Pure Mathematics
3 & 4

for A and AS level
The University of London modular mathematics syllabus

Graham Smithers
for

NATIONAL
EXTENSION
COLLEGE

CollinsEducational
An Imprint of HarperCollins*Publishers*

Published by Collins Educational
An imprint of HarperCollins*Publishers*
77–85 Fulham Palace Road
Hammersmith
London W6 8JB

© National Extension College Trust Ltd 1995
First published 1995
Reprinted 1995
ISBN 0 00 322396 5

This book was written by Graham Smithers for the National Extension College Trust Ltd. Part of the material was originally written by Tony Dacre and Stephen Webb.

Designed by Derek Lee
Cover design and implementation by Derek Lee
Page layout by Mary Bishop
Project editor, Hugh Hillyard-Parker

The author and publishers thank Pat Perkins and Clive Morris for their comments on this book.

Printed and bound in Great Britain by Scotprint Ltd, Musselburgh

The National Extension College is an educational trust and a registered charity with a distinguished body of trustees. It is an independent, self-financing organisation.

Since it was established in 1963, NEC has pioneered the development of flexible learning for adults. NEC is actively developing innovative materials and systems for distance-learning options from basic skills and general education to degree and professional training.

For further details of NEC resources that support *Advanced Modular Mathematics*, and other NEC courses, contact NEC Customer Services:

National Extension College Trust Ltd
18 Brooklands Avenue
Cambridge CB2 2HN
Telephone 0223 316644, Fax 0223 313586

CONTENTS

P3/P4

Advanced Modular Mathematics

FOREWORD

This book is one of a series covering the University of London Examination and Assessment Council's modular 'A' level Mathematics syllabus. It covers all the subject material for Pure Mathematics 3 and 4 (Modules P3 and P4). Sections 1–9 focus on the topics needed for P3, while Sections 10–16 move on to the more advanced topics of Module P4.

While this series of text books has been structured to match the University of London (ULEAC) syllabuses, we hope that the informal style of the text and approach to important concepts will encourage other readers, whose final examinations are from other examination Boards, to use the books for extra reading and practice.

This book is meant to be *used*: read the text, study the worked examples and work through the exercises, which will give you practice in the basic skills you need for maths at this level. There are many books for advanced mathematics, which include many more exercises: use this book to direct your studies, making use of as many other resources as you can. This book will act as a bridge between your new syllabus and the many older books that can still give even more practice in advanced mathematics.

Exercises are given at the end of each section; these range from the basic to exam-type questions. Many exercises, and worked examples, are based on *applications* of the mathematics in this book. We have given answers to all problems, so that you can check your work.

The National Extension College has more experience of flexible-learning materials than any other body (see p. ii). This series is a distillation of that experience: *Advanced Modular Mathematics* helps to put you in control of your own learning.

Permissions

We are grateful to the University of London Examinations and Assessment Council for permission to reproduce questions from past examination papers in the Exercises at the end of the following sections.

Section 2:   Exercise 11 (6382, P3 Specimen paper, Q3;
Exercise 12 (6382, June 1992, Q2)

Section 3:   Exercise 16 (6382, P3 Specimen paper, Q6)

Section 4:   Exercise 16 (6382, P3 Specimen paper, Q4)

Section 5:   Exercise 16 (6382, P3 Specimen paper, Q2)

Section 7:   Exercise 14 (6382, P3 Specimen paper, Q7)

Section 8:   Exercise 7 (6382, P3 Specimen paper, Q9)

The University of London Examinations and Assessment Council accepts no responsibility whatsoever for the accuracy or method of working in the answers given, which are entirely the responsibility of the author.

1

Inequalities revisited

In this section we'll be looking again at inequalities. You've already studied linear and quadratic inequalities in one variable (Module P1, Section 4) but now we move on to more complicated aspects of the subject. For example, you should already be able to solve $(x - 1)(x - 3) > 0$ (answer is $x > 3$ or $x < 1$) but what about this:

$$\frac{x - 1}{(x + 2)(x + 3)} > 0?$$

Havng done this, we'll then look at the modulus sign and its effect on inequalities.

More complicated inequalities

We need to find a method for solving inequalities like:

$$\frac{x - 1}{(x + 2)(x + 3)} > 0$$

or $\qquad (x + 1)(x + 3)(x - 3) < 0$

or $\qquad \dfrac{x(x + 4)}{x - 2} < 0$

which consist of some combination of linear factors. We'll take the first of these examples.

Example Find the set of values of x for which:

$$\frac{x - 1}{(x + 2)(x + 3)} > 0$$

Solution There are three factors each of which has a *critical point* – meaning the value of x for which the factor is zero. This point would be $x = 1$ for the factor $(x - 1)$, for example.

On one side of this critical point $(x - 1)$ is always positive, and on the other side it's always negative – there are no unexpected changes of sign at any other points. In the same way, the other factors have just one point each

1

where they change sign – these are $x = -2$ and $x = -3$. These three critical points divide the number line into four regions:

Figure 1.1

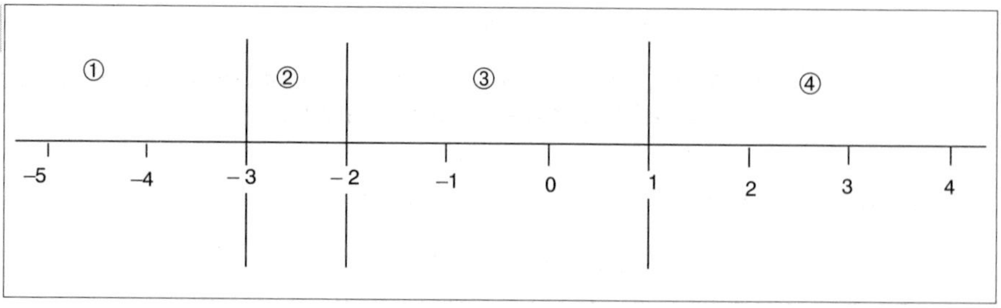

In each of these regions, the function has the same sign throughout. To find out what this sign is, we choose a convenient value of x and see what sign the factors have separately. For example, from region ④ we could pick the value $x = 3$. When x has this value, the function would be:

$$\frac{3-1}{(3+2)(3+3)} = \frac{2}{5 \times 6} = \frac{1}{15}$$

which is positive. So for *any value* of x in the region ④, the function is *positive*. We didn't really need to calculate the value of the function $x = 3$; we just wanted to know whether it's positive or negative. Instead of the value, we could have written: $\frac{+}{(+)(+)}$ which is positive overall.

Let's use this method to find the sign in region ③. We'll choose the value $x = 0$, which is always convenient. $(x-1)$ is now negative, and the other two still positive. The whole function is: $\frac{-}{(+)(+)}$ which is negative overall, because there is an *odd* number of negatives.

In region ② we can choose x to be $-2\frac{1}{2}$. With this value, $x - 1 = -3\frac{1}{2}$, (negative), $x + 2 = -\frac{1}{2}$ (negative), $x + 3 = \frac{1}{2}$ (positive).

The whole function is: $\frac{-}{(-)(+)}$ which is positive overall, having an *even* number of negatives.

Finally, in region ① we can choose x to be -4 and we find that all the factors are negative: $\frac{-}{(-)(-)}$ giving negative overall.

Let's set down our critical points and put the sign of the function between each point.

Region	①		②		③		④
Critical point		−3		−2		1	
Sign	−ve		+ve		−ve		+ve

Now the original question asked for values of x for which the function was *positive*. And so our answer is:

$$-3 < x < -2 \text{ or } x > 1$$

Naturally, you wouldn't expect to write as much as this down normally. Let's have a look at the second example.

Example   Find the set of values of x for which

$$(x + 1)(x + 3)(x - 3) < 0$$

Solution   The critical points are –1, –3 and 3. Putting these in ascending order, we get:

$$-3 \qquad -1 \qquad 3$$

We can now pick a value from each of the four regions:

① $x < -3,$ choose $x = -4$, (–) (–) (–), –ve overall

② $-3 < x < -1,$ choose $x = -2$, (–) (+) (–), +ve overall

③ $-1 < x < 3,$ choose $x = 0$, (+) (+) (–), –ve overall

④ $x > 3,$ choose $x = 4$, (+) (+) (+), +ve overall

We want the function to be negative, so we want x to be in either region ① or region ③. The solution is then:

$$x < -3 \quad \text{or} \quad -1 < x < 3$$

You should now be able to answer Exercise 1 on page 10.

Inequalities involving fractions

Now that you've got the basic idea, we'll have a look at typical exam questions and the techniques involved. Remember that in Module P1 we saw that multiplying an inequality through by a *negative* number *reversed* the sign, but multiplying through by a *positive* number left the sign *unchanged*? This means that we can't multiply through by a factor like $(x - 1)$ because we can't say whether it's positive or negative. So, for example, if we have to solve:

$$\frac{3}{x-1} < \frac{4}{x+2}$$

we *can't* multiply through by $(x - 1)$ and then $(x + 2)$ to give:

$$3(x + 2) < 4(x - 1) \qquad ✗ \text{ incorrect}$$

which we would have done had the inequality been an equation. We are allowed to add and subtract quite freely, however. Therefore what we do is subtract $\dfrac{4}{x+2}$ from both sides to give:

$$\frac{3}{x-1} - \frac{4}{x+2} < 0$$

then put these together as one fraction:

$$\frac{3(x+2) - 4(x-1)}{(x-1)\,(x+2)} < 0$$

$$\frac{3x + 6 - 4x + 4}{(x-1)\,(x+2)} < 0$$

$$\frac{10 - x}{(x-1)\,(x+2)} < 0$$

Critical points are at 10, 1 and –2. Testing with values between these points gives:

$$+ve \quad -2 \quad -ve \quad 1 \quad +ve \quad 10 \quad -ve$$

So the solution is:

$$-2 < x < 1 \quad \text{or} \quad x > 10$$

You should now be able to answer Exercise 2 on page 10.

Less than or equal to

Up to now we've only looked at strict inequalities like $x > 2$, meaning that x is *strictly greater* than 2 (and not equal to 2). If in addition x is allowed to take the value of the critical point, so that x is *greater than or equal to 2*, we change the symbol a little and write:

$$x \geq 2$$

Similarly, of course, $x \leq -1$ means that x is *less than or equal to –1.*

Note: In this connection, do remember that a fraction *can't have a denominator of 0*. Something like $\dfrac{2}{0}$ (try it on your calculator) is infinite; on the other hand, $\dfrac{0}{2}$ is perfectly OK and is just equal to 0.

This point can crop up in inequalities like:

$$\frac{x+2}{x-2} \geq 0$$

The two critical points are –2 and 2, and putting in suitable values we find:

$$+ve \quad -2 \quad -ve \quad 2 \quad +ve$$

Now *x is* allowed the value of –2 when the whole fraction has the value of 0, which the ≥ sign allows. It is *not* allowed the value of 2, however, so the solution is:

$$x \le -2 \text{ or } x > 2$$

Note: This restriction doesn't apply to critical points in the numerator.

You should now be able to answer Exercise 3 on page 11.

The modulus sign

The modulus of a function f(x), written $|f(x)|$, means that regardless of whether the value at any point is positive or negative, we always take the *positive* value. So if f(x) = 7, then $|f(x)| = 7$; and if f(x) = –5, then $|f(x)| = 5$. Let's compare the two functions:

$$g(x) = x - 2$$
$$\text{and} \quad h(x) = |x - 2|$$

For any value of $x \ge 2$, the values of the two functions are identical, e.g.:

$$g(7) = 7 - 2$$
$$= 5$$
$$\text{and} \quad h(7) = |7 - 2|$$
$$= |5|$$
$$= 5$$
$$\text{When} \quad x = 2,$$
$$g(2) = 2 - 2$$
$$= 0$$
$$\text{and} \quad h(2) = |2 - 2|$$
$$= |0|$$
$$= 0$$

The difference begins as *x* takes values less than 2; when $x = 1$ we have:

$$g(1) = 1 - 2$$
$$= -1$$
$$\text{and} \quad h(1) = |1 - 2|$$
$$= |-1|$$
$$= 1$$

This is explained more clearly if we sketch these two functions in one graph (see Figure 1.2). Note that the two graphs coincide for $x \ge 2$.

Figure 1.2

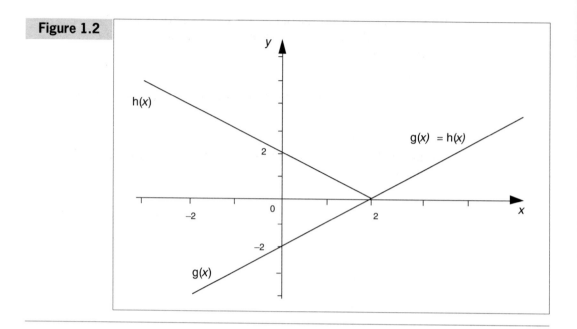

You should now be able to answer Exercise 4 on page 11.

The modulus sign and inequalities

How does the modulus sign affect inequalities? Suppose we were asked to solve:

$$|x - 2| < 1$$

We could have a look at the graph of $|x - 2|$, which we've already sketched, and draw in the line $y = 1$.

Figure 1.3

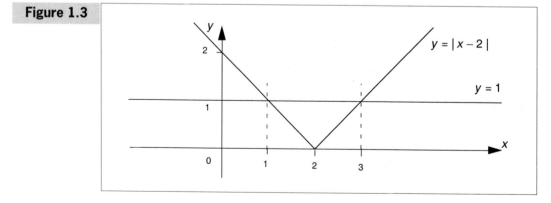

This intersects $|x-2|$ at the points where $x = 1$ and $x = 3$, and we can see from the graph that for values of x between these two critical points the inequality is true, i.e. the solution is:

$$1 < x < 3$$

We could also have found this without drawing the graph, starting by finding the critical points – the *two* points where:

$$|x-2| = 1$$

Since either +1 or –1 inside the modulus sign gives 1, we have to solve the two equations:

$$x - 2 = 1 \qquad \text{and} \quad x - 2 = -1$$

These give $x = 3$ and $x = 1$ respectively. Testing the inequality with values from the regions defined by these critical points would give:

	False	1	True	3	False

$\therefore \qquad 1 < x < 3$, as before.

Let's try another of these.

Example   Solve $|1 - x| < 3$

Solution $|1 - x| = 3$; in other words when

$$1 - x = 3 \qquad \text{or } 1 - x = -3$$

This gives the two critical points as $x = -2$ and $x = 4$.

Testing: False -2 True 4 False

The solution is: $-2 < x < 4$

You should now be able to answer Exercise 5 on page 11.

Mixed functions

We can still use the same method if there is another function involved.

Example   Find the set of values of x for which:

$$|3x - 2| < 1 - 4x$$

Solution   We have to solve the two equations:

$$3x - 2 = 1 - 4x \qquad \text{and} \quad 3x - 2 = -(1 - 4x)$$
$$7x = 3 \qquad\qquad\qquad 3x - 2 = -1 + 4x$$
$$\text{and} \qquad x = \frac{3}{7} \qquad\qquad\qquad x = -1$$

Testing between these two critical values gives:

True -1 False $\dfrac{3}{7}$ False

The solution is then:

$x < -1$

This is the first time where there has not been strict alternation between the critical values – let's have a look at the graphs and see why this is:

Figure 1.4

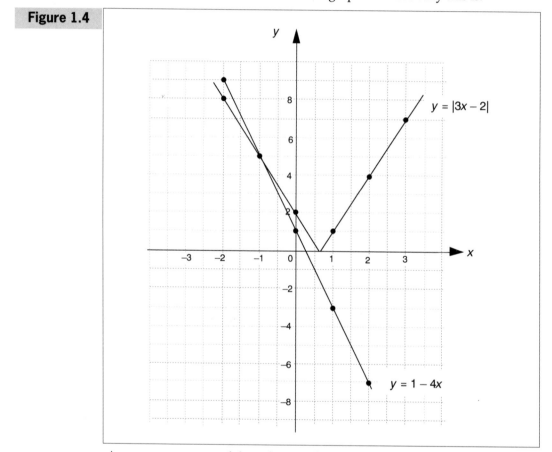

As you can see, one of the solutions doesn't exist. Perhaps by studying this particular pair, you could find out the condition that has to be satisfied for there only to be one crossing point. (Hint – think about the gradients.)

So be very careful with a mixture of 'normal' functions and those with modulus signs – you can't necessarily happily alternate true and false. In fact, under certain conditions there may be no solutions at all – can you see what these conditions are?

There's no danger of false solutions when *both* the functions are inside modulus signs. Let's have a look at an example of this.

| **Example** | Find the set of real values of x for which: |

$$|3x + 1| > 2|x - 1|$$

| **Solution** | Solving the two equations: |

$$3x + 1 = 2(x - 1)$$
$$= 2x - 2$$
$$x = -3$$

and
$$3x + 1 = -2(x - 1)$$
$$= -2x + 2$$
$$5x = 1$$
$$x = \frac{1}{5}$$

We have the critical points $x = \frac{1}{5}$ and $x = -3$.

Testing between these gives:

$$\text{True} \quad -3 \quad \text{False} \quad \tfrac{1}{5} \quad \text{True}$$

and so the answer is:

$$x < -3 \quad \text{or} \quad x > \frac{1}{5}$$

Should you prefer to use a sketch graph approach instead, then you would get the graph shown in Figure 1.5.

As you can see from the graph, the lines intersect at $x = -3$ and $x = \frac{1}{5}$, and so

$$|3x + 1| > 2|x - 1| \text{ for } x < -3 \text{ or } x > \frac{1}{5}$$

9

Figure 1.5

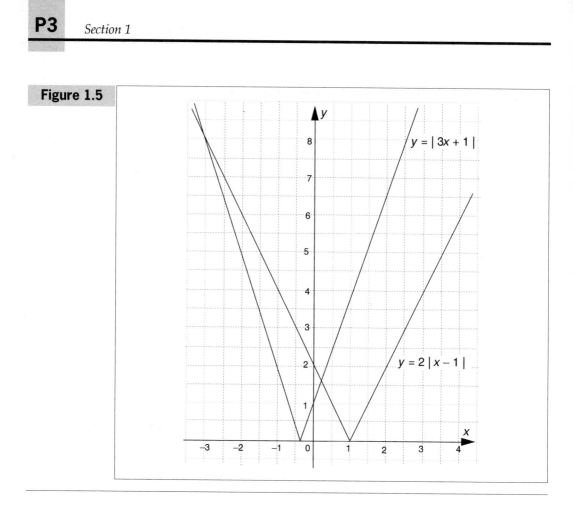

You should now be able to answer Exercises 6–10 on page 11.

EXERCISES

1 Find the sets of values of x satisfying:

(a) $\dfrac{x-2}{(x-4)(x+1)} < 0$ (c) $(x+5)(x+1)(x-2) > 0$

(b) $\dfrac{(x-2)(x+2)}{(x-1)(x+1)} < 0$

2 Find the sets of values of x for which:

(a) $\dfrac{x+2}{1-x} < 3$ (Be careful with your signs)

(b) $\dfrac{1}{x-2} > \dfrac{x}{x+4}$

(c) $\dfrac{x^2+12}{x} > 7$

(One of the three critical values is $x = 0$.)

3 Find the sets of values of x for which:

(a) $x^2 - 5x + 6 \geq 2$

(b) $\dfrac{x}{x+1} \leq \dfrac{1}{6}$

4 Sketch the following pairs of functions on one graph:

(a) $f(x) = x + 2,$

and $g(x) = |x + 2|$

(b) $f(x) = 1 - x,$

and $g(x) = |1 - x|$

5 Solve:

(a) $|x + 2| > 5$

(b) $|3 - x| < 2$

6 Find the set of values of x for which:

(a) $x > |3x - 8|$

(b) $|x + 1| > 2|1 - x|$

7 Sketch the graph of $y = x^2 - 12$. Hence, or otherwise, solve the equation

$|x^2 - 12| \geq x.$

8 (a)   On the same diagram, sketch the graphs of

$$y = \frac{1}{x-a} \text{ and } y = 4\,|x-a|,$$

where a is a positive constant. Show clearly the coordinates of any points of intersection with the coordinate axes.

(b)   Hence, or otherwise, find the set of values of x for which

$$\frac{1}{x-a} < 4\,|x-a|$$

9 Sketch the graphs of $y = \dfrac{1}{x}$ and $y = |x|$

Hence solve the inequality $\dfrac{1}{x} > |x|$

10 Sketch the graphs of $y = \dfrac{1}{x-1}$ and $y = |3x - 5|$

Hence solve the inequality $\dfrac{1}{x-1} < |3x - 5|$

SUMMARY   This section has looked again at inequalities. The manipulation of inequalities is made difficult by the range of numbers involved which replace the fixed quantities in equations. We have to be careful about the multiplication and division by negative numbers and variables. The modulus sign introduces new elements into inequalities such as mixed functions.

You should now be able to:

- solve inequalities such as $\dfrac{x-1}{(x+2)(x+3)} > 0$

  by using the critical values of 1, –2 and –3   (Ans: $-3 < x < -2$ or $x > 1$)

- solve inequalities such as $\dfrac{3}{x-1} < \dfrac{4}{x+2}$

  by first reducing it to $\dfrac{10-x}{(x-1)(x+2)} < 0$ (Ans: $-2 < x < 1$ or $x > 10$)

- solve inequalities such as $\lvert x-2 \rvert < 1$

  by using the critical values of 3 and 1.   (Ans: $1 < x < 3$)

- solve inequalities such as $\lvert x-2 \rvert < 1$ by means of sketch graphs.

- solve inequalities such as $\lvert 3x+1 \rvert > 2\lvert x-1 \rvert$

  by means of the critical values or sketch graphs. (Ans: $x < -3$ or $x > \frac{1}{5}$)

Series

In Module P2, Section 10, we saw how to use the binomial expansion on such as $(1 + x)^6$. But what about expanding $(1 + x)^{\frac{1}{2}}$ or $(1 - x)^{-2}$?

Then again, in Module P1, Section 6 we studied arithmetic progressions and geometric progressions so that we were able to work out such as:

$$\sum_{r=1}^{r=n} r \quad \text{and} \quad \sum_{r=1}^{r=\infty} (0.2)^r$$

But what about $\displaystyle\sum_{r=1}^{r=n} r^2$ and $\displaystyle\sum_{r=1}^{r=n} r(r + 1)$, for example?

Finally, is it possible to express *any* function in polynomial form? For example, we know that $(1 + x)^2 = 1 + 2x + x^2$ but can we get a similar expression for sin x (say)?

It is the aim of this Section to answer all of these questions.

Infinite series

We come now to what is really the main use of the binomial expansion as far as we're concerned – expressing brackets raised to awkward powers as infinite series. This sounds rather a strange thing to want to do and it may help to think why we turn fractions (which are exact and relatively short) into decimals (which can go on for ever and are usually only approximations).

The reason is that decimals have a common form – their value can be seen immediately and compared with other known values. They can also be added, multiplied, etc., more easily. Although they are not precise, for most purposes, two or three places of decimals are sufficient.

It's a very similar process with algebraic fractions and roots – provided certain conditions are met:

$$\frac{1}{1 - x} = 1 + x + x^2 + x^3 + x^4 + \ldots$$

In fact, if we substitute $x = \frac{1}{10}$ we have:

$$\frac{1}{1 - \frac{1}{10}} = \frac{10}{9} = 1 + \frac{1}{10} + \frac{1}{100} + \frac{1}{1000} + \ldots$$

$$= 1 + 0.1 + 0.01 + 0.001 + \ldots$$

$$= 1.1111\ldots$$

Just as three places of decimals are usually enough, so that $\frac{10}{9} \approx 1.111$, only terms with powers of x lower than or equal to 3 need usually be included, i.e.:

$$\frac{1}{1 - x} \approx 1 + x + x^2 + x^3$$

It's the same with square roots, $\sqrt{3}$ is actually:

$$1.7320508\ldots$$

but for most purposes we take it to be 1.732.

$\sqrt{1 + x}$, if it's expressed as an infinite series, would start:

$$1 + \frac{1}{2}x - \frac{1}{8}x^2 + \frac{1}{16}x^3 - \frac{5}{128}x^4 + \frac{7}{256}x^5 + \ldots$$

and we could take this to be $1 + \frac{1}{2}x - \frac{1}{8}x^2 + \frac{1}{16}x^3$ most of the time.

When you have understood this, the next task is to discover where these infinite series come from and how to work them out.

In fact, there is very little difference between working out the terms for an infinite series and the finite series that we've already looked at. We can't use the $\binom{n}{r}$ function because n is going to be either a fraction or a negative number, and anyway we won't be needing any but the first few terms.

Let's write out some of the expansion of $(1 + x)^n$, without using the $\binom{n}{r}$ function:

$$(1 + x)^n = 1 + \frac{n}{1}x + \frac{n(n-1)}{2 \times 1}x^2 + \frac{n(n-1)(n-2)}{3 \times 2 \times 1}x^3 + \ldots$$

This is true for any value of n – integer, fraction, positive or negative – but there sometimes has to be a restriction on the value of x. We'll discuss this more fully on page 19. Here are some examples:

$$n = 8: \quad (1 + x)^8 = 1 + \frac{8}{1}x + \frac{8 \times 7}{2 \times 1}x^2 + \frac{8 \times 7 \times 6}{3 \times 2 \times 1}x^3 + \ldots$$

$$= 1 + 8x + 28x^2 + 56x^3 + \ldots$$

$$n = \tfrac{1}{2}: \quad (1 + x)^{\frac{1}{2}} \;=\; 1 + \left(\tfrac{1}{2}\right)x + \frac{\left(\tfrac{1}{2}\right)\left(-\tfrac{1}{2}\right)}{2 \times 1}x^2 + \frac{\left(\tfrac{1}{2}\right)\left(-\tfrac{1}{2}\right)\left(-\tfrac{3}{2}\right)}{3 \times 2 \times 1}x^3 + \ldots$$

$$=\; 1 + \frac{x}{2} - \frac{x^2}{8} + \frac{x^3}{16} + \ldots$$

$$n = -1: \quad (1 + x)^{-1} \;=\; 1 + (-1)x + \frac{(-1)\,(-2)}{2 \times 1}x^2 + \frac{(-1)\,(-2)\,(-3)}{3 \times 2 \times 1}x^3 + \ldots$$

$$=\; 1 - x + x^2 - x^3 + \ldots$$

To avoid making errors try and get into the habit of writing expansions down in this fixed pattern. As before, if the x is replaced by $2x$ or $-x$, the expansion is basically unchanged.

$$(1 + 2x)^{\frac{1}{2}} = 1 + \left(\tfrac{1}{2}\right)(2x) + \frac{\left(\tfrac{1}{2}\right)\left(-\tfrac{1}{2}\right)}{2 \times 1}(2x)^2 + \frac{\left(\tfrac{1}{2}\right)\left(-\tfrac{1}{2}\right)\left(-\tfrac{3}{2}\right)}{3 \times 2 \times 1}(2x)^3 + \ldots$$

$$=\; 1 + x - \frac{x^2}{2} + \frac{x^3}{2} - \cdots$$

and $(1 - x)^{-2} = 1 + (-2)\,(-x) + \dfrac{(-2)\,(-3)\,(-x)^2}{2 \times 1} + \dfrac{(-2)\,(-3)\,(-4)\,(-x)^3}{3 \times 2 \times 1} + \ldots$

$$=\; 1 + 2x + 3x^2 + 4x^3 + \ldots$$

You should now be able to answer Exercise 1 on page 28.

Multiplying series

We do this quite simply multiplying term by term and then collecting, for example:

$$
\begin{aligned}
(1 - x + x^2)(1 + 3x + 4x^2) \;=\; &\; 1 + 3x + 4x^2 \\
& - x - 3x^2 - 4x^3 \\
& \quad\quad\; x^2 + 3x^3 + 4x^4 \\
\hline
& 1 + 2x + 2x^2 - x^3 + 4x^4
\end{aligned}
$$

Usually, however, the series are short because terms with powers of x higher than 3 can be ignored. This means an easier job multiplying out as we only keep terms up to and including x^3.

Example

Find the expansion of $\dfrac{1 + x}{1 - x}$ as an expression in ascending powers of x up to and including the term in x^3.

| **Solution** | Rewriting this as $(1 + x)(1 - x)^{-1}$, we need to find the first three terms of $(1 - x)^{-1}$: |

$$(1 - x)^{-1} \quad = \quad 1 + (-1)(-x) + \frac{(-1)(-2)(-x)^2}{2 \times 1} + \dots$$

$$= \quad 1 + x + x^2 + x^3 + \dots$$

So $\quad \dfrac{1 + x}{1 - x} \quad \approx \quad (1 + x)(1 + x + x^2 + x^3) = 1 + x + x^2 + x^3 + x + x^2 + x^3$

$$= \quad 1 + 2x + 2x^2 + 2x^3$$

when we ignore any terms with powers of x greater than 3.

We'll try another of these in the next example.

| **Example** | Express $\sqrt{\dfrac{1 - 2x}{1 + 2x}}$ as a series in ascending powers of x, up to and including the term in x^3. |

| **Solution** | We can rewrite the fraction as: |

$$(1 - 2x)^{\frac{1}{2}} \, (1 + 2x)^{-\frac{1}{2}}$$

and expand each of these separately.

$$(1 - 2x)^{\frac{1}{2}} \quad \approx 1 + \left(\tfrac{1}{2}\right)(-2x) + \frac{\left(\tfrac{1}{2}\right)\left(-\tfrac{1}{2}\right)(-2x)^2}{2} + \frac{\left(\tfrac{1}{2}\right)\left(-\tfrac{1}{2}\right)\left(-\tfrac{3}{2}\right)(-2x)^3}{6}$$

$$= 1 - x - \frac{x^2}{2} - \frac{x^3}{2}$$

$$(1 + 2x)^{-\frac{1}{2}} \quad \approx 1 + \left(-\tfrac{1}{2}\right)(2x) + \frac{\left(-\tfrac{1}{2}\right)\left(-\tfrac{3}{2}\right)(2x)^2}{2} + \frac{\left(-\tfrac{1}{2}\right)\left(-\tfrac{3}{2}\right)\left(-\tfrac{5}{2}\right)(2x)^3}{6}$$

$$= 1 - x + \frac{3x^2}{2} - \frac{5x^3}{2}$$

Then

$$\sqrt{\frac{1 - 2x}{1 + 2x}} \quad \approx \left(1 - x - \frac{x^2}{2} - \frac{x^3}{2}\right)\left(1 - x + \frac{3x^2}{2} - \frac{5x^3}{2}\right)$$

$$\approx 1 - x + \frac{3x^2}{2} - \frac{5x^3}{2} - x + x^2 - \frac{3x^3}{2} - \frac{x^2}{2} + \frac{x^3}{2} - \frac{x^3}{2}$$

$$= 1 - 2x + 2x^2 - 4x^3$$

up to and including the term in x^3.

You should now be able to answer Exercise 2 on page 28.

Rearrangements

In a way, the general expansion that has been quoted is quite limited – it only works when the terms inside the bracket start with 1. To expand something like

$$(4 + x)^{\frac{1}{2}}$$

we have to rearrange it somewhat to bring the bracket into the standard form:

$$(4 + x)^{\frac{1}{2}} = \left[4\left(1 + \frac{x}{4}\right) \right]^{\frac{1}{2}} = 4^{\frac{1}{2}}\left(1 + \frac{x}{4}\right)^{\frac{1}{2}}$$

$$= 2\left(1 + \frac{x}{4}\right)^{\frac{1}{2}}$$

$$\approx 2\left[1 + \left(\frac{1}{2}\right)\left(\frac{x}{4}\right) + \frac{\left(\frac{1}{2}\right)\left(-\frac{1}{2}\right)\left(\frac{x}{4}\right)^2}{2} + \frac{\left(\frac{1}{2}\right)\left(-\frac{1}{2}\right)\left(-\frac{3}{2}\right)\left(\frac{x}{4}\right)^3}{6} \right]$$

$$= 2\left[1 + \frac{x}{8} - \frac{x^2}{128} + \frac{x^3}{1024} \right]$$

$$= 2 + \frac{x}{4} - \frac{x^2}{64} + \frac{x^3}{512}$$

up to and including the term in x^3.

This procedure, or lack of it, is a very common source of error. Be particularly careful when bringing brackets up from the bottom line.

$$\frac{1}{2 - x} = (2 - x)^{-1}$$

$$= \left[2\left(1 - \frac{x}{2}\right) \right]^{-1}$$

$$= 2^{-1}\left(1 - \frac{x}{2}\right)^{-1}$$

$$\approx \frac{1}{2}\left[1 + (-1)\left(-\frac{x}{2}\right) + \frac{(-1)(-2)\left(-\frac{x}{2}\right)^2}{2} + \frac{(-1)(-2)(-3)\left(-\frac{x}{2}\right)^3}{6} \right]$$

$$= \frac{1}{2}\left[1 + \frac{x}{2} + \frac{x^2}{4} + \frac{x^3}{8} \right]$$

$$= \frac{1}{2} + \frac{x}{4} + \frac{x^2}{8} + \frac{x^3}{16} \quad \text{neglecting powers of } x \geq 4$$

You should now be able to answer Exercise 3 on page 29.

17

Larger terms

You occasionally come across questions where instead of the bracket containing something like $1 + 2x$, it contains something like $1 + x + x^2$. There is no change in the form of the expansion. $(2x)^3$ would be replaced by $(x + x^2)^3$ and the terms become a little more complicated to work out. Let's have a look at one of these.

Example

Expand $(1 + x + x^2)^{\frac{1}{2}}$ as a series in ascending powers of x up to and including the term in x^3.

Solution

Expanding as normal,

$$(1 + x + x^2)^{\frac{1}{2}} \approx 1 + \frac{1}{2}(x + x^2) + \frac{\left(\frac{1}{2}\right)\left(-\frac{1}{2}\right)(x + x^2)^2}{2!}$$

$$+ \frac{\left(\frac{1}{2}\right)\left(-\frac{1}{2}\right)\left(-\frac{3}{2}\right)(x + x^2)^3}{3!}$$

$$= 1 + \frac{1}{2}x + \frac{1}{2}x^2 - \frac{1}{8}(x + x^2)^2 + \frac{1}{16}(x + x^2)^3$$

(We can expand these brackets, but don't need to take all the terms.)

$$= 1 + \frac{1}{2}x + \frac{1}{2}x^2 - \frac{1}{8}[x^2 + 2x^3 + \ldots] + \frac{1}{16}[x^3 + \ldots]$$

$$= 1 + \frac{1}{2}x + \frac{1}{2}x^2 - \frac{1}{8}x^2 - \frac{x^3}{4} + \frac{x^3}{16}$$

$$= 1 + \frac{1}{2}x + \frac{3}{8}x^2 - \frac{3}{16}x^3 \text{ up to and including } x^3$$

Similarly, if the bracket contains something like $1 + \frac{2}{x}$, the series will be in ascending powers of $\frac{1}{x}$. For example

$$\left(1 + \frac{2}{x}\right)^{\frac{1}{2}} = 1 + \frac{1}{x} - \frac{1}{2x^2} + \frac{1}{2x^3} - \ldots$$

Check that you agree with this expansion.

You should now be able to answer Exercise 4 on page 29.

Validity of the expansion

Up to now we've assumed that the various infinite expansions are true regardless of the value of x. In fact, there is only a small range of permissible values of x for any particular expansion – we couldn't, for example, calculate the square root of 3 by putting:

$$\sqrt{3} = (3)^{\frac{1}{2}} = (1 + 2)^{\frac{1}{2}}$$

and then using the expansion of $(1 + x)^{\frac{1}{2}}$ replacing the x by 2. The terms would get larger and larger as they went on. On the other hand, we could calculate the square root of 1.01 by putting:

$$\sqrt{1.01} = (1.01)^{\frac{1}{2}} = (1 + 0.01)^{\frac{1}{2}}$$

with $x = 0.01$ here. The terms would very quickly become extremely small and we could find quite an accurate value by taking only the first few.

You need to know that if x is between -1 and 1, then the series is valid. In other words:

$$|x| < 1 \Rightarrow (1 + x)^{\frac{1}{2}} = 1 + \frac{1}{2}x - \frac{1}{8}x^2 + \frac{1}{16}x^3 \dots \text{ is true.}$$

Similarly:

$$|2x| < 1 \Rightarrow \text{the binomial expansion of } (1 + 2x)^{\frac{1}{2}} \text{ is valid, and}$$

$$|x - x^3| < 1 \Rightarrow \text{the binomial expansion of } (1 + x - x^3)^{-3} \text{ is valid.}$$

You should now be able to answer Exercise 5 on page 29.

Use of partial fractions

When we have a more complicated algebraic fraction that we would like to express as an ascending series in x, our work can be made easier by the use of partial fractions. (We first met these in Section 1 of Module P2.) Suppose, for example, that we wanted to find the first four non-zero terms in the expansion in ascending powers of x of:

$$\frac{1 - 8x}{(1 + x)(1 - 2x)}$$

In partial fractions $\dfrac{1 - 8x}{(1 + x)(1 - 2x)} \equiv \dfrac{A}{1 + x} + \dfrac{B}{1 - 2x}$

$$\equiv \frac{A(1 - 2x) + B(1 + x)}{(1 + x)(1 - 2x)}$$

$$\Rightarrow 1 - 8x \equiv A(1 - 2x) + B(1 + x)$$

19

$$x = \frac{1}{2} : \quad -3 = 0 + B\left(\frac{3}{2}\right) \quad \Rightarrow B = -2$$

$$x = -1 : \quad 9 = A(3) + 0 \quad \Rightarrow A = 3$$

i.e. $\quad \dfrac{1 - 8x}{(1 + x)(1 - 2x)} \equiv \dfrac{3}{1 + x} - \dfrac{2}{1 - 2x}$

So to find the series for LHS, we find each of the series for the RHS and subtract.

$$\frac{3}{1 + x} = 3(1 + x)^{-1} \qquad = 3[1 - x + x^2 - x^3 + \ldots]$$

$$\frac{2}{1 - 2x} = 2(1 - 2x)^{-1} \qquad = 2[1 + 2x + 4x^2 + 8x^3 + \ldots]$$

so finally:

$$\frac{1 - 8x}{(1 + x)(1 - 2x)} \approx 3[1 - x + x^2 - x^3] - 2[1 + 2x + 4x^2 + 8x^3]$$

$$= 1 - 7x - 5x^2 - 19x^3 \quad \text{(first four terms)}$$

When more than one series is involved, the whole expansion will only be valid for the smallest range of values of the parts. So for example, the expansion above is made up of $(1 + x)^{-1}$, which is valid for $|x| < 1$, and $(1 - 2x)^{-1}$, which is valid for $(2x) < 1$, i.e. $|x| < \frac{1}{2}$.

Since this last range is the smaller, the whole expansion will only be valid if $|x| < \frac{1}{2}$.

You should now be able to answer Exercise 6 on page 29.

The natural number series

We already know that $\displaystyle\sum_{r=1}^{r=n} r = 1 + 2 + 3 + \ldots + n$ and that this is an arithmetic progression (or A.P. for short), with $a = 1$ and $d = 1$. Therefore, using the sum formula for an A.P. we get:

$$\sum_{r=1}^{r=n} r = \frac{n(n + 1)}{2}$$

But what about $\displaystyle\sum_{r=1}^{r=n} r^2$ or $\displaystyle\sum_{r=1}^{r=n} r^3$?

The formulae for these are usually obtained by the *method of differences*. (A rather obscure method, but in any examination you would be guided carefully!)

To find $\displaystyle\sum_{r=1}^{r=n} r^2$ we proceed as follows:

$$(n+1)^3 - n^3 = 3n^2 + 3n + 1$$
$$\therefore \quad n^3 - (n-1)^3 = 3(n-1)^2 + 3(n-1) + 1$$
$$\therefore \quad (n-1)^3 - (n-2)^3 = 3(n-2)^2 + 3(n-2) + 1$$

$$\overset{.}{\underset{.}{.}}$$

$$3^3 - 2^3 = 3.2^2 + 3.2 + 1$$
$$2^3 - 1^3 = 3.1^2 + 3.1 + 1$$

Now *add this lot* and the left-hand side becomes $(n+1)^3 - 1^3$ whereas on the right-hand side we get $3\displaystyle\sum_{r=1}^{r=n} r^2 + 3\displaystyle\sum_{r=1}^{r=n} r + n$.

$$\therefore \quad (n+1)^3 - 1^3 = 3\sum_{r=1}^{r=n} r^2 + \frac{3n(n+1)}{2} + n$$

$$\therefore \quad 3\sum_{r=1}^{r=n} r^2 = (n+1)^3 - 1^3 - \frac{3n(n+1)}{2} - n$$

$$= n^3 + 3n^2 + 3n - \frac{3n(n+1)}{2} - n$$

$$= \frac{n}{2}\left[2n^2 + 6n + 6 - 3n - 3 - 2\right]$$

$$= \frac{n}{2}\left[2n^2 + 3n + 1\right]$$

$$= \frac{n}{2}(n+1)(2n+1)$$

$$\therefore \quad \sum_{r=1}^{r=n} r^2 = \frac{n}{6}(n+1)(2n+1)$$

Study this result carefully so that you become really familiar with the processes involved and feel confident about applying it in other questions.

Example	Using the formulae for $\displaystyle\sum_{r=1}^{r=n} r$ and $\displaystyle\sum_{r=1}^{r=n} r^2$, find a similar formula for $$\sum_{r=1}^{r=n} r\,(r+2)$$

Solution	$$\sum_{r=1}^{r=n} r\,(r+2) = \sum_{r=1}^{r=n} r^2 + 2\sum_{r=1}^{r=n} r$$ $$= \frac{n(n+1)(2n+1)}{6} + \frac{2n(n+1)}{2}$$ $$= \frac{n(n+1)}{6}\left[2n+1+6\right]$$ $$= \frac{n(n+1)(2n+7)}{6}$$

Example   Using the identity:

$$n^4 - (n-1)^4 = 4n^3 - 6n^2 + 4n - 1$$

and the standard results for $\sum_{r=1}^{r=n} r$ and $\sum_{r=1}^{r=n} r^2$, find $\sum_{r=1}^{r=n} r^3$.

Solution $$n^4 - (n-1)^4 = 4n^3 - 6n^2 + 4n - 1$$

$$\therefore \quad (n-1)^4 - (n-2)^4 = 4(n-1)^3 - 6(n-1)^2 + 4(n-1) - 1$$

$$\cdot \qquad \qquad \cdot$$

$$1^4 - 0^4 = 4 \times 1^3 - 6 \times 1^2 + 4 \times 1 - 1$$

Add both sides and get:

$$n^4 - 0^4 = 4\sum_{r=1}^{r=n} r^3 - 6\sum_{r=1}^{r=n} r^2 + 4\sum_{r=1}^{r=n} r - n$$

$$\therefore \quad 4\sum_{r=1}^{r=n} r^3 = n^4 + 6\sum_{r=1}^{r=n} r^2 - 4\sum_{r=1}^{r=n} r + n$$

$$= n^4 + \frac{6n\,(n+1)\,(2n+1)}{6} - \frac{4n\,(n+1)}{2} + n$$

$$= n\left[n^3 + (n+1)\,(2n+1) - 2(n+1) + 1\right]$$

$$= n\left[n^3 + 2n^2 + n\right]$$

$$= n^2\,(n^2 + 2n + 1)$$

$$= n^2\,(n+1)^2$$

$$\therefore \quad \sum_{r=1}^{r=n} r^3 = \frac{n^2\,(n+1)^2}{4} \quad \text{or} \quad \left[\frac{n\,(n+1)}{2}\right]^2$$

Once again, study this result carefully, so that you can apply the methods when the need arises.

Example   Find the values of the following:

(a) $\sum_{r=1}^{r=20} r^3$ (b) $\sum_{r=10}^{r=20} r^3$

Solution   (a)   Using the result $\sum_{r=1}^{r=n} r^3 = \left[\frac{n\,(n+1)}{2}\right]^2$ we get:

$$\sum_{r=1}^{r=20} r^3 = \left[\frac{20 \times 21}{2}\right]^2 = 210^2 = 44\,100$$

(b)   Since $\displaystyle\sum_{r=10}^{r=20} r^3$ $= 10^3 + 11^3 + \ldots + 20^3$

$$= (1^3 + 2^3 + \ldots + 10^3 + 11^3 + \ldots + 20^3) - (1^3 + 2^3 + \ldots + 9^3)$$

It follows that:

$$\sum_{r=10}^{r=20} r^3 = \sum_{r=1}^{r=20} r^3 - \sum_{r=1}^{r=9^*} r^3$$

$$= \left[\frac{20 \times 21}{2}\right]^2 - \left[\frac{9 \times 10}{2}\right]^2$$

$$= 44\,100 - 2025$$

$$= 42\,075$$

*Note carefully that this says $r = 9$, and not $r = 10$. It is so easy to go wrong at this step.

Example

(a)   Express $\dfrac{1}{r(r+1)}$ in partial fractions

(b)   Hence find $\displaystyle\sum_{r=1}^{r=n} \dfrac{1}{r(r+1)}$

Solution

(a)   If $\dfrac{1}{r(r+1)} = \dfrac{A}{r} + \dfrac{B}{r+1}$ then $1 = A(r+1) + Br$.

Putting $r = 0$ gives $A = 1$ and putting $r = -1$ gives $B = -1$.

$\therefore$ $\dfrac{1}{r(r+1)} = \dfrac{1}{r} - \dfrac{1}{r+1}$, the required partial fractions

(b)   Using part (a) we get:

$$\sum_{r=1}^{r=n} \frac{1}{r(r+1)} = \sum_{r=1}^{r=n}\left(\frac{1}{r} - \frac{1}{r+1}\right)$$

$$= \sum_{r=1}^{r=n} \frac{1}{r} - \sum_{r=1}^{r=n} \frac{1}{r+1}$$

$$= \left(\frac{1}{1} + \frac{1}{2} + \frac{1}{3} + \frac{1}{4} + \ldots + \frac{1}{n}\right) - \left(\frac{1}{2} + \frac{1}{3} + \frac{1}{4} + \ldots + \frac{1}{n} + \frac{1}{n+1}\right)$$

$\therefore$ we have to subtract these:

$$\begin{cases} 1 + \dfrac{1}{2} + \dfrac{1}{3} + \ldots + \dfrac{1}{n} \\[2mm] \quad\;\; \dfrac{1}{2} + \dfrac{1}{3} + \ldots + \dfrac{1}{n} + \dfrac{1}{n+1} \end{cases}$$

But when we subtract the 'middle block' cancels out leaving us with:

$$1 + 0 + \quad 0 + \quad \ldots \quad + 0 \quad - \frac{1}{n+1}$$

$$= 1 - \frac{1}{n+1} = \frac{n}{n+1}$$

$$\therefore \sum_{r=1}^{r=n} \frac{1}{r(r+1)} = \frac{n}{n+1}$$

You should now be able to answer Exercises 7 to 10 on page 29.

Maclaurin Series

In a Maclaurin Series we attempt to express a function – and for the moment let's suppose it can be *any* function – in the form:

$$f(x) = a_0 + a_1 x + a_2 x^2 + \ldots + a_n x^n + \ldots$$

In other words, our expression would be a polynomial if it were not for the fact that it continues for ever. This expression is an infinite series, whereas a polynomial is a finite series.

The next question, of course, is: Assuming it *is* possible to write the function in this way, how do we determine the values of a_0, a_1, a_2 and all the rest? Surprisingly, the answer is quick and easy – but just a little ingenious.

Notice what happens when we set $x = 0$. The result is:

$$f(0) = a_0$$

so the constant a_0 must be the value of the function at 0. Provided that it is possible to evaluate $f(x)$ at $x = 0$, this deals with the first a.

Notice also that by differentiating we get:

$$f'(x) = a_1 + 2a_2 x + 3a_3 x^2 + \ldots$$

Setting $x = 0$, $f'(0) = a_1$

So a_1 must be the value of $f'(x)$ at $x = 0$.

Continuing this process, it is reasonably easy to see that

$$f^n(0) = n! a_n$$

so that:

$$a_n = \frac{f^n(0)}{n!}$$

Provided that all the derivatives exist and that it is possible to evaluate them at $x = 0$, we have therefore shown that:

$$f(x) = f(0) + \frac{f'(0)x}{1!} \; x + \frac{f''(0)}{2!} \; x^2 + \; ... \; + \frac{f^n(0)}{n!} \; x^n + \; ...$$

This is the known as the **Maclaurin Series** for the function f.

Maclaurin Series for important functions

Using the general form of the Maclaurin Series that we have just proved, it is easy to create expressions for many of the important functions of mathematics. To do this, you will need a knowledge of the functions' derivatives, of course, but you are already very familiar with these from your work on Modules P1 and P2.

e^x

If $f(x) = e^x$, then:

$$f^n(x) = e^x \quad \text{for } n = 0, 1, 2 \; ...$$

This follows because the derivative of e^x is just e^x again. In the Maclaurin Series for e^x, we therefore have:

$$a_n = \frac{f^n(0)}{n!} = \frac{e^0}{n!} = \frac{1}{n!} \quad \text{and so this produces the formula:}$$

$$e^x = 1 + \frac{x}{1!} + \frac{x^2}{2!} + \frac{x^3}{3!} + \; ... \; + \frac{x^n}{n!} + \; ...$$

This is possibly the best-known series in the whole of mathematics. It happens to be valid for any x whatsoever. No matter whether x is positive or negative or how large a value it takes, the series will always converge to a finite value. Make sure you remember it for when you see it again.

ln (1 + x)

Unfortunately it is impossible to write down a Maclaurin Series for ln (x). Just try it and you will soon see why. The series would involve dividing by zero. ln $(1 + x)$ is a different matter, however.

If $\qquad f(x) = \ln (1 + x)$, then $a_0 = f(0) = \ln (1 + 0) = 0$

also $\qquad f'(x) = \dfrac{1}{1 + x}$

and so $\qquad a_1 = \dfrac{f'(0)}{1!} = \dfrac{1}{1 + 0} = 1$

further $f''(x) = \dfrac{-1}{(1 + x)^2}$

and so $a_2 = \dfrac{f''(0)}{2!} = \dfrac{-1}{2!}$

similarly, $f'''(x) = \dfrac{2}{(1 + x)^3}$

and so $a_3 = \dfrac{f'''(0)}{3!} = \dfrac{2}{3!}$

It is now easy to see that the higher-order derivatives of f will alternate in sign, with an increasing factorial in the numerator of the fraction and an increasing power of $(1 + x)$ in the denominator. In other words:

$$f^n(x) = \dfrac{(-1)^{(n-1)} (n-1)!}{(1 + x)^n}$$

so that $a_n = \dfrac{f^n(0)}{n!} = \dfrac{(-1)^{(n-1)} (n-1)!}{n!}$

Putting all this together gives a surprisingly simple formula for $\ln (1 + x)$.

$$\ln (1 + x) = x - \dfrac{x^2}{2} + \dfrac{x^3}{3} - \ldots - \dfrac{(-1)^n x}{n} + \ldots$$

Not surprisingly, however, this series does *not* converge when $x \le -1$. After all, $\ln (0)$ is infinite and logs of negative numbers do not exist. It can be shown, though, that for $-1 < x \le 1$ there is no problem – the series is valid.

sin x

If $f(x) = \sin x$, then: $a_0 = f(0) = \sin 0 = 0$

also $f'(x) = \cos x$

and so $a_1 = \dfrac{f'(0)}{1!} = \cos 0 = 1$

further $f''(x) = -\sin x$

and so $a_2 = \dfrac{f''(0)}{2!} = 0$

Do you see the pattern that is beginning to form? It is now reasonably clear that the derivatives are going to alternate between 0 and ±1, and that the non-zero derivatives will themselves alternate between +1 and –1. If you are not yet convinced, try a few more derivatives and you will soon see the point. The result is:

$$\sin x = x - \dfrac{x^3}{3!} + \dfrac{x^5}{5!} - \ldots + \dfrac{(-1)^{n+1} x^{2n-1}}{(2n-1)!} + \ldots$$

Despite the awkward formula for the nth term – which you should not attempt to commit to memory – the series as a whole is fairly easy to remember. Just recall that, starting with x, the powers of x go up in 2's and alternate in sign. Like the series for e^x, $\sin x$ converges for any value of x, but in this case, x must be in radians.

Example

Find the Maclaurin Series for $e^x \sin x$

Solution

Two methods are possible

One way would be to multiply the two series that we already know.

$$\therefore \quad e^x \sin x \quad = \quad \left(1 + x + \frac{x^2}{2} + \frac{x^3}{6} + \dots\right)\left(x - \frac{x^3}{6} + \frac{x^5}{120} \dots\right)$$

$$= \quad x + x^2 + \frac{x^3}{3} + \dots$$

Another way would be to use the derivatives. In summary form (and *using the derivatives of a product*) we get:

n	$f^n(x)$	$f^n(0)$
0	$e^x \sin x$	0
1	$e^x \sin x + e^x \cos x$	1
2	$2e^x \cos x$	2
3	$2e^x \cos x - 2e^x \sin x$	2
4	$-4e^x \sin x$	0

It is clear from the table that, since $f^{IV}(x) = -4f(x)$, the next four derivatives are merely a repetition of the first four multiplied by another -4 and so on. Using these facts we could easily write down as many terms of the Maclaurin Series as we wished. And so:

$$e^x \sin x \quad = \quad \frac{x}{1!} + \frac{2x^2}{2!} + \frac{2x^3}{3!} - \frac{4x^5}{5!} - \frac{8x^6}{6!} - \frac{8x^7}{7!} + \dots$$

$$= \quad x + x^2 + \frac{x^3}{3} - \frac{x^5}{30} - \frac{x^6}{90} - \frac{x^7}{630} + \dots$$

In an examination, you'll be told which method to use.

Example	Find the Maclaurin Series for sin $3x$

Solution	Once again, two methods are possible.

One way would be to use the expansion for sin x, i.e.

$$\sin x = x - \frac{x^3}{3!} + \frac{x^5}{5!} - \frac{x^7}{7!} + \dots$$

Replacing x by $3x$ this becomes:

$$\sin 3x = 3x - \frac{(3x)^3}{3!} + \frac{(3x)^5}{5!} - \frac{(3x)^7}{7!} + \dots$$

$$\therefore \quad \sin 3x = 3x - \frac{9x^3}{2} + \frac{81x^5}{40} - \frac{243x^7}{560} + \dots$$

Another way would be to use the derivatives.

$$f(x) = \sin 3x \qquad \Rightarrow f'(x) = 3\cos 3x \qquad \Rightarrow f''(x) = -9\sin 3x$$

$$\Rightarrow f'''(x) = -27\cos 3x \qquad \Rightarrow f^{IV}(x) = 81\sin 3x, \text{ etc.}$$

$$\therefore \quad f(0) = 0, \ f'(0) = 3, \ f''(0) = 0, \ f'''(0) = -27, \ f^{IV}(0) = 0, \text{ etc.}$$

$$\therefore \quad f(x) = 0 + \frac{3x}{1!} + \frac{0x^2}{2!} + \frac{27x^3}{3!} + \frac{0x^4}{4!} - \dots$$

$$\therefore \quad \sin 3x = 3x - \frac{9x^3}{2} + \dots, \text{ as before.}$$

The choice is yours.

You should now be able to answer Exercises 11–14 on pages 29–30.

EXERCISES

1 Write out the first four terms in the expansion of:

(a) $(1 + x)^{\frac{1}{3}}$ (b) $\sqrt{1 - x}$ (c) $\dfrac{1}{1 + 2x}$

(d) $(1 - 3x)^{\frac{2}{3}}$ (e) $\dfrac{1}{\sqrt{1 - 2x}}$ (f) $\left(1 + \dfrac{x}{2}\right)^{-2}$

2 Express as a series in ascending powers of x, up to and including the term in x^3:

(a) $\dfrac{1 + 2x}{1 - 2x}$ (b) $\dfrac{1 - x}{\sqrt{1 + x}}$

3 Put the following in the form $a(1 + bx)^n$. The expansion is not required.

(a) $(8 + x)^{\frac{1}{3}}$ (b) $\dfrac{1}{x + 2}$ (c) $\dfrac{1}{\sqrt{9 - x}}$

4 (a) Expand $(1 + 2x - x^2)^{-1}$ as a series in ascending powers of x, up to and including the term in x^3.

(b) Expand $\left(1 - \dfrac{4}{x}\right)^{\frac{1}{2}}$ as a series in ascending powers of $\dfrac{1}{x}$ up to and

including the term in $\dfrac{1}{x^2}$.

5 For the previous exercises 1 to 4, give the set of values of x for which the expansions are valid.

6 Express $f(x) = \dfrac{2 + 11x}{(2 + x)(1 - 2x)}$ in partial fractions.

Hence determine the coefficient of x^3 in the expansion of $f(x)$ in a series of ascending powers of x. State the range of values of x for which the expansion is valid.

7 Show that $\displaystyle\sum_{r=1}^{r=n} (n + 2r + 1) = 2n(n + 1)$

8 Find (a) $\displaystyle\sum_{r=1}^{r=20} r^2$ (b) $\displaystyle\sum_{r=10}^{r=20} r^2$

9 Prove that $\displaystyle\sum_{r=1}^{r=n} r(r + 1) = \frac{1}{3}n(n + 1)(n + 2)$

10 Express $\dfrac{1}{r(r + 2)}$ in partial fractions.

Hence find $\displaystyle\sum_{r=1}^{r=n} \dfrac{1}{r(r + 2)}$

11 Express $\dfrac{2}{4x^2 - 1}$ in partial fractions.

Hence, or otherwise, show that $\displaystyle\sum_{r=1}^{n} \dfrac{2}{4r^2 - 1} = \dfrac{2n}{2n + 1}$

12 Find the Maclaurin Series for the following (first four terms only):

(a) $\cos x$ (b) $\cos 2x$ (c) $x \cos x$ (d) e^{2x} (e) $\ln(2 + x)$.

13 By using the series expansions of e^x and $\cos x$, or otherwise, find the expansion of $e^x \cos 3x$ in ascending powers of x up to and including the term in x^3.

14 By using the power series expansion for $\cos x$ and the power series expansion for $\ln(1 + x)$, find the series expansion for $\ln(\cos x)$ in ascending powers of x up to and including the term in x^4.

Hence, or otherwise, obtain the first two non-zero terms in the series expansion for $\ln(\sec x)$ in ascending powers of x.

SUMMARY

In this section we have had a thorough look at series. We began with the binomial expansion:

$$(1 + x)^n = 1 + \frac{nx}{1!} + \frac{n(n-1)\,x^2}{2!} + \frac{n(n-1)\,(n-2)\,x^3}{3!} + \dots$$

which is

● always valid if n is a positive integer
● valid if n is *not* a positive integer if $|x| < 1$

We then developed and used the following series involving natural numbers:

$$\sum_{r=1}^{r=n} r = \frac{n\,(n+1)}{2}$$

$$\sum_{r=1}^{r=n} r^2 = \frac{n(n+1)\,(2n+1)}{6}$$

$$\sum_{r=1}^{r=n} r^3 = \left[\frac{n(n+1)}{2}\right]^2$$

Finally we used Maclaurin Series:

$$f(x) = f(0) + \frac{f'(0)\,x}{1!} + \frac{f''(0)\,x^2}{2!} + \frac{f'''(0)\,x^3}{3!} + \dots$$

to obtain expansions for such as e^x and $\sin x$.

Trigonometry

INTRODUCTION In this section we are going to look again at trigonometry. We've already seen how to solve the equation sin x = 0.5, over the domain $0 < x < \pi$, (answers are $x = \frac{\pi}{6}$ and $\frac{5\pi}{6}$) but what are the solutions for $x \in$ Á? And what about the solutions to an equation such as 2 cos x + 3 sin x = 1? We'll be answering questions like these in this Section.

Solutions for sin x = k

If we were asked to sketch a sine curve, we would probably put down something like:

Figure 3.1

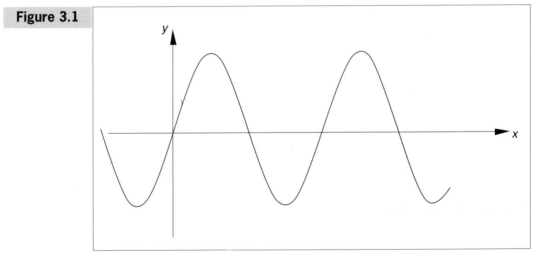

and understand that the curve went on and on in both directions. This property of the sine function, of repeating itself exactly every 360°, means that there are an infinite number of solutions for the equation sin x = k, provided k lies between –1 and +1. Let's have a look at a graphical illustration of the equation $\sin x = \frac{1}{2}$, for example:

Figure 3.2

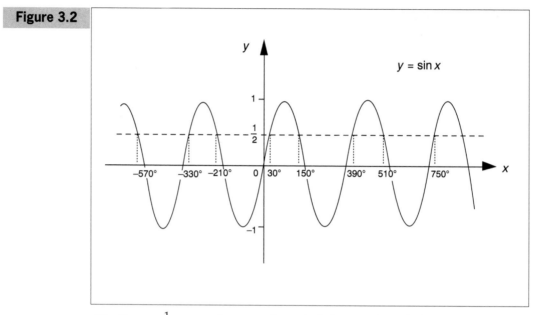

The line $y = \frac{1}{2}$ crosses the curve in an infinite number of places. We can see
that the x-co-ordinates of these points of intersection fall into two groups:

$$30° \quad + \quad \text{some multiple of } 360°$$
$$\text{and} \quad 150° \quad + \quad \text{some multiple of } 360°$$

There is quite a neat way of combining these two groups. Let's take the
solutions in order, starting with 30°:

$$30° \quad = \quad 0° + 30° \quad = \quad 0 \times 180° + 30°$$
$$150° \quad = \quad 180° - 30° \quad = \quad 1 \times 180° - 30°$$
$$390° \quad = \quad 360° + 30° \quad = \quad 2 \times 180° + 30°$$
$$510° \quad = \quad 540° - 30° \quad = \quad 3 \times 180° - 30°$$
$$750° \quad = \quad 720° + 30° \quad = \quad 4 \times 180° + 30°$$

Can you see the pattern? Each solution contains a multiple of 180°: if the
multiple is even, you add 30°; if it is odd, you subtract 30°. We can write
this in one formula as:

$$x = n180° + (-1)^n 30°, \text{ where } n \text{ is an integer}$$

n can be positive or negative or zero, so that the one formula covers all the
possible solutions. We call this the general solution in degrees. If we were
asked for the general solution in radians, we would write:

$$x = n\pi + (-1)^n \frac{\pi}{6}, \text{ where } n \text{ is an integer.}$$

Let's have a look at the other two functions, $\cos x$ and $\tan x$, which are
actually more straightforward.

Solutions for cos $x = k$

We'll start by illustrating the equation $\cos x = \frac{1}{2}$

($\cos x$ is an even function – its graph is symmetrical about the y-axis):

Figure 3.3

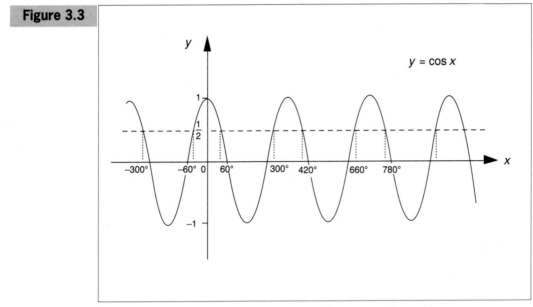

Using the symmetry of the curve, the solutions can be written as

$$0° \pm 60°$$
$$360° \pm 60°$$
$$720° \pm 60°$$

And so each solution is an integer multiple of 360° plus/minus 60°. Thus the general solutions can be written in degrees as

$$x = n360° \pm 60°, \text{ where } n \text{ is an integer.}$$

In radians, this general solution becomes

$$x = 2n\pi \pm \frac{\pi}{3}, \text{ where } n \text{ is an integer.}$$

Solutions for tan $x = k$

This has an easier solution, because the graph repeats itself every 180° and generally takes any one value only once in this cycle. Let's look at $\tan x = \frac{1}{\sqrt{3}}$:

Figure 3.4

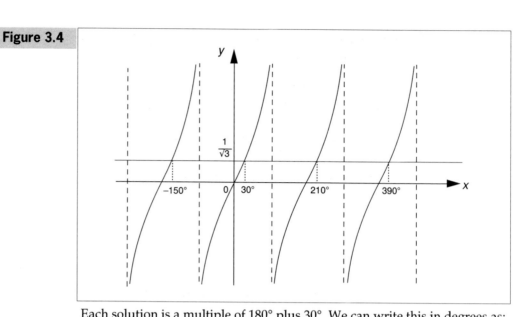

Each solution is a multiple of 180° plus 30°. We can write this in degrees as:

$$x = n180° + 30°, \text{ where } n \text{ is an integer}$$

In radians the general solution becomes

$$x = n\pi + \frac{\pi}{6}, \text{ where } n \text{ is an integer.}$$

Example

Write down (or obtain) the general solutions (in both degrees and radians) for the following equations:

(a) $\sin x = -\frac{1}{2}$ (b) $2 \cos x = \sqrt{3}$ (c) $\tan x = 1$ (d) $\sin 3x = \frac{1}{2}$

(e) $2 \cos 2x + 1 = 0$

Solutions

(a)   Using the calculator, $\sin x = -\frac{1}{2}$ gives $x = -30°$

$\therefore$ $x = n180° + (-1)^n(-30°)$ i.e. $x = n180° - (-1)^n 30°$, for integer n

In radians this can be written as $x = n\pi - (-1)^n \frac{\pi}{6}$

(b)   Using the calculator, $\cos x = \dfrac{\sqrt{3}}{2}$ gives $x = 30°$

$\therefore$ $x = n360° \pm 30°$ or $x = 2n\pi \pm \dfrac{\pi}{6}$

(c)   Using the calculator, $\tan x = 1$ gives $x = 45°$

$\therefore$ $x = n180° + 45°$ or $x = n\pi + \dfrac{\pi}{4}$

(d) We need to be careful over this one. Using the calculator, $\sin 3x = \frac{1}{2}$ gives an angle of 30°

∴ The general solution in degrees can be written as

$3x = n180° + (-1)^n\, 30°$ i.e. $x = n60° + (-1)^n\, 10°$

In radians, the general solution becomes $x = \dfrac{n\pi}{3} + (-1)^n\, \dfrac{\pi}{18}$.

(e) Using the calculator, $\cos 2x = -\frac{1}{2}$ gives an angle of 120°

∴ $2x = n360° \pm 120°$ i.e. $x = n180° \pm 60°$

In radians, the general solution becomes $x = n\pi \pm \dfrac{\pi}{3}$.

You should now be able to answer Exercise 1 on page 47.

Sums and differences of sines

Let's start by remembering the compound angle formulae for $\sin (A + B)$, etc.:

$$\sin (A + B) \equiv \sin A \cos B + \cos A \sin B \qquad \ldots ①$$
$$\sin (A - B) \equiv \sin A \cos B - \cos A \sin B \qquad \ldots ②$$

When we add these two identities, we get:

$$\sin (A + B) + \sin (A - B) \equiv 2 \sin A \cos B \qquad \ldots ③$$

and subtracting gives

$$\sin (A + B) - \sin (A - B) \equiv 2 \cos A \sin B \qquad \ldots ④$$

This is what we're after – ③ and ④ tell us how to change sums and differences into products, but at the moment they are not in the most handy form. We would prefer something like:

$$\sin P + \sin Q = \text{product}$$

and $\quad \sin P - \sin Q = \text{product}$

Let's take the identity ③ and put:

$$A + B = P \ \text{ and } \ A - B = Q$$

Adding these equations,

$$2A = P + Q \Rightarrow A = \frac{P + Q}{2}$$

and subtracting,

$$2B = P - Q \Rightarrow B = \frac{P - Q}{2}$$

Now rewrite the identities ③ and④ using these relationships:

$$\sin P + \sin Q \equiv 2 \sin \frac{P + Q}{2} \cos \frac{P - Q}{2}$$

$$\sin P - \sin Q \equiv 2 \cos \frac{P + Q}{2} \sin \frac{P - Q}{2}$$

You can see some examples of this type in the following equations.

Examples   **1**   Solve the equation

$$\sin 2x + \sin 4x = 0 \quad 0 \le x \le 180°$$

2   Give the general solution in radians for the equation

$$\sin 3x = \sin x$$

Solutions   **1**   Using the first of the identities above, we can rewrite this equation as

$$2 \sin \frac{2x + 4x}{2} \cos \frac{2x - 4x}{2} = 0$$

i.e. $2 \sin 3x \cos (-x) = 0$

so either   (a) $\sin 3x = 0$ or (b) $\cos (-x) = 0$.

(a) $\sin 3x = 0$,

The calculator gives an angle of $0°$

$\therefore \ 3x = n180° \pm 0°$

i.e. $x = n60°$

i.e. $x = 0, 60°, 120°$ or $180°$

(b) $\cos (-x) = 0$. Cos is an even function, as we've seen, so $\cos (-x) = \cos x$, and we can put

$\cos x = 0 \Rightarrow x = 90°$

Collecting these together:

$x = 0°, 60°, 90°, 120°$ or $180°$ if x is in the range $0 \le x \le 180°$

2 Rearrange this to give:

$$\sin 3x - \sin x = 0$$

Then use the second of our identities to rewrite this as:

$$2 \cos \frac{3x + x}{2} \sin \frac{3x - x}{2} = 0$$

i.e. $2 \cos 2x \sin x = 0$

so either (a) $\cos 2x = 0$ or (b) $\sin x = 0$

(a) $\cos 2x = 0$

so $2x = 2n\pi \pm \dfrac{\pi}{2}$

i.e. $x = n\pi \pm \dfrac{\pi}{4}$, where n is an integer

(b) $\sin x = 0$

so $x = n\pi + (-1)^n\, 0$

i.e. $x = n\pi$, where n is an integer

Collecting these:

$$x = n\pi \pm \frac{\pi}{4} \text{ or } x = n\pi, \text{ where } n \text{ is an integer}$$

Cosine functions

With practice you will be able to work out equations like those in the examples above. Let's complete our identities by looking at the corresponding results for sums and differences of cos functions:

Using $\cos (A + B)$ $=$ $\cos A \cos B - \sin A \sin B$

and $\cos (A - B)$ $=$ $\cos A \cos B + \sin A \sin B$

we find, by adding and subtracting these and putting

$$A = \frac{P + Q}{2}, \; B = \frac{P - Q}{2}$$

as before, that:

$$\cos P + \cos Q = 2 \cos \frac{P + Q}{2} \cos \frac{P - Q}{2}$$

$$\cos P - \cos Q = -2 \sin \frac{P + Q}{2} \sin \frac{P - Q}{2} \quad \text{(Note the sign)}$$

Example	Give the general solution in degrees for the equation:

$$\cos 3x - \cos x = \sin x$$

Solution	Using the subtraction rules above we get:

$$-2 \sin\left(\frac{3x + x}{2}\right) \sin\left(\frac{3x - x}{2}\right) = \sin x$$

i.e. $-2 \sin 2x \sin x = \sin x$

So either (a) $\sin x = 0$ or (b) $-2 \sin 2x = 1$

(a) $\sin x = 0$ so $x = n\,180°$

(b) $\sin 2x = -\dfrac{1}{2}$

so $2x = n\,180° - (-1)^n\,30°$ i.e. $x = n\,90° - (-1)^n\,15°$

Collecting them together we get

$x = n\,180°$ or $n\,90° - (-1)^n\,15°$

You should now be able to answer Exercises 2–5 on page 47.

Combining sine and cosine curves

Knowing the compound angle formulae for sine and cosine, we can probably write down the expansion of expressions like $2 \sin(\theta - 60°)$ and $3\sqrt{2} \cos(\theta + 45°)$ without too much trouble. They would be:

$$2 \sin(\theta - 60°) = 2\,[\sin \theta \cos 60° - \cos \theta \sin 60°]$$

$$= 2\left[\sin \theta \times \frac{1}{2} - \cos \theta \times \frac{\sqrt{3}}{2}\right]$$

$$= \sin \theta - \sqrt{3} \cos \theta$$

and $3\sqrt{2} \cos(\theta + 45°)$ $= 3\sqrt{2}\,[\cos \theta \cos 45° - \sin \theta \sin 45°]$

$$= 3\sqrt{2}\left[\cos \theta \times \frac{1}{\sqrt{2}} - \sin \theta \times \frac{1}{\sqrt{2}}\right]$$

$$= 3 \cos \theta - 3 \sin \theta$$

We are now going to see how we can reverse this procedure. Given something like:

$$f(\theta) = 3 \cos \theta - 4 \sin \theta$$

how can we express this as a single trigonometrical function?

Combining

The method we use is much the same as for partial fractions – we assume the basic form of the answer and then try and calculate the details. We can see from the second of our examples, which is quite similar, that the combination is going to be something like:

$$R \cos (\theta + \alpha)$$

where we have to find R and α. Putting this equal to our original function and expanding, we have:

$$3 \cos \theta - 4 \sin \theta \equiv R [\cos \theta \cos \alpha - \sin \theta \sin \alpha]$$
$$\equiv R \cos \theta \cos \alpha - R \sin \theta \sin \alpha$$

We have to choose the constants R and α so that the two sides are identically equal. Putting $\theta = 0$ and remembering that $\cos 0 = 1$ and $\sin 0 = 0$, we get:

$$3 = R \cos \alpha \qquad \qquad \dots ①$$

Putting $\theta = 90°$ and remembering that $\cos 90° = 0$ and $\sin 90° = 1$, we get:

$$-4 = -R \sin \alpha \Rightarrow 4 = R \sin \alpha \qquad \qquad \dots ②$$

Squaring both of these,

$$9 = R^2 \cos^2 \alpha \text{ and } 16 = R^2 \sin^2 \alpha$$

and adding,

$$25 = R^2 \cos^2 \alpha + R^2 \sin^2 \alpha$$
$$= R^2 [\cos^2 \alpha + \sin^2 \alpha]$$
$$= R^2 \text{ (because } \cos^2 \alpha + \sin^2 \alpha = 1)$$

We get: $R = 5$ (taking the positive solution only)

Dividing ② by ① gives: $\dfrac{R \sin \alpha}{R \cos \alpha} = \dfrac{4}{3}$

$$\tan \alpha = \frac{4}{3}$$

$$\alpha = \tan^{-1} \frac{4}{3} = 53.1° \text{ (to one d.p.)}$$

(Always assume that α is acute in these questions.)

Altogether then,

$$3 \cos \theta - 4 \sin \theta = 5 \cos (\theta + 53.1°)$$

You should now be able to answer Exercise 6 on page 47.

There are advantages in expressing the sums and differences in this form – equations are easier to solve and the maximum and minimum values can be read off directly. Let's have a look at an example of this.

Example (a) Express $2 \cos x + 3 \sin x$ in the form $R \cos (x - \alpha)$, where $R > 0$ and $0 < \alpha < 90°$, giving the exact value of R and the value of α correct to the nearest $0.1°$.

(b) Find all values of x in the interval $0°$ to $360°$ satisfying

$$2 \cos x + 3 \sin x = 1$$

(c) Find the maximum and minimum values of $\dfrac{1}{4 + 2 \cos x + 3 \sin x}$

distinguishing between them.

Solution (a) Let $2 \cos x + 3 \sin x = R \cos (x - \alpha)$

$$= R \cos x \cos \alpha + R \sin x \sin \alpha$$

$x = 0° :$ $\quad 2 = R \cos \alpha$ ... ①

$x = 90° :$ $\quad 3 = R \sin \alpha$ ... ②

Squaring these and adding,

$4 = R^2 \cos^2 \alpha,$ $\quad 9 = R^2 \sin^2 \alpha,$ and

$13 = R^2 \cos^2 \alpha + R^2 \sin^2 \alpha$

$= R^2 (\cos^2 \alpha + \sin^2 \alpha)$

$= R^2$ because $\cos^2 \alpha + \sin^2 \alpha = 1$

i.e. $\quad R = \sqrt{13}$

Dividing ② by ①, $\dfrac{R \sin \alpha}{R \cos \alpha} = \dfrac{3}{2}$

i.e. $\tan \alpha = \dfrac{3}{2} \Rightarrow \alpha = 56.3°$ (to 1 d.p.)

Then $2 \cos x + 3 \sin x = \sqrt{13} \cos (x - 56.3°)$

(b) We can rewrite the given equation as: $\sqrt{13} \cos (x - 56.3°) = 1$

i.e. $\cos (x - 56.3°) = \dfrac{1}{\sqrt{13}}$

But $\cos 73.9° = \dfrac{1}{\sqrt{13}}$

∴ $x - 56.3° = 73.9°$ or $286.1°$

∴ $x = 130.2°$ or $342.4°$ (to 1 d.p.)

(c) Suppose that:

$$f(x) = \dfrac{1}{4 + 2 \cos x + 3 \sin x}$$

$$= \dfrac{1}{4 + \sqrt{13} \cos (x - 56.3°)}$$

We have to think first about $\cos (x - 56.3°)$.

This has a: maximum value of +1 at $x = 56.3°$

    minimum value of –1 at $x = 236.3°$

Then f(x) has a: maximum value of $\dfrac{1}{4 - \sqrt{13}}$ at $x = 236.3°$

    minimum value of $\dfrac{1}{4 + \sqrt{13}}$ at $x = 56.3°$

(Note that the maximum and minimum values are reversed, because the value of the fraction increases as the denominator decreases, and vice versa.)

Have a go at a couple of this type yourself. Don't be put off if the function is in terms of a multiple angle, $3 \cos 5x - 2 \sin 5x$, for example. The working is exactly the same, and the final form would be $R \cos (5x + \alpha)$ as before.

You should now be able to answer Exercises 7–10 on pages 47–48.

Small angle approximations

We saw in Section 2 that the Maclaurin Expansions for $\sin x$ and $\cos x$ (where x is measured in radians) are

$$\sin x = x - \frac{x^3}{3!} + \frac{x^5}{5!} - \dots$$

and $$\cos x = 1 - \frac{x^2}{2!} + \frac{x^4}{4!} - \dots$$

Similarly it can be shown that

$$\tan x = x + \frac{x^3}{3} + \frac{2x^5}{15} + \dots$$

And so if x is small (so the powers of x higher than two can be ignored) we get the approximations:

$$\sin x \approx x$$

$$\cos x \approx 1 - \frac{x^2}{2}$$

$$\tan x \approx x$$

You need to be really familiar with these approximations.

Example   If θ is small and in radians, find approximations for the following:

(a) $\sin 2\theta$ (b) $\cos 3\theta$ (c) $\dfrac{\sin 3\theta}{\tan 4\theta}$ (d) $\dfrac{\tan^2 \theta}{1 - \cos \theta}$ (e) $\sec \theta$.

| Solution | (a) $\sin 2\theta \approx 2\theta$ |

(b) $\cos 3\theta \approx 1 - \dfrac{(3\theta)^2}{2} = 1 - \dfrac{9\theta^2}{2}$

(c) $\dfrac{\sin 3\theta}{\tan 4\theta} \approx \dfrac{3\theta}{4\theta} = 0.75$

(d) $\dfrac{\tan^2\theta}{1 - \cos\theta} \approx \dfrac{\theta^2}{1 - (1 - \frac{\theta^2}{2})} = \dfrac{\theta^2}{\frac{\theta^2}{2}} = 2$

(e) $\sec\theta = \dfrac{1}{\cos\theta} = \dfrac{1}{1 - \frac{\theta^2}{2}}$

$$= \left(1 - \frac{\theta^2}{2}\right)^{-1} *$$

$$= 1 + \frac{(-1)}{1}\left(\frac{-\theta^2}{2}\right) + \frac{(-1)\,(-2)}{2!}\left(\frac{-\theta^2}{2}\right)^2 + \dots$$

$$= 1 + \frac{\theta^2}{2}$$

(*A binomial expansion is needed here.)

You should now be able to answer Exercises 11–14 on page 48.

Inverse trigonometric functions and their graphs

We saw in P1 how to find the inverse of a $1 - 1$ function, we simply reflect the original function in the line $y = x$. Let's now look at the inverse functions for $\sin x$, $\cos x$ and $\tan x$ over suitable domains.

sin⁻¹ x

The function $f : x \mapsto \sin x \left(x \in \mathbb{R}, -\dfrac{\pi}{2} \leq x \leq \dfrac{\pi}{2}\right)$ is 1 to 1 (but it wouldn't have been had we taken a larger domain). Consequently we can find the inverse function f^{-1} by reflecting in the line $y = x$.

Figure 3.5

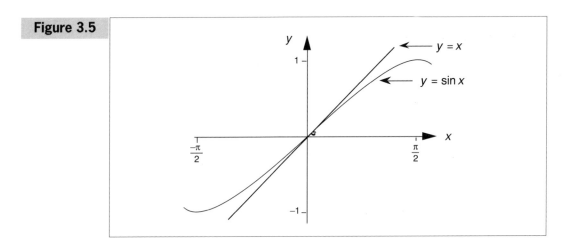

(You might like to check that $y = x$ is a *tangent* to $y = \sin x$ at the origin.)

Figure 3.6

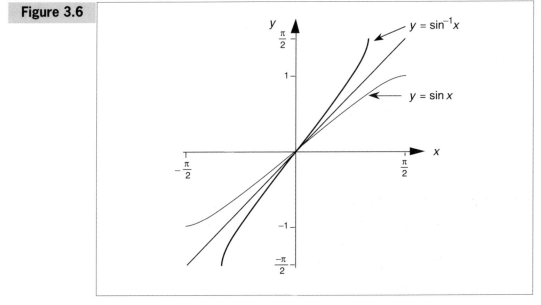

∴   The function f^{-1} is given by

$$f^{-1} : x \mapsto \sin^{-1} x \ (x \in \mathbb{R}, -1 \le x \le 1)$$

(Remember: the *domain* of f^{-1} is the *range* of f).

cos⁻¹ x

The function $f : x \mapsto \cos x$ $(x \in \mathbb{R}, 0 \leq x \leq \pi)$ is 1 to 1 (but it wouldn't have been over a larger domain). The inverse function f^{-1} is found by reflecting in the line $y = x$.

Figure 3.7

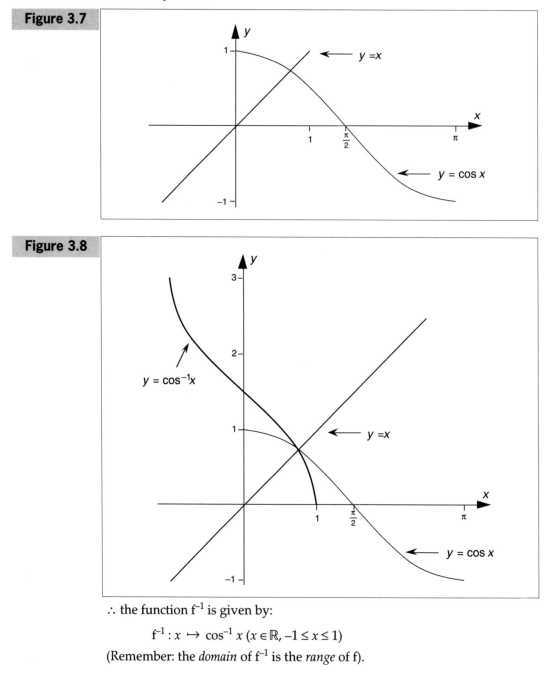

Figure 3.8

∴ the function f^{-1} is given by:

$$f^{-1} : x \mapsto \cos^{-1} x \ (x \in \mathbb{R}, -1 \leq x \leq 1)$$

(Remember: the *domain* of f^{-1} is the *range* of f).

tan⁻¹ x

The function f: $x \mapsto \tan x \left(x \in \mathbb{R}, -\frac{\pi}{2} < x < \frac{\pi}{2}\right)$ is 1 to 1 (but it wouldn't have been for a larger domain). The inverse function f^{-1} is found by reflecting in the line $y = x$.

Figure 3.9

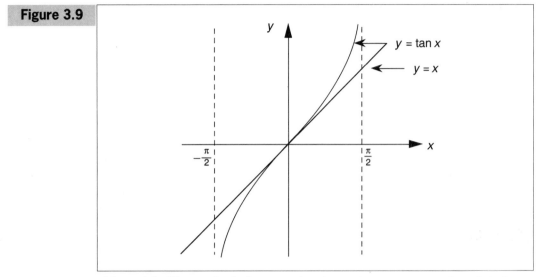

(You might like to check that $y = x$ is a *tangent* to $y = \tan x$ at the origin.)

Figure 3.10

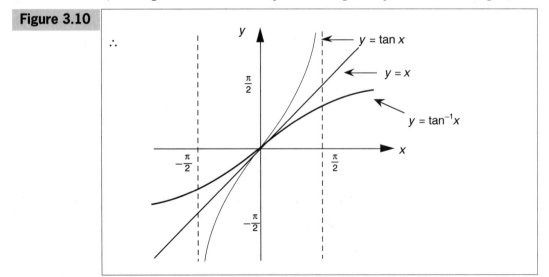

∴   the function f^{-1} is given by:

$f^{-1} : x \mapsto \tan^{-1} x \ (x \in \mathbb{R}, -\infty < x < \infty)$

(Remember: the *domain* of f^{-1} is the *range* of f.)

Differentiating inverse trigonometric functions

To differentiate the function $y = \sin^{-1} x$, we have to turn this equation round to give:

$$\sin y = x$$

Differentiation with respect to x now gives:

$$\cos y \, \frac{dy}{dx} = 1$$

so

$$\frac{dy}{dx} = \frac{1}{\cos y}$$

We would like the result to be in terms of x, so we use the fact that $\sin y = x$ and that $\sin^2 y + \cos^2 y = 1$ to give:

$$x^2 + \cos^2 y = 1 \Rightarrow \cos^2 y = 1 - x^2 \Rightarrow \cos y = \sqrt{1 - x^2}$$

and putting this back in,

$$\frac{dy}{dx} = \frac{1}{\sqrt{1 - x^2}}$$

Differentiating $\cos^{-1} x$ gives exactly the same result except that there is a minus sign in front (because cos differentiated gives $-\sin$), i.e.

if $y = \cos^{-1} x$, then $\dfrac{dy}{dx} = -\dfrac{1}{\sqrt{1 - x^2}}$

Similarly if $y = \tan^{-1} x$, then $\dfrac{dy}{dx} = \dfrac{1}{1 + x^2}$

As with other functions we quite frequently have to differentiate a function of a function, something like $\sin^{-1} x^2$ or $\tan^{-1} (1 - x)$ for example. With this in mind, we can generalise these last differentials.

$$y = \sin^{-1} f(x) \quad \Rightarrow \quad \frac{dy}{dx} = f'(x) \times \frac{1}{\sqrt{1 - f(x)^2}}$$

$$y = \cos^{-1} f(x) \quad \Rightarrow \quad \frac{dy}{dx} = -f'(x) \times \frac{1}{\sqrt{1 - f(x)^2}}$$

$$y = \tan^{-1} f(x) \quad \Rightarrow \quad \frac{dy}{dx} = f'(x) \times \frac{1}{1 + f(x)^2}$$

So that, for example,

$$y = \sin^{-1}(x^2) \quad \Rightarrow \quad \frac{dy}{dx} = 2x \times \frac{1}{\sqrt{1-(x^2)^2}} = \frac{2x}{\sqrt{1-x^4}}$$

and

$$y = \tan^{-1}(1-x) \quad \Rightarrow \quad \frac{dy}{dx} = -1 \times \frac{1}{1+(1-x)^2} = \frac{-1}{x^2-2x+2}$$

You should now be able to answer Exercises 15–17 on page 48.

EXERCISES

1 Find general solutions for the following equations, giving each answer both in degrees and radians.

(a) $\sin x = \dfrac{\sqrt{3}}{2}$ (b) $\cos x = -\dfrac{1}{\sqrt{2}}$ (c) $\tan x = -1$ (d) $\sin x = -1$

(e) $\cos x = 0$ (f) $\tan x = 0$ (g) $\sin 2x = 0.5$

(h) $\cos 2x = \dfrac{\sqrt{3}}{2}$ (i) $\tan\left(x - \dfrac{\pi}{3}\right) = 1$

2 Solve the equation $\cos 4\theta + \cos 2\theta = 0$ for $0 \le \theta \le 180°$.

3 Find all solutions for:

$$\cos \theta + \cos 5\theta = 2 \cos 2\theta, \quad 0 \le \theta \le 360°$$

4 Find all values of θ for which $0 \le \theta \le \dfrac{\pi}{2}$ and $\sin 8\theta = \sin 2\theta$

5 Solve the equation $\sin 2\theta + \sin 6\theta = 2 \sin 4\theta$ for $0 \le \theta \le \pi$

6 Find the values of R and α (where $R > 0$ and α is acute) such that:

(a) $\sqrt{3} \cos \theta - \sin \theta = R \cos (\theta + \alpha)$
(b) $\cos \theta + \sin \theta = R \cos (\theta - \alpha)$ $\Big\}$

7 Find, to the nearest 0.1 of a degree, the acute angle α for which:

$$4 \cos \theta - 3 \sin \theta \equiv 5 \cos (\theta + \alpha)$$

Calculate the values of θ in the interval $-180° \le \theta \le 180°$ for which the function: $f(\theta) = 4 \cos \theta - 3 \sin \theta - 4$
attains its greatest value, its least value and the value of zero.

8 Calculate, to one decimal place, in the interval $0° \le x \le 360°$, those values of x for which:

$$3 \cos x + \sin x = 2$$

9 (a) Express $\cos\theta - \sin\theta$ in the form $R\cos(\theta + \alpha)$, where R is positive and $0 < \alpha < \dfrac{\pi}{2}$

(b) Find both solutions, in the interval $0 \le x \le 2\pi$, of the equation:

$$\cos 2x - \sin 2x = \sqrt{2}$$

10 Solve the equation $4\sin\theta - 7\cos\theta + 3 = 0$, giving all values of θ between $0°$ and $360°$ correct to the nearest $0.1°$.

11 If θ is small and in radians, give the approximate value of the following:

(a) $\sin 4\theta$ (b) $\cos 2\theta$ (c) $\tan 3\theta$

(d) $\cos^2 2\theta$ (e) $\dfrac{\tan 2\theta}{\theta}$ (f) $\dfrac{\theta\sin 3\theta}{1 - \cos\theta}$

12 Express $\sin\left(\dfrac{1}{6}\pi + x\right)$ in terms of $\sin x$ and $\cos x$. Hence show that, when x is sufficiently small for terms of x^3 and higher powers of x to be ignored:

$$4\sin\left(\dfrac{1}{6}\pi + x\right) = 2 + (2\sqrt{3})\,x - x^2$$

13 Show that, when x is small:

$$(1 - \sin^2 2x)\cos 3x \approx 1 - \dfrac{17}{2}x^2$$

14 It is given that one root of the equation:

$$\cos x - 6\sin x = x^2$$

is sufficiently small for powers of x above the second to be neglected. Use approximations for $\cos x$ and $\sin x$ to obtain an estimate for this root to two decimal places.

15 Differentiate with respect to x:

(a) $\sin^{-1}(4x)$ (b) $\cos^{-1}(2x)$ (c) $\tan^{-1}(2x)$ (d) $\cos^{-1}(-x)$

(e) $\tan^{-1}x^2$ (f) $\sin^{-1}(e^x)$ (g) $\cos^{-1}\left(\dfrac{1}{x}\right)$ (h) $\tan^{-1}\left(\dfrac{1}{x^2}\right)$

16 Find the positive constant R and the acute angle A for which

$$\cos x + \sin x \equiv R\cos(x - A)$$

(a) Find the general solution of the equation

$$\cos x + \sin x = 1.$$

(b) Deduce the greatest value of $\sin x + \cos x$.

17 Differentiate the following with respect to x:

(a) $x\sin^{-1}x$ (b) $x^2\cos^{-1}x$ (c) $x + \tan^{-1}x$ (d) $\sqrt{x}\tan^{-1}\sqrt{x}$

SUMMARY   You should now be able to:

- use the following general solutions in radians:

$$\sin x = k \quad \Rightarrow \quad x = n\pi + (-1)^n \alpha$$
$$\cos x = k \quad \Rightarrow \quad x = 2n\pi \pm \alpha$$
$$\tan x = k \quad \Rightarrow \quad x = n\pi + \alpha$$

where α is the value obtained from the calculator and n is an integer

- use the following general solutions in degrees:

$$\sin x = k \quad \Rightarrow \quad x = n180° + (-1)^n \alpha°$$
$$\cos x = k \quad \Rightarrow \quad x = n360° \pm \alpha°$$
$$\tan x = k \quad \Rightarrow \quad x = n180° + \alpha°$$

where $\alpha°$ is the value obtained from the calculator and n is an integer

- express $a \cos \theta + b \sin \theta$ in the form $R \cos (\theta - \alpha)$ where $R > 0$ and $0 < \alpha < \dfrac{\pi}{2}$

- use the result that $R \cos (\theta - \alpha)$ attains its maximum value of R when $\theta - \alpha = 0$

- use the result that $R \cos (\theta - \alpha)$ attains its minimum value of $- R$ when $\theta - \alpha = 180°$ (or $\theta - \alpha = \pi$)

- use the following approximations, where x is small and measured in radians:

$$\sin x \approx x$$
$$\cos x \approx 1 - \frac{x^2}{2}$$
$$\tan x \approx x$$

- sketch the graphs of the inverse functions $\sin^{-1}x$, $\cos^{-1}x$ and $\tan^{-1}x$ giving, in each case, the range and domain

- use the following differentiation results:

$$y = \sin^{-1} f(x) \quad \Rightarrow \quad \frac{dy}{dx} = f'(x) \times \frac{1}{\sqrt{1 - f^2(x)}}$$

$$y = \cos^{-1} f(x) \quad \Rightarrow \quad \frac{dy}{dx} = f'(x) \times \frac{-1}{\sqrt{1 - f^2(x)}}$$

$$y = \tan^{-1} f(x) \quad \Rightarrow \quad \frac{dy}{dx} = f'(x) \times \frac{1}{1 + f^2(x)}$$

Hyperbolic functions

INTRODUCTION Hyperbolic functions are defined in terms of e^x and have a number of very useful properties. In particular they are helpful in:

- solving certain types of integration problem
- providing a parametric representation of the hyperbola
- solving certain types of problem in mechanics.

As you will see, hyperbolic functions also have much in common with the trigonometrical functions that we have already studied. Once we've covered the basics, we'll look at their inverses, derivatives and integrals.

Definitions

Before we can investigate the properties of hyperbolic functions, we must clearly know how they are defined – and how they are pronounced. Their definitions and pronunciations are:

function	definition	pronunciation
sinh x	$\frac{1}{2}(e^x - e^{-x})$	shine
cosh x	$\frac{1}{2}(e^x + e^{-x})$	cosh
tanh x	$\dfrac{\sinh x}{\cosh x}$	tansh (or than)
sech x	$\dfrac{1}{\cosh x}$	shec (or setch)
cosech x	$\dfrac{1}{\sinh x}$	coshec (cosetch)
coth x	$\dfrac{1}{\tanh x}$	coth

Note: tanh, sech, cosech and coth are defined in terms of sinh and cosh in exactly the same way that the trigonometrical functions tan, sec, cosec and cot are defined in terms of sin and cos.

Try to commit these definitions to memory right away. In particular, remember the difference between sinh and cosh:

<u>si</u>nh has a m<u>in</u>us where c<u>os</u>h has a p<u>los</u>!

This may sound silly, but it can be very effective.

Examples

1 Show that $\tanh x = \dfrac{e^{2x} - 1}{e^{2x} + 1}$

2 Express coth x in terms of e^{-2x}

3 Show that $\cosh x + \sinh x = e^x$

and write down a similar result for $\cosh x - \sinh x$

4 Use the findings of problem 3 to show that $\cosh^2 x - \sinh^2 x = 1$

5 Show that $\sinh^2 x = \frac{1}{2}\cosh 2x - \frac{1}{2}$ and write down a similar result for $\cosh^2 x$

Solutions

The solutions to these problems are summarised below.

1 Use the basic definitions of tanh x, sinh x and cosh x, then cancel the $\frac{1}{2}$ in the resulting fraction and multiply top and bottom by e^x.

2 Use the same approach as in 1, but multiply top and bottom by e^{-x}.

This gives coth $x = \dfrac{1 + e^{-2x}}{1 - e^{-2x}}$.

3 The definitions of sinh and cosh are all that are needed here.

The useful results are

$$\cosh x + \sinh x = e^x$$

and $\cosh x - \sinh x = e^{-x}$

4 $\cosh^2 x - \sinh^2 x = \left[\cosh x + \sinh x\right]\left[\cosh x - \sinh x\right]$

$$= e^x e^{-x} = 1$$

5 $\sinh^2 x = \frac{1}{4}(e^x - e^{-x})^2 = \frac{1}{4}(e^{2x} - 2 + e^{-2x})$

$$= \frac{1}{4}(e^{2x} + e^{-2x}) - \frac{1}{2}$$

$$= \frac{1}{2}\cosh 2x - \frac{1}{2}$$

A similar approach shows that:

$$\cosh^2 x = \tfrac{1}{2}\cosh 2x + \tfrac{1}{2}$$

Useful identities

We will now discover a few helpful facts about hyperbolic functions. In the process we will see how they can be manipulated, and will pick up valuable information for later use.

cosh² x – sinh² x = 1

This property can be proved in a number of ways – for example, by following the series of steps indicated in the previous exercise. Here, however, we will do it from scratch.

By definition:

$$\cosh^2 x - \sinh^2 x = \tfrac{1}{4}(e^x + e^{-x})^2 - \tfrac{1}{4}(e^x - e^{-x})^2$$
$$= \tfrac{1}{4}\left[(e^{2x} + 2 + e^{-2x}) - (e^{2x} - 2 + e^{-2x})\right]$$
$$= \tfrac{1}{4}(e^{2x} + 2 + e^{-2x} - e^{2x} + 2 - e^{-2x})$$
$$= \tfrac{1}{4}(4) = 1$$

cosh² x + sinh² x = cosh 2x

Using the definitions again:

$$\cosh^2 x + \sinh^2 x = \tfrac{1}{4}\left[(e^{2x} + 2 + e^{-2x}) + (e^{2x} - 2 + e^{-2x})\right]$$
$$= \tfrac{1}{4}\left[2(e^{2x} + e^{-2x})\right]$$
$$= \tfrac{1}{2}(e^{2x} + e^{-2x})$$
$$= \cosh 2x \text{ by definition.}$$

tanh² x + sech² x = 1

We already know that $\cosh^2 x - \sinh^2 x = 1$

So, dividing by $\cosh^2 x$,

$$1 - \frac{\sinh^2 x}{\cosh^2 x} = \frac{1}{\cosh^2 x}$$

i.e. $1 - \tanh^2 x = \mathrm{sech}^2 x$ by definition.

Rearranging, we get the property we wanted to prove.

sinh (x + y) = sinh x cosh y + cosh x sinh y

It is much easier to prove this from right to left.

Again using the basic definitions:

$$\sinh x \cosh y + \cosh x \sinh y$$

$$= \tfrac{1}{4} \left[(e^x - e^{-x})(e^y + e^{-y}) + (e^x + e^{-x})(e^y - e^{-y}) \right]$$

$$= \tfrac{1}{4} \left[(e^{x+y} - e^{-x-y} + e^{x-y} - e^{-x+y}) + (e^{x+y} - e^{-x-y} - e^{x-y} + e^{-x+y}) \right]$$

$$= \tfrac{1}{4} \left[2(e^{x+y} - e^{-x-y}) \right]$$

$$= \tfrac{1}{2} (e^{x+y} - e^{-x-y})$$

$$= \sinh (x+y) \text{ by definition.}$$

As you can see from the above working, all these 'useful identities' are proved in the same sort of way. It is just a matter of quoting the appropriate definition(s), then using a little algebra – multiplying powers of e in particular – to produce the answer you need. Sometimes things can get rather messy and out of hand, so take care to check your algebra as you go.

Examples   Prove the following identities.

1 $\coth^2 x - \operatorname{cosech}^2 x = 1$

2 $\sinh 2x = 2\sinh x \cosh x$

3 $\cosh (x + y) = \cosh x \cosh y + \sinh x \sinh y$

4 $\cosh^3 x = \tfrac{1}{4} \left[\cosh 3x + 3\cosh x \ \right]$

5 $\sinh^3 x = \tfrac{1}{4} \left[\sinh 3x - 3\sinh x \ \right]$

Solutions   The answers can be summarised below:

1   Divide the identity $\cosh^2 x - \sinh^2 x = 1$ by $\sinh^2 x$ and rearrange.

2   Put $y = x$ in the last of the 'useful identities'.

3   Using the basic definitions, the right-hand side is

$$\tfrac{1}{4} (e^x + e^{-x})(e^y + e^{-y}) + \tfrac{1}{4} (e^x - e^{-x})(e^y - e^{-y})$$

$$= \tfrac{1}{4} \left[2e^x e^y + 2e^{-x} e^{-y} \right]$$

$$= \tfrac{1}{2} (e^{x+y} + e^{-x-y}) = \cosh (x + y)$$

4 Various methods are possible here, for example:

$$\begin{aligned}
\cosh 3x &= \cosh(2x + x) \\
&= \cosh 2x \cosh x + \sinh 2x \sinh x \\
&\quad \text{by the result of problem 3} \\
&= [\cosh^2 x + \sinh^2 x]\cosh x + [2\sinh x \cosh x]\sinh x \\
&\quad \text{by the results of problems 3 and 2} \\
&= \cosh^3 x + 3\sinh^2 x \cosh x \\
&= \cosh^3 x + 3[\cosh^2 x - 1]\cosh x \\
&\quad \text{by the first of the 'useful identities'} \\
&= 4\cosh^3 x - 3\cosh x
\end{aligned}$$

Rearranging produces the required result.

5 Again, several methods are possible. For example, taking the same approach as in problem 4, express $\sinh 3x$ first in terms of the sinh's and cosh's of $2x$ and x, then in terms of $\sinh x$ and $\cosh x$ and finally in the required form.

Osborne's Rule

We have seen that corresponding to each of the standard trigonometric formulae there is one for hyperbolic functions. For example:

$$\cos^2 x + \sin^2 x = 1 \text{ whereas } \cosh^2 x - \sinh^2 x = 1$$

and $\quad \cos^2 x - \sin^2 x = \cos 2x \text{ whereas } \cosh^2 x + \sinh^2 x = \cosh 2x$

We have proved these by going back to the definitions of $\cosh x$ and $\sinh x$ in terms of e^x but Osborne's rule gives us a method for remembering them: *to obtain a hyperbolic formula from a standard trigonometric one, change cos into cosh and sin into sinh, and change the sign for a product of two sines.*

Thus:

$$\sin A \sin B \text{ is changed to } - \sinh A \sinh B$$
$$\sin^2 B = \sin B \sin B \text{ becomes } - \sinh^2 B \text{ and}$$
$$\tan^2 C = \frac{\sin^2 C}{\cos^2 C} \text{ becomes } - \tanh^2 C.$$

Some examples of Osborne's Rule

Below I have listed some trigonometric formulae together with the corresponding hyperbolic ones.

(a) $\sec^2 A = 1 + \tan^2 A$ $\quad\quad\quad$ whereas $\text{sech}^2 A = 1 - \tanh^2 A$

(b) $\sin 3A = 3\sin A - 4\sin^3 A$ $\quad$ whereas $\sinh 3A = 3\sinh A + 4\sinh^3 A$

(c) $\cos (A + B) = \cos A \cos B - \sin A \sin B$

whereas $\cosh (A + B) = \cosh A \cosh B + \sinh A \sinh B$

(d) $\tan (A + B) = \dfrac{\tan A + \tan B}{1 - \tan A \tan B}$

wheres $\tanh (A + B) = \dfrac{\tanh A + \tanh B}{1 + \tanh A \tanh B}$

(e) $\cos 3A = 4 \cos^3 A - 3 \cos A$ whereas $\cosh 3A = 4 \cosh^3 A - 3 \cosh A$.

Solving equations of the type: $A \sinh x + B \cosh x = C$

Equations of this type are favourites with examiners. For this reason alone it is important to know how to tackle them. However, there is an even better reason. When we take a look at inverse hyperbolic functions in the next section, we will need to solve a number of equations of this type.

Example	Solve the equation:

$$6 \sinh x + 9 \cosh x = 7$$

Solution	As always with hyperbolic functions (and most other things in mathematics) follow the rule: 'If in doubt, appeal to the basic definitions.' In this case the equation becomes

$$\frac{6(e^x - e^{-x})}{2} + \frac{9(e^x + e^{-x})}{2} = 7$$

Multiplying by 2 and collecting terms, we get

$$15e^x + 3e^{-x} = 14$$

Now multiply by e^x and bring the $14e^x$ across to the left:

$$15e^{2x} - 14e^x + 3 = 0$$

Although this may look unpromising, it is really no more than a quadratic equation. Set $X = e^x$ and you get:

$$15X^2 - 14X + 3 = 0$$

i.e. $(3X - 1)(5X - 3) = 0$

so that $X = \dfrac{1}{3}$ or $\dfrac{3}{5}$

Remembering that $X = e^x$, you will now see that this means

$$x = \ln \frac{1}{3} \ \text{ or } \ \ln \frac{3}{5}$$

and our original equation is solved as required.

You should now be able to answer Exercises 1–5 on page 66.

Graphing hyperbolic functions

As with any mathematical function of x, it is useful to gain a feel for the way in which sinh x, cosh x, tanh x and the rest vary as x ranges over its permitted set of values. This is best done by drawing graphs.

In the case of the hyperbolic functions, x's permitted set consists of everything between $-\infty$ and $+\infty$. After all, there is nothing to stop us using any value of x we please when we calculate these functions, since e^x is defined for all real x. For the purpose of the graphs, though, we will restrict ourselves to the small number of values in the following tables.

$y = \sinh x$

The calculator gives:

Table 4.1

x	0	1	2	3	4
sinh x	0	1.18	3.63	10.02	27.29

By the way, there is no need to bother with separate calculations for $x = -1$, -2, -3, -4. From the definition of sinh x, it is clear that sinh is an *odd* function, i.e. sinh $(-x) = -\sinh x$. (Check that this is so.)

The resulting graph is shown in Figure 4.1.

Figure 4.1

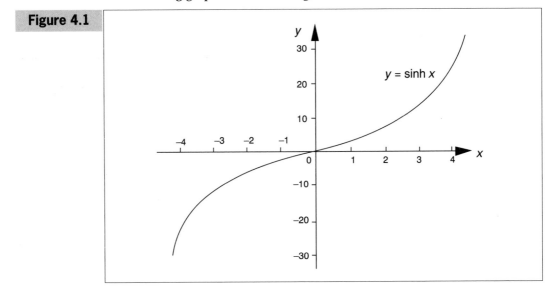

y = cosh x

The calculator gives:

Table 4.2

x	0	1	2	3	4
cosh x	1	1.54	3.76	10.07	27.31

From its definition, cosh x is an *even* function. In other words,
cosh $(-x)$ = cosh x . So once again we need do no calculations for negative x
values. The graph is shown in Figure 4.2.

Figure 4.2

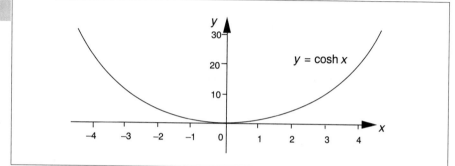

y = tanh x

Since tanh x $= \dfrac{\sinh x}{\cosh x}$, the calculator gives:

Table 4.3

x	0	1	2	3	4
tanh x	0	0.762	0.964	0.995	0.999

Also, tanh x is an *odd* function, i.e. tanh $(-x)$ $= -$ tanh x , and so the graph is:

Figure 4.3

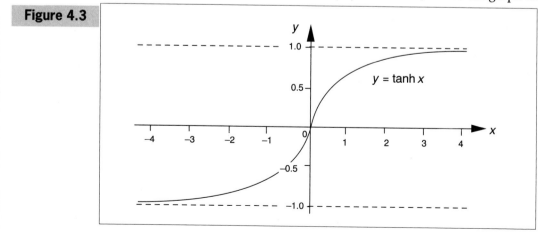

Notice that the dotted lines on the graph represent *asymptotes*. As the table of values suggests, for positive x, tanh x gets closer and closer to 1 without ever quite making it all the way. This means that the graph of $y = $ tanh x gets closer and closer to the line $y = 1$ as x increases – but never quite meets up with it. The behaviour of tanh x can be proved more rigorously by noting that

$$\tanh x = \frac{\sinh x}{\cosh x} = \frac{\frac{1}{2}(e^x - e^{-x})}{\frac{1}{2}(e^x + e^{-x})} = \frac{1 - e^{-2x}}{1 + e^{-2x}}$$

Clearly the numerator of this fraction is always smaller than the denominator. So tanh $x < 1$.

However, since $e^{-2x} \rightarrow 0$ as $x \rightarrow \infty$, it is also clear that both numerator and denominator $\rightarrow 1$ as $x \rightarrow \infty$. Therefore

$$\tanh x \rightarrow 1 \text{ as } x \rightarrow \infty$$

The graphs of sech x, cosech x and coth x can be found in a similar way and are as follows:

Figure 4.4

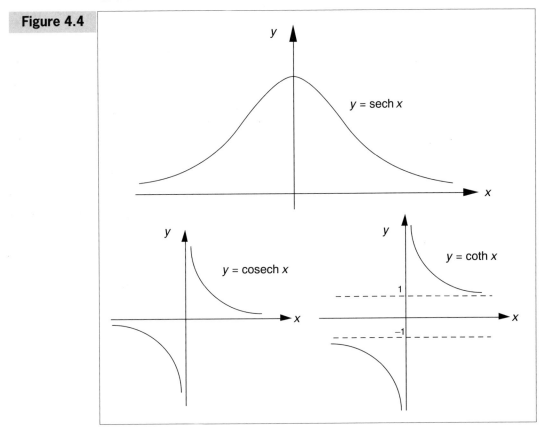

Inverse hyperbolic functions and their graphs

When dealing with the inverses of hyperbolic functions, it is conventional to use the names:

$$\sinh^{-1} x,\ \cosh^{-1} x,\ \tanh^{-1} x\ \text{ etc.}$$

Notice that these names are very similar to the equivalent inverse trigonometrical functions: $\sin^{-1}x$, $\cos^{-1}x$ and $\tan^{-1}x$.

Let's take a look at each of these inverse hyperbolic functions in turn and work out how to draw their graphs.

sinh⁻¹ x

The graph of sinh which we drew in the previous section leaves no doubt about the existence of $\sinh^{-1}$. For any value k that you care to name, you will always be able to find a unique h for which $k = \sinh h$. Just refer to the graph of sinh x, mark the position of k on the y-axis and read off the corresponding value of h from the x-axis. This h is the value of $\sinh^{-1} k$ by definition.

Since the inverse exists, we graph it by reflections

$$y = \sinh x \text{ in the line } y = x$$

This reflection is shown in Figure 4.5.

Figure 4.5

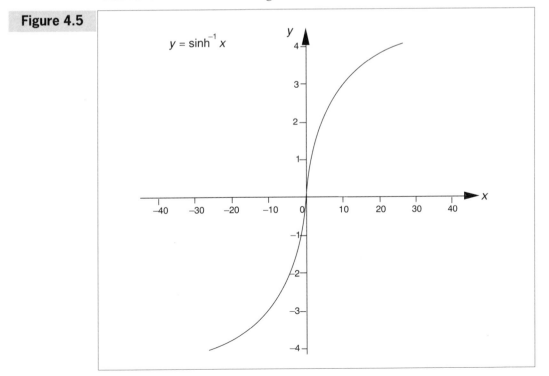

$y = \sinh^{-1} x$

cosh⁻¹ x

We drew the graph of cosh x in the previous section. Unlike sinh, the task of producing cosh's inverse function is complicated by one or two awkward facts.

Firstly, note that cosh x is always 1 or bigger. This means that if k is any value less than 1 it is impossible to find an h for which $k = \cosh h$. Such a number just doesn't exist.

Secondly, notice that if k is any value greater than 1 there are *two* values of h such that $k = \cosh h$. One is positive, the other negative. Which of these should we call $\cosh^{-1} k$?

These problems can be resolved, however, if we are willing to agree that:

for $x < 1$, $\cosh^{-1} x$ is undefined

for $x > 1$, $\cosh^{-1} x$ is defined to be the *positive y* for

which $x = \cosh y$.

(Note that for $x = 1$ there is no doubt. Because 0 is the only value of y for which $\cosh y = 1$, we must have $\cosh^{-1} 1 = 0$)

In fact, this is exactly the way mathematicians choose to define $\cosh^{-1} x$. When we graph the function, we therefore reflect the right hand section of $y = \cosh x$ in the line $y = x$. This reflection is shown in Figure 4.6.

Figure 4.6

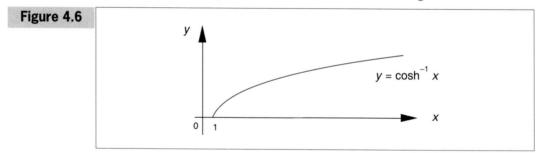

$$y = \cosh^{-1} x$$

tanh⁻¹ x

The graph of tanh in the previous section shows that all its values lie between –1 and +1, implying that, for any h outside this range, there is no k such that $h = \tanh k$. In other words $\tanh^{-1} x$ cannot be defined when $x \leq -1$ or $x \geq 1$. As long as you bear this in mind, though, the rest is easy – just reflect $y = \tanh x$ in the line $y = x$.

Figure 4.7

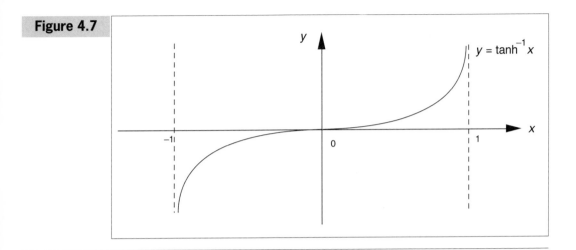

You should now be able to answer Exercises 6–8 on pages 66–67.

Formulae for inverse hyperbolic functions

Of course, it is very helpful to have graphs – but it would be much better still if we could write down formulae for $\sinh^{-1} x$ and the rest. We would then be able to calculate their values directly and might also have a powerful method for finding other properties and uses for these functions. In the following pages we will see that such formulae can be found. Firstly, consider $\sinh^{-1} x$.

sinh⁻¹ x

Once again remember that if $y = \sinh^{-1} x$ then y is a solution of the equation:

$$\sinh y = x$$

We need to solve this equation for y.

Using the basic definition of sinh yet again, we get: $\quad \frac{1}{2}(e^y - e^{-y}) = x$

Therefore $\qquad\qquad\qquad\qquad e^y - 2x - e^{-y} = 0$

and multiplying by e^y, $\qquad\qquad e^{2y} - 2xe^y - 1 = 0$

Set $X = e^y$ to give $\qquad\qquad\quad X^2 - 2xX - 1 = 0$

This quadratic equation has the solution:

$$X = \frac{2x \pm \sqrt{(4x^2 + 4)}}{2} = x \pm \sqrt{(x^2 + 1)}$$

Now $X = e^y$ and so must be positive. However, $\sqrt{(x^2 + 1)} > x$
(Just square both sides and you'll see why.) So $x - \sqrt{(x^2 + 1)}$ is negative.
This means that the only possible root is:

$$X = x + \sqrt{(x^2 + 1)}$$

and therefore

$$y = \ln(x + \sqrt{[x^2 + 1]})$$

In other words we have shown that:

$$\sinh^{-1} x = \ln(x + \sqrt{[x^2 + 1]})$$

cosh⁻¹ x

To find a formula for $y = \cosh^{-1} x$ we have to solve the equation:

$$\cosh y = x$$

(Remember that it is y that we want to find, not x. x is the given value for
which we need the corresponding y.)

Using the basic definition of cosh we get:

$$\frac{e^y + e^{-y}}{2} = x$$

Clearing the fractions and the multiplying through by e^y, we get

$$e^{2y} - 2xe^{\,y} + 1 = 0$$

$\therefore$ Using the quadratic formula, this reduces to

$$e^y = \frac{2x \pm \sqrt{4x^2 - 4}}{2}$$

or $\qquad e^y = x \pm \sqrt{x^2 - 1}$

i.e. $\qquad y = \ln\left(x \pm \sqrt{x^2 - 1}\right)$

But which of the possible values (the one with + or the one with the –) shall
we choose? We faced this problem before when we were looking at the
graph of $y = \cosh^{-1} x$. And as we make the same choice again – we pick the
positive y. This leaves us with

$$\cosh^{-1} x = \ln\left(x + \sqrt{x^2 - 1}\right)$$

tanh⁻¹ x

To find the formula for $y = \tanh^{-1} x$ we have to solve the equation
$\tanh y = x.$

The basic definitions give us:

$$\frac{e^y - e^{-y}}{e^{\,y} + e^{-y}} = x$$

Clearing the fractions and then multiplying through by e^y, we get

$$e^{2y}(1-x) = 1 + x$$

or $\qquad e^{2y} = \dfrac{1+x}{1-x}$

i.e. $\qquad y = \dfrac{1}{2}\ln\left(\dfrac{1+x}{1-x}\right)$

$\therefore \qquad \tanh^{-1} x = \dfrac{1}{2}\ln\left(\dfrac{1+x}{1-x}\right)$

You should now be able to answer Exercises 9–11 on page 67.

Derivatives

As with most other functions, we can differentiate sinh, cosh, $\sinh^{-1}$, $\cosh^{-1}$ and the rest to produce their derivatives. The following table contains all the derivatives that you need to know.

Table 4.4

Function y	derivative $\dfrac{dy}{dx}$
$\sinh x$	$\cosh x$
$\cosh x$	$\sinh x$
$\tanh x$	$\operatorname{sech}^2 x$
$\operatorname{sech} x$	$-\operatorname{sech} x \tanh x$
$\operatorname{cosech} x$	$-\operatorname{cosech} x \coth x$
$\coth x$	$-\operatorname{cosech}^2 x$
$\sinh^{-1} x$	$\dfrac{1}{\sqrt{(x^2+1)}}$
$\cosh^{-1} x$	$\dfrac{1}{\sqrt{(x^2-1)}}$
$\tanh^{-1} x$	$\dfrac{1}{(1-x^2)}$

All these results follow directly from the basic definitions of the functions, using the standard 'rules' of differentiation, but you will also find the earlier identities very useful on occasions. Consider the following proofs:

y = sinh x

By definition, $\qquad y = \frac{1}{2}(e^x - e^{-x})$

and so $\qquad \dfrac{dy}{dx} = \frac{1}{2}(e^x - [-e^{-x}]) \quad = \frac{1}{2}(e^x + e^{-x})$

$\qquad\qquad\qquad = \cosh x$ by definition.

y = tanh x

$$y = \frac{\sinh x}{\cosh x}$$

So, using the quotient rule of differentiation,

i.e. $\qquad$ if $y = \dfrac{u}{v}$, $\quad$ then $\dfrac{dy}{dx} = \dfrac{v\,\dfrac{du}{dx} - u\,\dfrac{dv}{dx}}{v^2}$

$$\frac{dy}{dx} = \frac{\cosh x \cosh x - \sinh x \sinh x}{\cosh^2 x}$$

$$= \frac{\cosh^2 x - \sinh^2 x}{\cosh^2 x}$$

$$= \frac{1}{\cosh^2 x} = \text{sech}^2 x \text{ as required.}$$

Note: Here we have assumed that the derivative of $\cosh x$ is $\sinh x$. (You can prove this later.) We have also used the fact that $\cosh^2 x - \sinh^2 x = 1$ which is one of the useful earlier identities.

y = sinh⁻¹ x

In this case we could use the formula for $\sinh^{-1} x$ that we produced earlier. However, it's just as easy – and possibly more instructive – to take the following approach:

$\qquad\qquad y = \sinh^{-1} x \quad$ implies

$\qquad\qquad \sinh y = x$

and so, using the function-of-a-function rule,

$$\cosh y \, \frac{dy}{dx} = 1$$

Therefore $\qquad \dfrac{dy}{dx} = \dfrac{1}{\cosh y}$

But, by the most familiar of the useful earlier identities,

$$\cosh^2 y = \sinh^2 y + 1 = x^2 + 1$$

and so $\qquad \dfrac{dy}{dx} = \dfrac{1}{\sqrt{(1 + x^2)}}$

y = tanh^{-1} x

$$\tanh y = x$$

Therefore

$$\text{sech}^2 y \, \frac{dy}{dx} = 1$$

$$\frac{dy}{dx} = \frac{1}{\text{sech}^2 y}$$

But, from earlier work, $\text{sech}^2 y = 1 - \tanh^2 y = 1 - x^2$

So

$$\frac{dy}{dx} = \frac{1}{1 - x^2}$$

You are now in a position to tackle any of the functions in the table for yourself.

Integrals

The integrals you need to know and be familiar with are shown in Table 4.5.

Table 4.5

function y	integral $\int y\,dx$
$\sinh x$	$\cosh x$
$\cosh x$	$\sinh x$
$\tanh x$	$\ln(\cosh x)$
$\sinh^{-1} x$	$x \sinh^{-1} x - \sqrt{(x^2 + 1)}$
$\cosh^{-1} x$	$x \cosh^{-1} x - \sqrt{(x^2 - 1)}$
$\tanh^{-1} x$	$x \tanh^{-1} x + \frac{1}{2} \ln(1 - x^2)$

The integrals of $\sinh x$ and $\cosh x$ follow directly from the table of derivatives. The rest can quickly be verified using differentiation to work backwards from the integral. However, to show how you might tackle one of the harder integrals, if you did not already know the answer, let us take a closer look at $\sinh^{-1} x$.

sinh^{-1} x

The technique here is to use integration by parts. If you have forgotten how this works, recall that:

$$\int u \frac{dv}{dx} \, dx = uv - \int v \frac{du}{dx} \, dx$$

where u and v are functions of x. In this case write:

$$\int \sinh^{-1} x \, dx \quad \text{as} \quad \int \sinh^{-1} x \times 1 \, dx$$

So that $u = \sinh^{-1} x$ and $\dfrac{dv}{dx} = 1$

$\therefore \quad \dfrac{du}{dx} = \dfrac{1}{\sqrt{x^2 + 1}}$ and $v = x$

So $\quad \displaystyle\int \sinh^{-1} x \, dx \quad = \int \sinh^{-1} x \times 1 \, dx$

$$= (\sinh^{-1} x) \times x - \int x \times \frac{1}{\sqrt{x^2 + 1}} \, dx$$

$$= x \sinh^{-1} x - \int \frac{x}{\sqrt{x^2 + 1}} \, dx$$

$$= x \sinh^{-1} x - \sqrt{x^2 + 1} \text{ as required.}$$

The integrals of the other inverse functions in Table 4.5 can be proved in a similar way. Give them a try.

You should now be able to answer Exercises 12–16 on page 67.

EXERCISES

1 Solve the equation $\sinh x + \cosh x = 1$

2 Solve the equation $2 \sinh x + 5 \cosh x = 8$

3 Solve the equation $2 \sinh x + 4 \cosh x = 1$

4 For what values of k does the equation

$3 \sinh x + 5 \cosh x = k$ have two distinct solutions?

5 For what values of k does the equation

$3 \sinh x + k \cosh x = 4$ have two distinct solutions?

6 Sketch the function f: $x \mapsto \text{sech } x \ (x \in \mathbb{R}, x \geq 0)$.

Hence sketch the inverse function f^{-1}

7 Sketch the function f : $x \mapsto \text{cosech } x \ (x \in \mathbb{R}, -\infty \leq x \leq \infty)$.

Does the inverse function f^{-1} exist? If so, sketch it.

8 Sketch the function $f : x \mapsto \coth x \ (x \in \mathbb{R}, -\infty \le x \le \infty)$.

Does the inverse function f^{-1} exist? If so, sketch it.

9 Prove that $\operatorname{sech}^{-1} x = \ln\left(\dfrac{1}{x} + \sqrt{\dfrac{1}{x^2} - 1}\right)$

10 Prove that $\operatorname{cosech}^{-1} x = \ln\left(\dfrac{1}{x} + \sqrt{\dfrac{1}{x^2} + 1}\right)$

11 Prove that $\coth^{-1} x = \dfrac{1}{2} \ln\left(\dfrac{x+1}{x-1}\right)$

12 Define $\sinh x$ and $\cosh x$. Hence prove that

$$\cosh^4 x - \sinh^4 x = \cosh 2x$$

13 Differentiate the following with respect to x:

    (a) $\cos 2x \cosh 2x$ (b) $x \sinh 3x$ (c) $\cosh^2 x^2$ (d) $\operatorname{sech} 2x$

    (e) $2\sinh 3x$ (f) $\tanh^{-1} 2x$

14 Solve the equation $2\sinh^2 x + 8 = 7 \cosh x$

15 Find

    (a) $\int \cosh 3x \, dx$

    (b) $\int x \cosh 3x \, dx$

    (c) $\int \sinh^{-1} 3x \, dx$

    (d) $\int x \tanh (x^2) \, dx$

    (e) $\int \sinh^3 x \cosh x \, dx$

    (f) $\int \sinh^2 x \, dx$

16 Find the value of x for which $4 \tanh x - \operatorname{sech} x = 1$, giving your solution in terms of natural logarithms.

SUMMARY

Now that you have completed this section on hyperbolic functions you should

- know how to define the various hyperbolic functions
- be able to use Osborne's Rule to obtain a set of hyperbolic identities
- be able to prove most hyperbolic identities from basic definitions
- be able to sketch the graphs of hyperbolic functions
- define, graph and derive formulae for inverse hyperbolic functions
- differentiate and integrate certain hyperbolic functions and their inverses.

SECTION 5

Further integration

INTRODUCTION

We've already tackled the beginning of integration in Modules P1 and P2, but there is still a set of integrals that we have so far avoided. They are:

$$\int \frac{dx}{1 + x^2} \,, \quad \int \frac{dx}{\sqrt{1 - x^2}} \,, \quad \int \frac{dx}{\sqrt{1 + x^2}} \quad \text{and} \quad \int \frac{dx}{\sqrt{x^2 - 1}}$$

In this section, we are going to look again at

- a particular type of partial fraction and its uses in integration
- the substitution method for integration

Having done this we'll be able to tackle the integrals mentioned above.

Using partial fractions in integration

We've already seen partial fractions being used in integration problems. For example:

$$\int \frac{5x + 1}{(x - 1)\,(2x + 1)} \, dx \;=\; \int \left(\frac{2}{x - 1} + \frac{1}{2x + 1} \right) dx$$

$$= \; 2 \ln (x - 1) + \frac{1}{2} \ln (2x + 1) + c$$

$$= \; \ln \left((x - 1)^2 \, \sqrt{2x + 1} \right) + c$$

And a more difficult one:

$$\int \frac{x + 8}{x(x - 2)^2} \, dx \;=\; \int \left(\frac{2}{x} - \frac{2}{x - 2} + \frac{5}{(x - 2)^2} \right) dx$$

$$= \; 2 \ln x - 2 \ln (x - 2) - 5(x - 2)^{-1} + c$$

$$= \; 2 \ln \left(\frac{x}{x - 2} \right) - \frac{5}{x - 2} + c$$

But there is one type that needs special consideration.

$$\int \frac{6-2x}{(x+2)(x^2+1)}\,dx \;=\; \int \left(\frac{2}{(x+2)}+\frac{-2x+2}{(x^2+1)}\right)dx$$

$$= \int \frac{2dx}{(x+2)} - \int \frac{2xdx}{(x^2+1)} + \int \frac{2dx}{(x^2+1)}$$

$$= 2\ln(x+2) - \ln(x^2+1) - 2\tan^{-1}x + c$$

where as usual c is a constant of integration.

It is now clear why the partial fraction form is so helpful. Every part of it corresponds to some well-known integral:

$$\frac{A}{px+q} \qquad \text{is integrated to produce} \qquad \frac{A}{p}\ln(px+q)$$

$$\frac{Cx+D}{rx^2+s} \;=\; \frac{Cx}{rx^2+s} + \frac{D}{rx^2+s}$$

produces
$$\frac{C}{2r}\ln(rx^2+s) + \frac{D}{\sqrt{(rs)}}\tan^{-1}\left(x\sqrt{\frac{r}{s}}\right)$$

Before moving on, make sure that you understand – and believe – these facts. The first is reasonably obvious, but the second is less so. To prove it, verify that differentiating the ln and $\tan^{-1}$ functions produces appropriate results. It should be stressed that you do *not* need to remember the detail of these formulae. They are plainly too complicated to be memorised. The important point is that you know the kind of function which must appear as a result of the integration – in particular, of course, the trickier ones like natural logs and $\tan^{-1}$s.

Example Evaluate $\displaystyle\int \frac{x+4}{x(x+4)}\,dx$

Solution Expressing the integrand in partial fractions gives:

$$\int \left(\frac{1}{x}+\frac{-x+1}{(x^2+4)}\right)dx$$

$$= \int \frac{dx}{x} - \int \frac{xdx}{(x^2+4)} + \int \frac{dx}{x^2+4}$$

$$= \ln x - \frac{1}{2}\ln(x^2+4) + \frac{1}{2}\tan^{-1}\left(\frac{x}{2}\right) + c$$

You should now be able to answer Exercises 1–3 on page 81.

The substitution method

You have already seen a good deal of integration. As a result you may well feel by now that, with a range of solution methods under your belt, you could tackle most integrals with confidence. However, it is for a good reason that integration is considered one of the more difficult aspects of mathematics.

By comparison with differentiation, which is a largely mechanical process, integration demands a broader knowledge of the properties of functions, a greater ability to 'spot' the relevance of standard techniques and – from time to time – more than a little ingenuity. In fact, there are a great many functions which cannot be integrated at all in the sense that we know it, and there are many other integrals which appear virtually impossible until a simple key is found to provide a solution. This section is about such a class of problems – and about approaches to solving them. The first of these is the method of substitution. (You first met this in Module P2.)

Substitution, or 'change of variable' as it is often known, involves the sequence of steps set out below. Read them now, but at this stage don't spend too much time attempting to understand them. They are really for future reference.

Note that we assume we are integrating with respect to x.

1 Define a suitable[†] function $x = f(u)$

(Note: It is often more convenient to define u in terms of x instead,

i.e. $u = f^{-1}(x)$)

2 Differentiate to produce $dx = f'(u)du$

(Or, if more convenient, $du = f^{-1'}(x)dx$)

3 Replace dx and the corresponding integrand in x

by du and the corresponding integrand in u

4 If you are dealing with a definite integral, change the limits of integration (which are values of x) by replacing them with the corresponding values of u

5 Carry out the resulting integration[†] with respect to u

6 If the integral is indefinite, revert to the original variable x by using the inverse function $u = f^{-1}(x)$

[†]The function used for the substitution is suitable if the integration of step 5 is possible. Any number of functions might be tried in this way, but very few will result in success.

By this stage you could well be wondering what all this talk of substitution is about. As with any mathematical method, the only way to gain a proper understanding is to see the method at work and try it for yourself. In this section we shall be looking at a number of different substitutions, each appropriate to a particular type of integral.

Simple substitutions

We first give a few fairly simple examples of the method.

Example

$$\int 4x^3\sqrt{(x^4 + 2)}\, dx$$

Solution

In this case a suitable substitution is:

$$u = x^4 + 2$$

Since

$$du = 4x^3\, dx$$

it follows that:

$$\int 4x^3\sqrt{(x^4 + 2)}\, dx = \int u^{\frac{1}{2}}\, du$$

and so the integral becomes:

$$\int u^{\frac{1}{2}}\, du = \frac{2u^{\frac{3}{2}}}{3} + c$$

where c is a constant of integration.

We are dealing here with an indefinite integral, and so we now revert to x to produce:

$$\frac{2}{3}\left(x^4 + 2\right)^{\frac{3}{2}} + c$$

If you have a keen eye for integration, you may have spotted the solution without using this method. In general, though, it usually pays to base your substitution on the contents of the square root bracket in integrals of this sort; an example follows.

Example	$\displaystyle\int \frac{dx}{x^2 + 8x + 17}$

Solution	In this case, complete the square first of all.

This gives us $\displaystyle\int \frac{dx}{(x + 4)^2 + 1}$

Now substitute $u = x + 4$ so that $du = dx$.

∴   the integral becomes $\displaystyle\int \frac{du}{u^2 + 1} = \tan^{-1} u + c$

$$= \tan^{-1}(x + 4) + c$$

Example	$\displaystyle\int_4^9 \frac{dx}{3 + \sqrt{x}}$

Solution	Set $x = u^2$, so that $3 + \sqrt{x} = 3 + u$ and $dx = 2u\, du$. Also, since the limits on x are 4 and 9, and $u = \sqrt{x}$, the limits on u must be 2 and 3. The integral is therefore:

$$\int_2^3 \frac{2u\, du}{3 + u} = \int_2^3 \left(2 - \frac{6}{3 + u}\right) du$$

$$= \left[2u - 6\ln(3 + u)\right]_2^3$$

$$= (6 - 6\ln(6)) - (4 - 6\ln(5))$$

$$= 2 - 6\ln\left(\frac{6}{5}\right)$$

Finally, another example before you try a few for yourself.

Example	$\displaystyle\int \frac{e^x}{1 + e^x} dx$

Solution	Set $u = e^x$, so that $du = e^x dx$ and the integral is:

$$\int \frac{du}{1 + u} = \ln(1 + u) + c$$

$$= \ln(1 + e^x) + c$$

You should now be able to answer Exercises 4–9 on page 81.

So far, you will notice, all the substitutions have been given. You have not needed to invent any for yourself. This is hardly surprising – you could not be expected to know what changes of variable would work before you had seen a few successful examples.

Unfortunately, the substitution method is one of those areas in which it is difficult to lay down ground rules about what will or will not work. It is often a matter of experience, trial and error – and perhaps a little luck. With practice, however, you can develop a 'feel' for it, and succeed in integrating some of the most horrendous functions. If you never quite manage to master this art, don't worry – in most examination questions the substitutions are either given or very well known.

One insight you may have gained from the previous exercise is that it often pays to simplify the denominator of the integrand. Notice the way in which we consistently replaced an 'awkward' function – for example, e^x or $\cos x$ or $\ln x$ – by something much easier to handle – like u. This usually resulted in an integral that we could tackle directly or by using partial fractions.

In addition to this very general pointer, there are several standard situations where particular substitutions will always bring rewards. These are investigated in the next few pages.

Trigonometrical substitutions

There are many cases of a similar type where substitutions based on trigonometrical functions prove successful. As a first example of its kind, consider the following integral.

Example	$\displaystyle\int \frac{dx}{\sqrt{(16-9x^2)}}$

Solution	A suitable approach here is to set $x = \frac{4}{3}\sin u$

For then, $dx = \frac{4}{3}\cos u\ du$

and $\quad \sqrt{(16-9x^2)} \quad = \quad \sqrt{(16-16\sin^2)} \quad = \quad 4\sqrt{(1-\sin^2 u)}$

$\qquad\qquad\qquad\qquad\quad = \quad 4\sqrt{(\cos^2 u)} \quad = \quad 4\cos u$

The integral is therefore:

$$\int \frac{\left(\frac{4}{3}\right)\cos u}{4\cos u}\,du \quad = \quad \int \frac{du}{3} = \frac{u}{3} + c$$

$$= \quad \frac{1}{3}\sin^{-1}\frac{3x}{4} + c$$

This example is just a special case of the general form:

$$\int \frac{dx}{\sqrt{(a^2 - b^2 x^2)}} \quad \text{which can be shown, using the substitution:}$$

$$x = \frac{a}{b} \sin u, \text{ to give:}$$

$$\int \frac{dx}{\sqrt{(a^2 - b^2 x^2)}} = \frac{1}{b} \sin^{-1}\left(\frac{bx}{a}\right) + c$$

You should now be able to answer Exercise 10 on page 81.

Trigonometrical substitutions of the sort we have just seen are applicable to a broader set of problems. A great many integrals which involve **quadratic surds** – that is, square roots containing quadratic functions – can be tackled successfully using similar methods. There are in fact a few general rules which are often extremely effective in producing solutions.

They are outlined below:

surd contained in integrand	recommended substitution
$\sqrt{(a^2 - b^2 x^2)}$	$x = \dfrac{a}{b} \sin u$
$\sqrt{(a^2 + b^2 x^2)}$	$x = \dfrac{a}{b} \tan u$
$\sqrt{(a^2 x^2 - b^2)}$	$x = \dfrac{b}{a} \sec u$

These substitutions are helpful because of the well-known identities which relate the trigonometrical functions sin, cos, tan and sec. To show this, using the appropriate recommendations for the three cases above, we have:

$$\sqrt{(a^2 - b^2 x^2)} = \sqrt{(a^2 - a^2 \sin^2 u)} = a \cos u$$
$$\sqrt{(a^2 + b^2 x^2)} = \sqrt{(a^2 + a^2 \tan^2 u)} = a \sec u$$
$$\sqrt{(a^2 x^2 - b^2)} = \sqrt{(b^2 \sec^2 u - b^2)} = b \tan u$$

In every one of these different instances, notice the way in which the function has been simplified. All mention of the awkward surd or square root has vanished. However, the recommended substitutions do not guarantee success. The only way to find out whether they work in any particular case is to try them out.

Example   Integrate the following functions:

(a) $\dfrac{x}{\sqrt{(4 - x^2)}}$ (b) $\dfrac{1}{x^2 \sqrt{(9 + x^2)}}$ (c) $x\sqrt{(x^2 - 1)}$

Solution
(a) The recommended substitution is $x = 2 \sin u$

So $dx = 2 \cos u \, du$ and the function becomes:

$$\frac{2 \sin u}{2 \cos u} \quad \text{i.e.} \quad \frac{\sin u}{\cos u}$$

The integral is therefore:

$$\int \frac{\sin u \times 2 \cos u}{\cos u} \, du \;=\; \int 2 \sin u \, du = -2 \cos u + c$$

$$= -2 \sqrt{1 - \left(\frac{x}{2}\right)^2} + c$$

$$= -\sqrt{(4 - x^2)} + c$$

(b) Try $x = 3 \tan u$ so that $dx = 3 \sec^2 u \, du$ and the function becomes:

$$\frac{1}{9 \tan^2 u \times 3 \sec u}$$

Therefore the integral is:

$$\int \frac{3 \sec^2 u}{27 \tan^2 u \sec u} \, du \;=\; \int \frac{1}{9} \frac{\sec u}{\tan^2 u} \, du \;=\; \int \frac{1}{9} \frac{\cos u}{\sin^2 u} \, du$$

$$= \frac{1}{9} \int (\operatorname{cosec} u \cot u \, du \,)$$

$$= \frac{-1}{9} \operatorname{cosec} u + c$$

$$= \frac{-1}{9} \sqrt{(1 + \cot^2 u)} + c$$

$$= \frac{-1}{9} \sqrt{\left(1 + \left(\frac{3}{x}\right)^2\right)} + c$$

$$= \frac{-1}{9x} \sqrt{(x^2 + 9)} + c$$

(c) Try $x = \sec u$ so that $dx = \sec u \tan u \, du$ and the function becomes
$\sec u \tan u$

The integral is thus:

$$\int \sec^2 u \tan^2 u \, du \;=\; \frac{1}{3} \tan^3 u + c$$

$$= \frac{1}{3}(x^2 - 1)^{\frac{3}{2}} + c$$

You should now be able to answer Exercises 11–12 on page 82.

As a final example of trigonometrical substitution, we introduce another standard result:

$$\int \frac{dx}{a^2 + b^2x^2} = \frac{1}{ab} \tan^{-1}\left(\frac{bx}{a}\right) + c$$

Example

Use the substitution $x = \dfrac{a}{b} \tan u$ to prove this result.

Solution

The solution is summarised as follows:

Again, the simplest way to verify this integral is to work backwards using differentiation. However, it is more instructive to do as the exercise suggests. So:

$$dx = \frac{a}{b} \sec^2 u \ du \text{ and } a^2 + b^2x^2 = a^2 + a^2\tan^2 u$$

$$= a^2 (1 + \tan^2 u)$$

$$= a^2 \sec^2 u$$

The integral is thus:

$$\int \frac{a \sec^2 u}{ba^2 \sec^2 u} du = \frac{1}{ab} u + c$$

$$= \frac{1}{ab} \tan^{-1}\left(\frac{bx}{a}\right) + c$$

Example

Evaluate $\displaystyle\int_0^{1.5} \frac{5}{9 + 4x^2} \ dx$

Solution

Comparing $\displaystyle\int \frac{1}{9 + 4x^2} \ dx$ with $\displaystyle\int \frac{1}{a^2 + b^2 x^2} \ dx$,

we see that $a = 3$ and $b = 2$. (Take positive values only.)

$$\therefore \int \frac{1}{9 + 4x^2} \ dx = \frac{1}{6} \tan^{-1} \frac{2x}{3} + c$$

$$\therefore \int_0^{1.5} \frac{5}{9 + 4x} \ dx = \left[\frac{5}{6} \tan^{-1} \frac{2x}{3}\right]_0^{1.5} = \frac{5\pi}{24}$$

You should now be able to answer Exercise 13 on page 82.

Hyperbolic substitutions

In cases where trigonometrical changes of variables fail to work for integrands containing quadratic surds, it may well pay to try hyperbolic substitutions. The table below shows the two most common instances.

surd contained in integrand	recommended substitution
$\sqrt{(a^2 + b^2x^2)}$	$x = \dfrac{a}{b} \sinh u$
$\sqrt{(a^2x^2 - b^2)}$	$x = \dfrac{b}{a} \cosh u$

These are helpful because of the well-known identity which links the functions sinh and cosh, i.e.

$$\cosh^2 u - \sinh^2 u = 1$$

Thus, using the appropriate substitutions for the two cases above, we have:

$$\sqrt{(a^2 + b^2x^2)} = \sqrt{(a^2 + a^2 \sinh^2 u)} = a \cosh u$$
$$\sqrt{(a^2x^2 - b^2)} = \sqrt{(b^2 \cosh^2 u - b^2)} = b \sinh u$$

Try the recommended substitutions in the exercise below.

Example Integrate the following functions

(a) $\dfrac{1}{\sqrt{(9 + 4x^2)}}$ (b) $\sqrt{(x^2 - 1)}$

Solution (a) Using the change of variable suggested in the table, i.e.

$$x = \frac{3}{2} \sinh u$$

we have $dx = \frac{3}{2} \cosh u \, du$ and the function to be integrated becomes:

$$\frac{1}{\sqrt{(9 + 9\sinh^2 u)}} = \frac{1}{3 \cosh u}$$

So the integral is:

$$\frac{1}{2} \int \frac{3 \cosh u}{3 \cosh u} \, du = \int \frac{1}{2} \, du = \frac{1}{2} u + c$$

$$= \frac{1}{2} \sinh^{-1}\left(\frac{2x}{3}\right) + c$$

(b) The recommended substitution is $x = \cosh u$

Thus $dx = \sinh u \, du$ and the function to be integrated is $\sinh u$

The integral is therefore:

$$\int \sinh^2 u \ du \ = \ \int \left(\tfrac{1}{2}\cosh 2u - \tfrac{1}{2}\right) du$$

using a result proved in Section 4 when we first met hyperbolic functions,

$$= \ \tfrac{1}{4}\sinh 2u - \tfrac{1}{2}u + c$$

$$= \ \tfrac{1}{2}\sinh u \cosh u - \tfrac{1}{2}u + c$$

using another result of Section 4,

$$= \ \tfrac{1}{2}x\,\sqrt{(x^2 - 1)} - \tfrac{1}{2}\cosh^{-1} x + c$$

Example   Find $\displaystyle\int \frac{dx}{\sqrt{x^2 + 6x + 10}}$

Solution   Completing the square gives $x^2 + 6x + 10 \equiv (x + 3)^2 + 1$

$\therefore$ The integral becomes $\displaystyle\int \frac{dx}{\sqrt{(x + 3)^2 + 1}}$

Substituting $x + 3 = \sinh y$, and using $dx = \cosh y \ dy$, we get

$$\int \frac{\cosh y}{\sqrt{\sinh^2 y + 1}}\,dy$$

$$= \ \int \frac{\cosh y}{\sqrt{\cosh^2 y}}\,dy \quad (\text{using the identity } \cosh^2 y - \sinh^2 y = 1)$$

$$= \ \int \frac{\cosh y}{\cosh y}\,dy$$

$$= \ \int 1 \ dy$$

$$= \ y + c$$

$$= \ \sinh^{-1}(x + 3) + c$$

You should now be able to answer Exercises 14–15 on page 82.

The substitution tan x = t

This is a standard substitution with which you should be familiar.

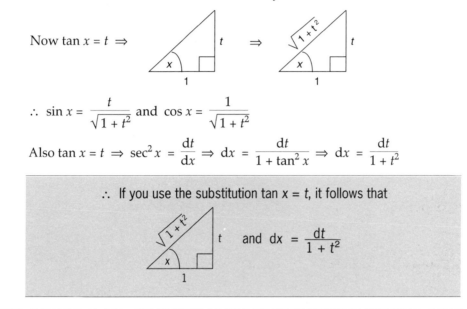

Now $\tan x = t \Rightarrow$ $\Rightarrow$

$\therefore \ \sin x = \dfrac{t}{\sqrt{1 + t^2}} \ \text{ and } \ \cos x = \dfrac{1}{\sqrt{1 + t^2}}$

Also $\tan x = t \Rightarrow \sec^2 x = \dfrac{dt}{dx} \Rightarrow dx = \dfrac{dt}{1 + \tan^2 x} \Rightarrow dx = \dfrac{dt}{1 + t^2}$

$\therefore$ If you use the substitution $\tan x = t$, it follows that

$t \quad \text{and} \quad dx = \dfrac{dt}{1 + t^2}$

Example

Find $\displaystyle\int \dfrac{dx}{1 + \sin^2 x}$ by means of the substitution $\tan x = t$

Solution

$\tan x = t \Rightarrow$ $t \ \Rightarrow \sin x = \dfrac{t}{\sqrt{1 + t^2}}$

Also $dx = \dfrac{dt}{1 + t^2}$

$\therefore \displaystyle\int \dfrac{dx}{1 + \sin^2 x} = \int \dfrac{\frac{dt}{1 + t^2}}{1 + \left(\dfrac{t}{\sqrt{1 + t^2}}\right)^2} = \int \dfrac{dt}{(1 + t^2) + t^2} = \int \dfrac{dt}{1 + 2t^2}$

But this is one of our standard integrals

$\therefore \displaystyle\int \dfrac{dt}{1 + 2t^2} = \dfrac{1}{\sqrt{2}} \tan^{-1} t\sqrt{2} + c$

$\therefore \displaystyle\int \dfrac{dx}{1 + \sin^2 x} = \dfrac{1}{\sqrt{2}} \tan^{-1} \left(\sqrt{2} \tan x\right) + c$

You should now be able to answer Exercise 16 on page 82.

The substitution $\tan \frac{x}{2} = t$

Using the identity $\tan 2A = \dfrac{2 \tan A}{1 - \tan^2 A}$ it follows that

$$\tan \frac{x}{2} = t \Rightarrow \tan x = \frac{2t}{1 - t^2} \Rightarrow$$

(I'll leave you to check that final step – use Pythagoras.)

Also $\tan \dfrac{x}{2} = t \Rightarrow \dfrac{1}{2} \sec^2 \dfrac{x}{2} = \dfrac{dt}{dx} \Rightarrow dx = \dfrac{2dt}{1 + \tan^2 \frac{x}{2}} \Rightarrow dx = \dfrac{2dt}{1 + t^2}$

$\therefore$ If you use the substitution $\tan \dfrac{x}{2} = t$, it follows that

$2t \quad$ and $\quad dx = \dfrac{2dt}{1 + t^2}$

Example

Find $\displaystyle\int \dfrac{dx}{2 \sin x - \cos x + 3}$ by means of the substitution $\tan \dfrac{x}{2} = t$

Solution

$\tan \dfrac{x}{2} = t \Rightarrow$

$2t \Rightarrow \sin x = \dfrac{2t}{1 + t^2}$ and $\cos x = \dfrac{1 - t^2}{1 + t^2}$

Also $dx = \dfrac{2dt}{1 + t^2}$

$\therefore \displaystyle\int \dfrac{dx}{2 \sin x - \cos x + 3} = \int \dfrac{\dfrac{2dt}{1 + t^2}}{2\left(\dfrac{2t}{1 + t^2}\right) - \left(\dfrac{1 - t^2}{1 + t^2}\right) + 3}$

$= \displaystyle\int \dfrac{2dt}{2(2t) - (1 - t^2) + 3(1 + t^2)}$

$= \displaystyle\int \dfrac{2dt}{4t^2 + 4t + 2} = \int \dfrac{2dt}{(2t + 1)^2 + 1}$

Now put $y = 2t + 1$, so that $dy = 2dt$

$\therefore$ the integral becomes $\displaystyle\int \frac{dy}{y^2 + 1} = \tan^{-1} y + c = \tan^{-1} (2t + 1) + c$

$\therefore \displaystyle\int \frac{dx}{2 \sin x - \cos x + 3} = \tan^{-1}\left(2 \tan\frac{x}{2} + 1\right) + c$

You should now be able to answer Exercise 17 on page 82.

EXERCISES

1 Find: (a) $\displaystyle\int \frac{dx}{9x^2 + 4}$ (b) $\displaystyle\int \frac{dx}{4x^2 + 1}$ (c) $\displaystyle\int \frac{dx}{x^2 + 25}$

2 Find: $\displaystyle\int \frac{3x + 2}{(x - 1)(4x^2 + 1)}\, dx$

3 Find: $\displaystyle\int \frac{x^2 + 6x + 3}{(x - 1)(x^2 + 4x + 5)}\, dx$

Find the following integrals using the given substitutions

4 $\displaystyle\int \frac{dx}{2 - \sqrt{x}}$ using $x = u^2$

5 $\displaystyle\int \frac{dx}{x \ln(x)}$ using $u = \ln(x)$

6 $\displaystyle\int_1^2 \frac{e^x}{1 - e^{2x}}\, dx$ using $u = e^x$

7 $\displaystyle\int_2^5 \frac{x^3 + 2x}{(x - 1)^3}\, dx$ using $x = u + 1$

8 $\displaystyle\int_0^{\frac{\pi}{2}} \frac{\sin^3 x}{(1 + \cos x)^2}\, dx$ using $u = \cos x$

9 $\displaystyle\int \frac{e^{3x}}{e^{2x} - 1}\, dx$ using $u = e^x$

10 Find: (a) $\displaystyle\int_0^1 \frac{dx}{\sqrt{(1 - x^2)}}$ (b) $\displaystyle\int_1^3 \frac{dx}{\sqrt{(3 + 2x - x^2)}}$

11 Find: $\displaystyle\int \frac{\sqrt{x^2-1}}{x}\, dx$

12 Find: $\displaystyle\int \frac{x^2}{\sqrt{1-x^2}}\, dx$

13 Find:

(a) $\displaystyle\int \frac{dx}{x^2+4}$

(b) $\displaystyle\int \frac{dx}{x^2+2x+5}$

(c) $\displaystyle\int \frac{x+2}{x^2+2x+5}\, dx$

14 Find:

(a) $\displaystyle\int \frac{dx}{\sqrt{1+x^2}}$ (b) $\displaystyle\int \frac{dx}{\sqrt{x^2-1}}$

(c) $\displaystyle\int \frac{x+3}{\sqrt{4+x^2}}\, dx$ (d) $\displaystyle\int \frac{x+3}{\sqrt{4x^2-1}}\, dx$

15 Find

(a) $\displaystyle\int \frac{dx}{x^2+4x+13}$

(b) $\displaystyle\int \frac{dx}{\sqrt{x^2+4x+3}}$

16 Using the substitution $t = \tan x$, evaluate

$$\int_0^{\frac{\pi}{4}} \frac{dx}{3\cos^2 x + \sin^2 x}$$

giving your answer in terms of π.

17 Use the substitution $\tan \dfrac{x}{2} = t$ to find the following:

(a) $\displaystyle\int \frac{dx}{1+\cos x}$ (b) $\displaystyle\int \frac{dx}{1+\sin x + \cos x}$ (c) $\displaystyle\int \operatorname{cosec} x\, dx$

SUMMARY

In this Section we have used substitutions to obtain the following standard results:

● $\int \dfrac{dx}{a^2 + b^2 x^2} = \dfrac{1}{ab} \tan^{-1}\left(\dfrac{bx}{a}\right) + c$

● $\int \dfrac{dx}{\sqrt{a^2 - b^2 x^2}} = \dfrac{1}{b} \sin^{-1}\left(\dfrac{bx}{a}\right) + c$

● $\int \dfrac{dx}{\sqrt{a^2 + b^2 x^2}} = \dfrac{1}{b} \sinh^{-1}\left(\dfrac{bx}{a}\right) + c$

● $\int \dfrac{dx}{\sqrt{b^2 x^2 - a^2}} = \dfrac{1}{b} \cosh^{-1}\left(\dfrac{bx}{a}\right) + c$

Furthermore, integrals such as $\int \dfrac{dx}{x^2 + 6x + 13}$ can be found by completing the square.

(The answer in this case is $\frac{1}{2}\tan^{-1}\left(\dfrac{x + 3}{2}\right) + c$.)

● When using the substitution $\tan x = t$ remember that

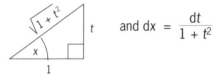

and $dx = \dfrac{dt}{1 + t^2}$

● When using the substitution $\tan \dfrac{x}{2} = t$ remember that

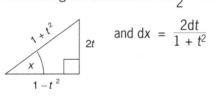

and $dx = \dfrac{2dt}{1 + t^2}$

Vectors

Using vectors, both the magnitude and direction of a quantity can be represented in a single expression. This leads to a simplification and reduction in working, especially for topics in applied mathematics and some geometrical problems in pure mathematics. In this section we shall start with vectors in two dimensions and extend our work to three dimensions.

Scalars and vectors

A scientist doing some research into the effects of walking long distances might be quite interested in someone who had just completed a walk of 45 km, and even more interested if the walk was 85 km long. We can extract the most important piece of information for our purposes by asking the single question – 'how far?' This type of quantity, where only the amount or size is relevant, is called a *scalar*. A scalar can generally be represented as a point on the number line – the length of the two walks, for example, could be shown by

Figure 6.1

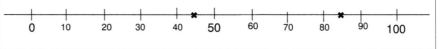

Someone studying geography might possibly be interested in the answer to more than one question – not only 'how far', but also 'and in what direction?' In this case, a single number line would not be enough – we'd have to add another dimension to give some indication of this additional piece of information. Taking our example again, if the walks were 45 km in a NE (north east) direction and 85 km in a W (west) direction, both relative to the same starting point, we could represent them thus:

Figure 6.2

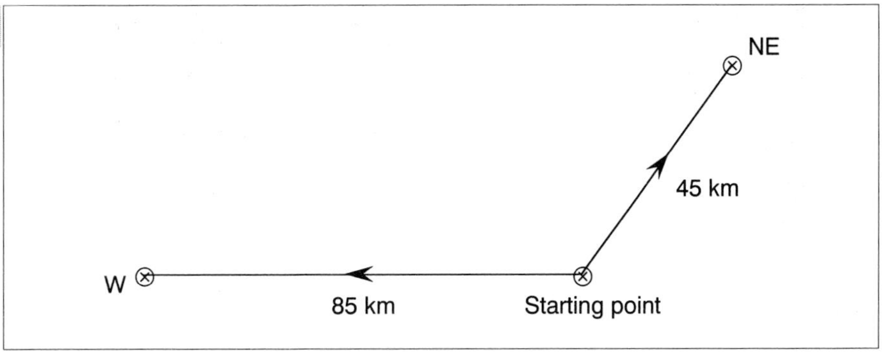

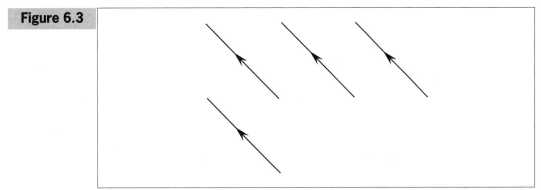

Notice that we have to indicate the sense in which the displacement took place by putting an arrow pointing the appropriate way; this is to distinguish 85 km W from 85 km E.

Quantities that answer two questions, how much and in what direction, are called *vectors*. If it's necessary to make it clear whether a particular quantity is scalar or vector, we write the scalar as a normal letter, e.g. 'a' when writing by hand or italicised '*a*', as in this book, whereas the corresponding vector is in bold type, '**a**' (printed) or underlined '<u>a</u>' (handwritten).

Now that you are clear about scalars and vectors let's see how to combine two or more vectors by adding or subtracting. Before we do this, there is one more distinction to make – between displacement vectors and position vectors.

An example of a displacement vector could be 'a distance of 10 km in a NW direction'. If N is at the top of this page and we choose the scale correctly, any of the vectors in Figure 6.3 would fit this description, and in that sense they are all equal.

Figure 6.3

A fixed vector, or position vector, is defined relative to a given point (say *O*) and for any combination of length and direction, as above for example, there is only one vector fitting this description (see Figure 6.4):

Figure 6.4

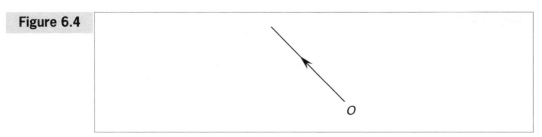

You should now be able to answer Exercise 1 on page 104.

Adding displacement vectors

Suppose we had the two displacement vectors **a** and **b**, represented by two lines, as shown in Figure 6.5:

Figure 6.5

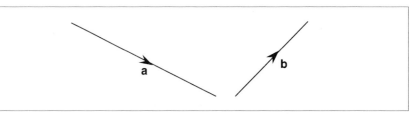

If we want to add these, we put the beginning point of **b** in contact with the end point of **a**.

Figure 6.6

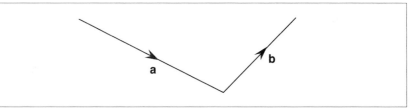

Then the sum of these is defined as the vector joining the beginning point to the end point of the 'journey'.

Figure 6.7

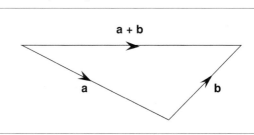

It doesn't matter how many vectors make up the 'journey', so long as the tail of each vector only joins at the beginning point of another vector, so that a path can be made from the tail of the beginning vector to the head of the end vector passing through all the arrows in the same direction.

Figure 6.8

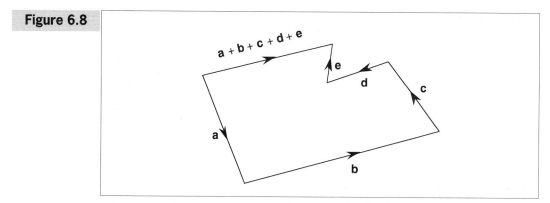

Vectors are frequently given in the form of a displacement between two points – $\overrightarrow{AB}$ is the directed line from A to B.

Figure 6.9

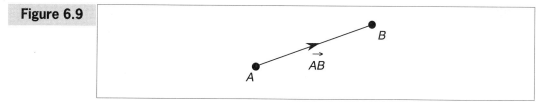

To add the vectors in this form, we have to make sure that the letter ending one vector begins another – we can add $\overrightarrow{AB}$ and $\overrightarrow{BC}$, for example:

Figure 6.10

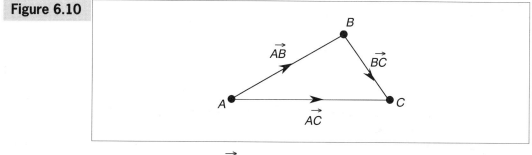

and the result will be $\overrightarrow{AC}$ i.e.

$$\overrightarrow{AB} + \overrightarrow{BC} = \overrightarrow{AC}$$

But we can't add $\overrightarrow{OP}$ and $\overrightarrow{OQ}$ (Figure 6.11) in the same way since the letter O begins both vectors.

Figure 6.11

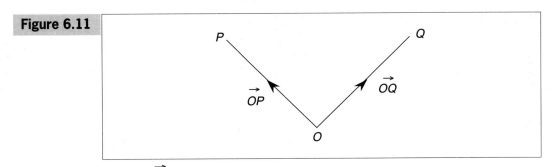

To find $\overrightarrow{PQ}$ in this case, we would have to put the letter O between the two other points:

$$\overrightarrow{PQ} = \overrightarrow{PO} + \overrightarrow{OQ}$$

and $\overrightarrow{PO}$ is $\overrightarrow{OP}$ the wrong way round, or $-\overrightarrow{OP}$:

Figure 6.12

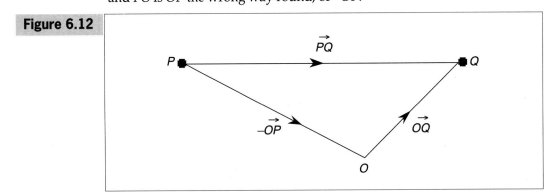

When vectors are given in relation to a fixed origin O, you would quite often write something like $\overrightarrow{OA}$ as **a** and $\overrightarrow{OS}$ as **s**, so that:

$$\overrightarrow{OP} = \mathbf{p} \qquad \text{and} \qquad \overrightarrow{OQ} = \mathbf{q}$$

$$\text{and} \qquad \overrightarrow{PQ} = \overrightarrow{PO} + \overrightarrow{OQ}$$

$$= -\overrightarrow{OP} + \overrightarrow{OQ}$$

$$= -\mathbf{p} + \mathbf{q}$$

i.e.

$$\overrightarrow{PQ} = \mathbf{q} - \mathbf{p}$$

Multiplication by a scalar

If a vector is multiplied by a *scalar* quantity, leading to $2\mathbf{a}$ or $\frac{1}{2}\mathbf{b}$, the result is a vector in the same direction but with magnitude changed according to the factor.

Figure 6.13

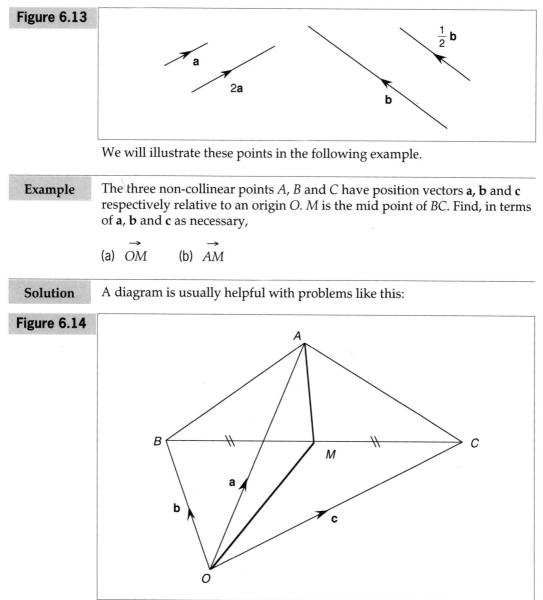

We will illustrate these points in the following example.

Example

The three non-collinear points A, B and C have position vectors $\mathbf{a}$, $\mathbf{b}$ and $\mathbf{c}$ respectively relative to an origin O. M is the mid point of BC. Find, in terms of $\mathbf{a}$, $\mathbf{b}$ and $\mathbf{c}$ as necessary,

(a) $\overrightarrow{OM}$ (b) $\overrightarrow{AM}$

Solution   A diagram is usually helpful with problems like this:

Figure 6.14

(a)   We have to find a route from O to M using vectors we know. One route we could try is to go from O to B and then to M. The first half OB

we know to be **b**, but we don't as yet know BM. We do know that BM is half of BC and we can find BC quite easily:

$$\vec{BC} = \vec{BO} + \vec{OC}$$
$$= -\mathbf{b} + \mathbf{c}$$

so $\quad \vec{BM} = \tfrac{1}{2}\vec{BC} = \tfrac{1}{2}(\mathbf{c} - \mathbf{b})$

and then $\vec{OM} = \vec{OB} + \vec{BM}$
$$= \mathbf{b} + \tfrac{1}{2}(\mathbf{c} - \mathbf{b})$$
$$= \mathbf{b} + \tfrac{1}{2}\mathbf{c} - \tfrac{1}{2}\mathbf{b}$$
$$= \tfrac{1}{2}\mathbf{b} + \tfrac{1}{2}\mathbf{c}$$
$$= \tfrac{1}{2}(\mathbf{b} + \mathbf{c})$$

(b)   Now we can find AM without too much difficulty:

$$\vec{AM} = \vec{AO} + \vec{OM}$$
$$= -\vec{OA} + \vec{OM}$$
$$= -\mathbf{a} + \tfrac{1}{2}(\mathbf{b} + \mathbf{c}) = \tfrac{1}{2}(\mathbf{b} + \mathbf{c} - 2\mathbf{a})$$

You should now be able to answer Exercise 2 on page 105.

The vector equation of a line

In Figure 6.15 we have a normal (cartesian) framework divided into a grid of unit squares upon which we put a counter P. P can only change position according to the rule that it moves up twice as many spaces as it moves to the right. So if it started at the point (2,3) and moved to the right, it would pass through the points (3,5), (4,7), (5,9), etc.

Figure 6.15

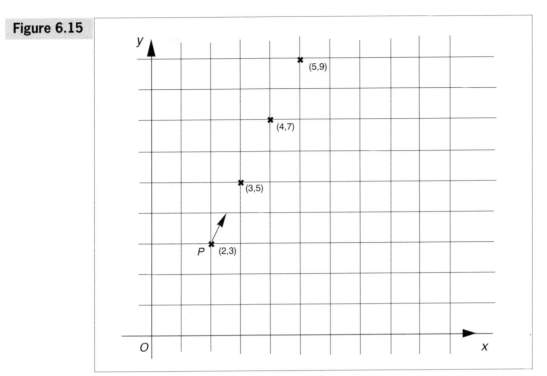

In general, after it had moved s spaces to the right it would have moved $2s$ spaces up – and its co-ordinates would be

$$x = 2 + s$$
$$y = 3 + 2s$$

These are the *parametric equations* of this particular line. Writing them in vector form combines these two equations into one equation:

$$\begin{pmatrix} x \\ y \end{pmatrix} = \begin{pmatrix} 2 + s \\ 3 + 2s \end{pmatrix}$$

$$= \begin{pmatrix} 2 \\ 3 \end{pmatrix} + s \begin{pmatrix} 1 \\ 2 \end{pmatrix}$$

Instead of writing $\begin{pmatrix} x \\ y \end{pmatrix}$ for a general position vector on the line, we usually write **r**. Our *vector equation* of this line is then

Line P: $\qquad \mathbf{r} = \begin{pmatrix} 2 \\ 3 \end{pmatrix} + s \begin{pmatrix} 1 \\ 2 \end{pmatrix}$ $\qquad\qquad$ ... ①

where s is the parameter.

In this form, you can see quite clearly one of the points the line passes through, (2,3), and the ratio of sideward movement to upward movement, $\begin{pmatrix} 1 \\ 2 \end{pmatrix}$. As another example the vector equation of the path taken by a counter Q, which moves down 1 for every 2 moves to the right and passes through the point (4,–3), is

$$\text{Line } Q : \mathbf{r} = \begin{pmatrix} 4 \\ -3 \end{pmatrix} + t \begin{pmatrix} 2 \\ -1 \end{pmatrix} \qquad \ldots ②$$

where t is the parameter.

To find a few of the points Q passes through, we could give some different values to t:

$$t = 0, \quad \begin{pmatrix} x \\ y \end{pmatrix} = \begin{pmatrix} 4 \\ -3 \end{pmatrix} + 0 \begin{pmatrix} 2 \\ -1 \end{pmatrix} = \begin{pmatrix} 4 \\ -3 \end{pmatrix} \therefore \text{ point is } (4 , -3)$$

$$t = 3, \quad \begin{pmatrix} x \\ y \end{pmatrix} = \begin{pmatrix} 4 \\ -3 \end{pmatrix} + 3 \begin{pmatrix} 2 \\ -1 \end{pmatrix} = \begin{pmatrix} 10 \\ -6 \end{pmatrix} \therefore \text{ point is } (10, -6)$$

$$t = -2, \quad \begin{pmatrix} x \\ y \end{pmatrix} = \begin{pmatrix} 4 \\ -3 \end{pmatrix} - 2 \begin{pmatrix} 2 \\ -1 \end{pmatrix} = \begin{pmatrix} 0 \\ -1 \end{pmatrix} \therefore \text{ point is } (0 , -1)$$

You should now be able to answer Exercise 3 on page 105.

Equation of a line passing through two given points

Now we will see how we can find the vector equation of a line which passes through two given points.

Suppose the two points are A (3,2) and B (5,7). We are not given the ratio of space up to spaces across, but we can work out what it must be from looking at the difference between the two points.

Figure 6.16

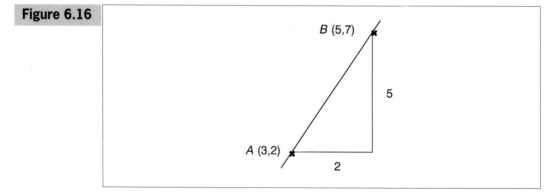

To get from A to B we have to go 5 up while moving across 2, which means that the direction vector is $\begin{pmatrix} 2 \\ 5 \end{pmatrix}$ and the vector equation of the line passing through A and B is

$$\mathbf{r} = \begin{pmatrix} 3 \\ 2 \end{pmatrix} + \lambda \begin{pmatrix} 2 \\ 5 \end{pmatrix}$$

$$\uparrow \qquad\qquad \uparrow \qquad\qquad \uparrow$$

position   parameter   direction ratios
vector

Note that this is the equation for the whole of the line passing through A and B. If we are interested only in the precise section of the line between A and B, we have to put restrictions on the set of values that the parameter λ can take. If we put $\lambda = 0$,

$$\begin{pmatrix} x \\ y \end{pmatrix} = \begin{pmatrix} 3 \\ 2 \end{pmatrix} + 0\begin{pmatrix} 2 \\ 5 \end{pmatrix} = \begin{pmatrix} 3 \\ 2 \end{pmatrix}, \text{ the position vector } \overrightarrow{OA}$$

If we put $\lambda = 1$

$$\begin{pmatrix} x \\ y \end{pmatrix} = \begin{pmatrix} 3 \\ 2 \end{pmatrix} + 1\begin{pmatrix} 2 \\ 5 \end{pmatrix} = \begin{pmatrix} 5 \\ 7 \end{pmatrix}, \text{ the position vector } \overrightarrow{OB}$$

These are the two extreme points – values of λ between 0 and 1 will give points between A and B. So if we are asked for the vector equation of the line segment AB (as opposed to the line passing through A and B), we would put

$$\mathbf{r} = \begin{pmatrix} 3 \\ 2 \end{pmatrix} + \lambda \begin{pmatrix} 2 \\ 5 \end{pmatrix}; \ 0 \le \lambda \le 1$$

You should now be able to answer Exercise 4 on page 105.

Coordinates and position vectors in two dimensions

Conventionally, we let $\mathbf{i}$ be a unit vector in the x-direction and $\mathbf{j}$ a unit vector in the y-direction, so that it we wanted to write the column vector $\begin{pmatrix} 4 \\ 3 \end{pmatrix}$ on one line, we would put $4\mathbf{i} + 3\mathbf{j}$. We have to be careful not to confuse coordinates and position vectors. The *coordinates* of a general point in two dimensions are always written (x, y), with a comma separating the coordinates. However, the *position vector* of this general point is written in column form $\begin{pmatrix} x \\ y \end{pmatrix}$ or on one line as $x\mathbf{i} + y\mathbf{j}$.

Vectors in three dimensions

We've been looking at vectors in two dimensions so far – there are no complications when we add a further dimension. The direction ratios now involve three figures: the three dimensions are represented by unit vectors **i**, **j** and **k**. The general position vector **r** now means

$$x\mathbf{i} + y\mathbf{j} + z\mathbf{k} \quad \text{or} \quad \begin{pmatrix} x \\ y \\ z \end{pmatrix} \quad \text{in column form}$$

and the coordinates of this general point are (x, y, z).

The equation of a line in three dimensions has the same form as before. The line

$$\mathbf{r} = \begin{pmatrix} 1 \\ 2 \\ 3 \end{pmatrix} + \lambda \begin{pmatrix} 2 \\ -1 \\ 6 \end{pmatrix} \qquad \textit{Vector equation}$$

for example, passes through the point with co-ordinates, $x = 1$, $y = 2$, $z = 3$ with direction ratios $x : y : z = 2 : -1 : 6$.

Since $\mathbf{r} = \begin{pmatrix} x \\ y \\ z \end{pmatrix}$ we can separate out the three parts of this equation and put them into parametric form:

$$\begin{aligned} x &= 1 + 2\lambda \qquad &\textit{Parametric equations} \\ y &= 2 - \lambda \\ z &= 3 + 6\lambda \end{aligned}$$

There is no single cartesian equation for this line corresponding to something like $y = 2x - 4$ in two dimensions. Instead, we have to solve these parametric equations for λ:

$$\lambda = \frac{x-1}{2} = \frac{y-2}{-1} = \frac{z-3}{6} \qquad \textit{Cartesian equations}$$

You have to be able to change from vector to cartesian form or the other way round and it helps at the beginning to put each of the cartesian equations equal to λ, find the parametric equations and then the vector equation. You may note that the direction ratios of the vector equation are the bottom line of the cartesian equations (i.e. $2 : -1 : 6$) and the position vector has as components the values of x, y and z which make the tops of the fractions zero (in this case 1, 2 and 3, i.e. $\begin{pmatrix} 1 \\ 2 \\ 3 \end{pmatrix}$.

Thus, when working in three dimensions the same conditions apply as in two-dimensions: a line passing through the points A with position vector **a** and B with position **b** is given by

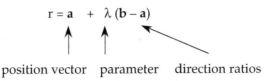

$$r = \mathbf{a} + \lambda (\mathbf{b} - \mathbf{a})$$

position vector   parameter   direction ratios

You should now be able to answer Exercises 5–6 on page 105.

The length of vectors

We can find the distance between the two points in two dimensions quite easily – if the points are $A(x_A, y_A)$ and $B(x_B, y_B)$, then the distance is given by Pythagoras's theorem:

Figure 6.17

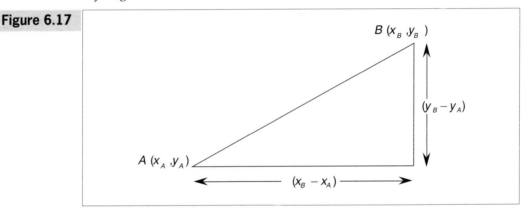

i.e. the length of $\overrightarrow{AB}$ written $|\overrightarrow{AB}|$ is given by:

$$|\overrightarrow{AB}| = \sqrt{(x_B - x_A)^2 + (y_B - y_A)^2}$$

There is quite a simple extension of this to three dimensions: if the points are $A(x_A, y_A, z_A)$ and $B(x_B, y_B, z_B)$, then the length of $\overrightarrow{AB}$ is given by:

$$|\overrightarrow{AB}| = \sqrt{(x_B - x_A)^2 + (y_B - y_A)^2 + (z_B - z_A)^2}$$

For example, the distance between the points $A\ (3,1,2)$ and $B\ (-1,2,-4)$ would be:

$$\sqrt{(-1-3)^2 + (2-1)^2 + (-4-2)^2} = \sqrt{16 + 1 + 36}$$
$$= \sqrt{53}$$

Exactly the same formula applies if we are given the points A and B in the form of position vectors, i.e.

$$\overrightarrow{OA} = x_A\mathbf{i} + y_A\mathbf{j} + z_A\mathbf{k} \text{ and } \overrightarrow{OB} = x_B\mathbf{i} + y_B\mathbf{j} + z_B\mathbf{k}$$

> The length of the vector $\overrightarrow{AB}$, where A and B have position vectors
> $\begin{pmatrix} x_A \\ y_A \\ z_A \end{pmatrix}$ and $\begin{pmatrix} x_B \\ y_B \\ z_B \end{pmatrix}$ respectively, is given by
>
> $$|\overrightarrow{AB}| = \sqrt{(x_B - x_A)^2 + (y_B - y_A)^2 + (z_B - z_A)^2}$$

If one of these points is the origin, this formula becomes quite simple.

> If $\overrightarrow{OB} = \begin{pmatrix} x_B \\ y_B \\ z_B \end{pmatrix}$, the length of OB is given by
>
> $$|\overrightarrow{OB}| = \sqrt{x_B^2 + y_B^2 + z_B^2}$$

We will now look at some examples of this.

Example   Find the lengths of the following vectors.

(a) $\overrightarrow{AB}$, where $\overrightarrow{OA} = \begin{pmatrix} 1 \\ 2 \\ 3 \end{pmatrix}$ and $\overrightarrow{OB} = \begin{pmatrix} 3 \\ 5 \\ 7 \end{pmatrix}$

(b) $\overrightarrow{PQ}$, where $\overrightarrow{OP} = -i + 2j + 2k$ and $\overrightarrow{OQ} = -3j + j + 4k$

(c) $\overrightarrow{OR}$, where $\overrightarrow{OR} = \begin{pmatrix} -1 \\ 5 \\ 2 \end{pmatrix}$

Solution

(a) $\overrightarrow{AB} = \overrightarrow{OB} - \overrightarrow{OA} = \begin{pmatrix} 2 \\ 3 \\ 4 \end{pmatrix}$. By the formula, this has length

$$\sqrt{2^2 + 3^2 + 4^2} = \sqrt{29} \text{ units.}$$

(b) $\overrightarrow{PQ} = \overrightarrow{OQ} - \overrightarrow{OP} = -2i - j + 2k.$ This has length

$$|\overrightarrow{PQ}| = \sqrt{(-2)^2 + (-1)^2 + 2^2} = 3 \text{ units}$$

(c) From the formula

$$|\overrightarrow{OR}| = \sqrt{(-1)^2 + 5^2 + 2^2} = \sqrt{30} \text{ units}$$

You should now be able to answer Exercise 7 on page 106.

We're now going to see if we can find the angle between any two vectors, but before we do this, we need to look at a way of multiplying vectors, which is called the *scalar product*, because the result is a scalar quantity.

The scalar product

Suppose we have two vectors **a** and **b**, and a light is shining directly down onto **b**. The length of the shadow of **a** on **b** is called the *projection* of **a** on **b**. This projection is the distance that vector **a** moves in the direction **b**.

Figure 6.18

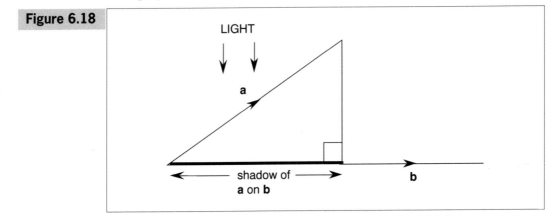

Then the scalar product of **a** and **b**, which can also be called the *dot product* because it is written **a . b**, is defined by:

$$\mathbf{a} \cdot \mathbf{b} = \text{projection of } \mathbf{a} \text{ on } \mathbf{b} \times \text{length of } \mathbf{b} \qquad \dots [*]$$

In Figure 6.19 we have marked the lengths of the vectors **a** and **b** and the angle between them, which we can call θ.

Figure 6.19

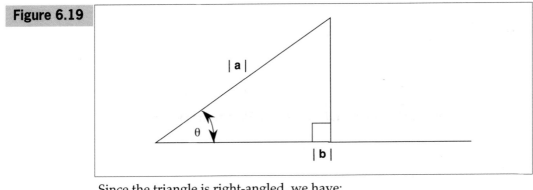

Since the triangle is right-angled, we have:

$$\cos \theta = \frac{\text{adjacent}}{\text{hypotenuse}} = \frac{\text{projection of } \mathbf{a} \text{ on } \mathbf{b}}{|\mathbf{a}|}$$

Rearranging, projection of **a** on **b** = $|\,\mathbf{a}\,|\,\cos\theta$

and putting this into [*] gives

$$\mathbf{a}\,.\,\mathbf{b}\ =\ |\,\mathbf{a}\,|\,\cos\theta\times|\,\mathbf{b}\,|$$
$$=\ |\,\mathbf{a}\,|\,|\,\mathbf{b}\,|\,\cos\theta \qquad\qquad \dots\ ①$$

This is one way of defining the scalar product but there is another way, direct from the components of the two vectors. Suppose the two vectors **a** and **b** were

$$\begin{pmatrix} x_a \\ y_a \\ z_a \end{pmatrix} \text{ and } \begin{pmatrix} x_b \\ y_b \\ z_b \end{pmatrix} \text{ respectively}$$

Then $\mathbf{a}\,.\,\mathbf{b}\ =\ x_a x_b + y_a y_b + z_a z_b \qquad\qquad \dots\ ②$

For example, if **a** is $\begin{pmatrix} 2 \\ 1 \\ 2 \end{pmatrix}$ and **b** is $\begin{pmatrix} 3 \\ -2 \\ 8 \end{pmatrix}$ then

$$\mathbf{a}\,.\,\mathbf{b}\ =\ \begin{pmatrix} 2 \\ 1 \\ 2 \end{pmatrix} . \begin{pmatrix} 3 \\ -2 \\ 8 \end{pmatrix}\ =\ 2\times3 + 1\times-2 + 2\times8 = 6 - 2 + 16\ = 20$$

Note that we end up with a *scalar* (i.e. a number): hence the name scalar product.

The angle between vectors

Combining these two results ① and ②, we can find the angle θ between the vectors **a** and **b**.

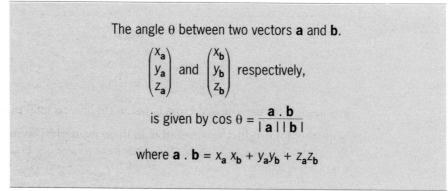

The angle θ between two vectors **a** and **b**.

$$\begin{pmatrix} x_a \\ y_a \\ z_a \end{pmatrix} \text{ and } \begin{pmatrix} x_b \\ y_b \\ z_b \end{pmatrix} \text{ respectively,}$$

is given by $\cos\theta = \dfrac{\mathbf{a}\,.\,\mathbf{b}}{|\,\mathbf{a}\,|\,|\,\mathbf{b}\,|}$

where $\mathbf{a}\,.\,\mathbf{b} = x_a\,x_b + y_a y_b + z_a z_b$

Example	Find the angle between the vectors:

(a) $\mathbf{a} = \begin{pmatrix} 3 \\ -1 \\ 2 \end{pmatrix}$ and $\mathbf{b} = \begin{pmatrix} 2 \\ 1 \\ -3 \end{pmatrix}$

(b) $\mathbf{p} = 3\mathbf{i} + 2\mathbf{j} - 6\mathbf{k}$ and $\mathbf{q} = -\mathbf{j} + \mathbf{k}$

(c) $\mathbf{u} = \begin{pmatrix} a \\ -2a \\ -5a \end{pmatrix}$ and $\mathbf{v} = \begin{pmatrix} -2a \\ 7a \\ 5a \end{pmatrix}$, where a is a scalar

Solution	(a) The angle is given by:

$$\cos\theta = \frac{\mathbf{a}.\mathbf{b}}{|\mathbf{a}||\mathbf{b}|} = \frac{(3 \times 2) + (-1 \times 1) + (2 \times -3)}{\sqrt{3^2 + (-1)^2 + 2^2}\ \sqrt{2^2 + 1^2 + (-3)^2}}$$

$$= \frac{6 - 1 - 6}{\sqrt{14}\ \sqrt{14}}$$

$$= \frac{-1}{14}$$

so the angle θ is 94.1° (correct to one decimal place)

(b) Here, $\cos\theta = \dfrac{3 \times 0 + 2 \times -1 + -6 \times 1}{\sqrt{3^2 + 2^2 + (-6)^2}\ \sqrt{(-1)^2 + 1^2}} = \dfrac{-8}{7\sqrt{2}}$

and the angle is 143.9° (to one decimal place)

(c) $\mathbf{u}.\mathbf{v} = -2a^2 - 14a^2 - 25a^2 \quad = -41a^2$

$|\mathbf{u}| = \sqrt{a^2 + 4a^2 + 25a^2} \quad = \sqrt{30a^2} \quad = a\sqrt{30}$

$|\mathbf{v}| = \sqrt{4a^2 + 49a^2 + 25a^2} \quad = \sqrt{78a^2} \quad = a\sqrt{78}$

and $\cos\theta = \dfrac{-41a^2}{a\sqrt{30}\ a\sqrt{78}} = \dfrac{-41}{\sqrt{30}\ \sqrt{78}}$

The angle between these vectors is 147.9° (to one decimal place).

Note: the dot product was negative in these examples, giving an angle of more than 90°. This is possible because the angle between two vectors takes into account the direction of the vectors – both vectors have to be pointed away from the vertex.

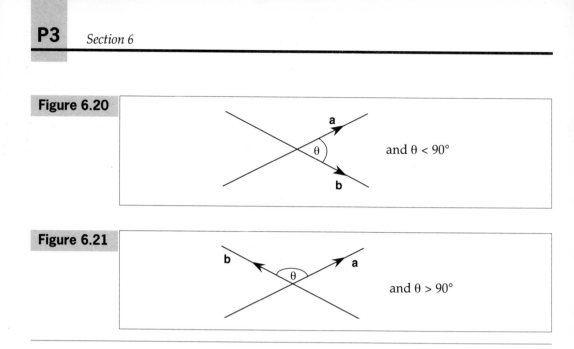

Figure 6.20

and θ < 90°

Figure 6.21

and θ > 90°

You should now be able to answer Exercises 8–10 on page 106.

Perpendicular vectors

The formula by which we calculate the angle makes it easy to see when two vectors are perpendicular to each other. In this case the angle between them is, of course, 90°.

$$\cos 90° = \frac{\mathbf{a} \cdot \mathbf{b}}{|\,\mathbf{a}\,|\,|\,\mathbf{b}\,|} \quad \text{but } \cos 90° = 0$$

i.e. $\mathbf{a} \cdot \mathbf{b} = 0$

This is a very important result which we will emphasise by putting it in a box.

> If **a** and **b** are two non-zero vectors
>
> **a** . **b** = 0 ⇔ **a** and **b** are mutually perpendicular

The double-ended implication sign, ⇔, means that the two statements amount to exactly the same thing – if either one is true, so is the other.

Further properties of the scalar product

We have just seen how if the vectors **a** and **b** are perpendicular, **a** . **b** = 0. Furthermore, we have

1   **a** . **b** = **b** . **a** for any vectors **a** and **b**. (This is because the components of **a** and **b** are multiplied and the order for ordinary multiplication is not important).

2 $\mathbf{a} . (\mathbf{b} + \mathbf{c}) = \mathbf{a} . \mathbf{b} + \mathbf{a} . \mathbf{c}$

This is true of course for ordinary multiplication: for example $2 \times (4 + 3) = 2 \times 4 + 2 \times 3$ and actually because of this it's true for the scalar product.

3 $\mathbf{a} . \mathbf{a} = | \mathbf{a} |^2$

Suppose $\mathbf{a} = \begin{pmatrix} x_A \\ y_A \\ z_A \end{pmatrix}$ then $\mathbf{a} . \mathbf{a} = \begin{pmatrix} x_A \\ y_A \\ z_A \end{pmatrix} . \begin{pmatrix} x_A \\ y_A \\ z_A \end{pmatrix} = x_A^2 + y_A^2 + z_A^2$

$$= \left(\sqrt{x_A^2 + y_A^2 + z_A^2} \right)^2$$

$$= | \mathbf{a} |^2$$

Let's see how we can use these to show certain properties of geometrical figures.

Pythagoras's theorem

Suppose we have a right-angled triangle ABC

Figure 6.22

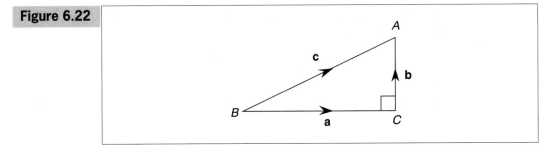

with $\overrightarrow{BC} = \mathbf{a}$ $\overrightarrow{CA} = \mathbf{b}$ and $\overrightarrow{BA} = \mathbf{c}$

Then $\mathbf{c} = \mathbf{a} + \mathbf{b}$ and $\mathbf{a}$ and $\mathbf{b}$ are perpendicular, i.e. $\mathbf{a} . \mathbf{b} = 0$.

If we dot each side of the equation with itself

$\mathbf{c} . \mathbf{c}$	$= (\mathbf{a} + \mathbf{b}) . (\mathbf{a} + \mathbf{b})$	
	$= \mathbf{a} . \mathbf{a} + \mathbf{a} . \mathbf{b} + \mathbf{b} . \mathbf{a} + \mathbf{b} . \mathbf{b}$	(property 2)
	$= \mathbf{a} . \mathbf{a} + 2\mathbf{a} . \mathbf{b} + \mathbf{b} . \mathbf{b}$	(property 1)
	$= \mathbf{a} . \mathbf{a} + \mathbf{b} . \mathbf{b}$	($\mathbf{a} . \mathbf{b} = 0$)
i.e. $| \mathbf{c} |^2$	$= | \mathbf{a} |^2 + | \mathbf{b} |^2$	(property 3)

The cosine rule

Figure 6.23

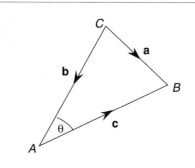

Draw a triangle *ABC* and put in the vectors **a**, **b** and **c** in such a way that
a = **b** + **c**. Also add the angle θ as shown.

Dot each side of this equation with itself

$$\mathbf{a}.\mathbf{a} = (\mathbf{b} + \mathbf{c}).(\mathbf{b} + \mathbf{c})$$

$$= \mathbf{b}.\mathbf{b} + \mathbf{b}.\mathbf{c} + \mathbf{c}.\mathbf{b} + \mathbf{c}.\mathbf{c} \qquad \text{(property 2)}$$

$$= \mathbf{b}.\mathbf{b} + 2\mathbf{b}.\mathbf{c} + \mathbf{c}.\mathbf{c} \qquad \text{(property 1)}$$

$$\Rightarrow |\mathbf{a}|^2 = |\mathbf{b}|^2 + 2\mathbf{b}.\mathbf{c} + |\mathbf{c}|^2 \quad \dots \text{①} \qquad \text{(property 3)}$$

Now to find the angle θ between **b** and **c**, we notice that the arrows are in
opposite direction. We have to reverse one of them, **b** say, so that:

$$\cos\theta = \frac{-\mathbf{b}.\mathbf{c}}{|\mathbf{b}||\mathbf{c}|} \Rightarrow \mathbf{b}.\mathbf{c} = -|\mathbf{b}||\mathbf{c}|\cos\theta$$

Putting this into ①, $|\mathbf{a}|^2 = |\mathbf{b}|^2 + |\mathbf{c}|^2 - 2|\mathbf{b}||\mathbf{c}|\cos\theta$

You should now be able to answer Exercise 11 on p. 106.

Vectors and geometrical properties of figures

We have seen how to apply scalar product in order to obtain some
geometrical properties of triangles. However, vectors themselves can also
be used to derive many further interesting properties.

Example   *O, A* and *B* are three non-collinear points; the position vectors of *A* and *B*
with respect to *O* are **a** and **b** respectively. *M* is the mid-point of *OA* and *T*
is the point of trisection of *OB* nearer *O*. If *TA* cuts *MB* at *P* find:

(a) the ratio *TP* : *TA*

(b) the ratio *MP* : *MB*

(c) the position vector of *P* in terms of **a** and **b**.

Solution	First we need a good diagram.

Figure 6.24

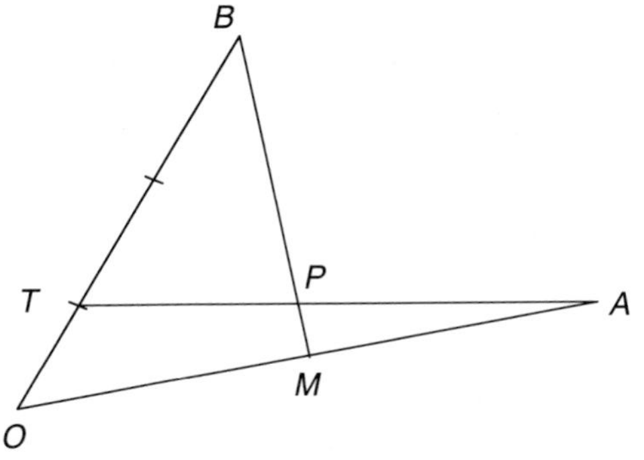

The procedure in questions such as these is to

- find two different expressions for the position vector of the point of intersection (these will involve unknown parameters)

- equate these expressions and hence find the values of the unknown parameters. All results will then follow.

One possible route to *P* is:

$$\overrightarrow{OP} = \overrightarrow{OT} + \overrightarrow{TP}$$

But $\overrightarrow{TP}$ is a scalar multiple of $\overrightarrow{TA}$ and so we can write $\overrightarrow{TP} = \lambda \overrightarrow{TA}$ where λ is an unknown scalar.

$$\begin{aligned}
\overrightarrow{OP} &= \overrightarrow{OT} + \lambda \overrightarrow{TA} \\
&= \overrightarrow{OT} + \lambda (\overrightarrow{TO} + \overrightarrow{OA}) \\
&= \tfrac{1}{3}\mathbf{b} + \lambda (-\tfrac{1}{3}\mathbf{b} + \mathbf{a}) \qquad \qquad \dots \text{①}
\end{aligned}$$

Another possible route to *P* is:

$$\overrightarrow{OP} = \overrightarrow{OM} + \overrightarrow{MP}$$

But $\overrightarrow{MP}$ is a scalar multiple of $\overrightarrow{MB}$ and so we can write $\overrightarrow{MP} = \mu \overrightarrow{MB}$ where μ is an unknown scalar.

$$\begin{aligned}
\therefore \qquad \overrightarrow{OP} &= \overrightarrow{OM} + \mu \overrightarrow{MB} \\
&= \overrightarrow{OM} + \mu (\overrightarrow{MO} + \overrightarrow{OB}) \\
&= \tfrac{1}{2}\mathbf{a} + \mu \left(-\tfrac{1}{2}\mathbf{a} + \mathbf{b}\right) \qquad \qquad \dots \text{②}
\end{aligned}$$

Equating the expressions from ① and ② we get:

$$\tfrac{1}{3}b + \lambda\left(-\tfrac{1}{3}b + a\right) = \tfrac{1}{2}a + \mu\left(-\tfrac{1}{2}a + b\right)$$

By comparing coefficients of **a** and **b**, this gives us

$$\tfrac{1}{3} - \tfrac{\lambda}{3} = \mu \quad \text{(coefficients of } \mathbf{b}\text{)} \qquad \dots ③$$

$$\lambda = \tfrac{1}{2} - \tfrac{\mu}{2} \quad \text{(coefficients of } \mathbf{a}\text{)} \qquad \dots ④$$

Now solve ③ and ④ simultaneously to give

$$\lambda = \tfrac{2}{5} \text{ and } \mu = \tfrac{1}{5}$$

Now we can answer the question!

(a) $\overrightarrow{TP} = \lambda\overrightarrow{TA}$ and $\lambda = \tfrac{2}{5}$ $\qquad \therefore \overrightarrow{TP} = \tfrac{2}{5}\overrightarrow{TA}$ $\qquad \therefore TP:TA \equiv 2:5$

(b) $\overrightarrow{MP} = \mu\overrightarrow{MB}$ and $\mu = \tfrac{1}{5}$ $\qquad \therefore \overrightarrow{MP} = \tfrac{1}{5}\overrightarrow{MB}$ $\qquad \therefore MP:MB \equiv 1:5$

(c) $\overrightarrow{OP} = \tfrac{1}{3}b + \lambda\left(-\tfrac{1}{3}b + a\right)$ (from ①) and $\lambda = \tfrac{2}{5}$

$$\therefore \overrightarrow{OP} = \tfrac{1}{3}b + \tfrac{2}{5}\left(-\tfrac{1}{3}b + a\right)$$

$$\therefore \overrightarrow{OP} = \tfrac{1}{5}(2a + b)$$

You should now be able to answer Exercises 12–20 on pages 106–108.

EXERCISES

1 State whether the following are scalar or vector quantities

    (a) a temperature of 50°C

    (b) a wind of 60 km/h from the north west

    (c) a height of 1.60 metres

    (d) an acceleration of 10 m/s²

    (e) a current of 15 knots in an easterly direction

    (f) a high tide of 3.6 metres

2 *P* has position vector **p** relative to an origin *O* and *Q* is a point such that $OQ = 2OP$. *R* has position vector **r** relative to the same origin and *S* is a point such that $OS = 2OR$. *T* is the mid-point of *QS*. Find, in terms of **p** and **r**

(a) $\overrightarrow{PR}$ (b) $\overrightarrow{QT}$ (c) $\overrightarrow{OT}$ (d) $\overrightarrow{TR}$.

3 Give the vector equation of the lines satisfying the following conditions:

Passing through the point	*Rule for changing position*
(a) (2,1)	2 up for every 3 across (→)
(b) (0,1)	1 down for every 1 across (→)
(c) (−3, 1)	4 up for every 3 back (←)

4 (a) Find the vector equation of the line passing through:

   (i) (2, −1)   and (3, 2)
   (ii) (4, 7)   and (6, 5)

(b) Find the vector equation of the following line segments:

   (i) (−1, 3)   and (4, 5)
   (ii) (0, −1)   and (−1, −3)

5 Find the vector equation for the line passing through:

(a) the point (2,1,6) with direction ratios $\begin{pmatrix} -1 \\ 2 \\ -1 \end{pmatrix}$

(b) the point (0,6,1) with direction ratios $\begin{pmatrix} 3 \\ 2 \\ 1 \end{pmatrix}$

For both these equations, find the corresponding cartesian forms.

6 Find the vector equation of the line passing through the points:

(a) (1, 0, 2)   and (5, 1, 3)
(b) (2, −1, 0)   and (−1, −4, 3)

Find the corresponding parametric and cartesian forms for each of them.

7 Find the lengths of the following vectors:

(a) $\overrightarrow{AB}$, where $\overrightarrow{OA} = \begin{pmatrix} 3 \\ -1 \\ 2 \end{pmatrix}$ $\overrightarrow{OB} = \begin{pmatrix} 1 \\ 2 \\ 8 \end{pmatrix}$

(b) $\overrightarrow{CD}$, where $\overrightarrow{OC} = \begin{pmatrix} -1 \\ 0 \\ -1 \end{pmatrix}$ $\overrightarrow{OD} = \begin{pmatrix} 2 \\ -2 \\ -3 \end{pmatrix}$

(c) $\overrightarrow{EF}$, where $\overrightarrow{OE} = 2\mathbf{i} - 3\mathbf{j} + \mathbf{k}$, $\overrightarrow{OF} = -\mathbf{i} - \mathbf{j} + 2\mathbf{k}$

(d) $\overrightarrow{OG}$, where $\overrightarrow{OG} = \begin{pmatrix} 3 \\ 2 \\ 6 \end{pmatrix}$

(e) $\overrightarrow{OH}$, where $\overrightarrow{OH} = \mathbf{i} - \mathbf{j} + 2\mathbf{k}$

8 Referred to an origin O, the position vectors of points A and B are given respectively by

$$\overrightarrow{OA} = 3\mathbf{i} + \mathbf{j} + 3\mathbf{k},$$

$$\overrightarrow{OB} = 5\mathbf{i} - 4\mathbf{j} + 3\mathbf{k}.$$

Show that the cosine of angle AOB is equal to $\dfrac{4}{\sqrt{38}}$

9 With respect to an origin O, the position vectors of the points L, M and N are:

$$a(4\mathbf{i} + 7\mathbf{j} + 7\mathbf{k}), \quad a(\mathbf{i} + 3\mathbf{j} + 2\mathbf{k}), \quad a(2\mathbf{i} + 4\mathbf{j} + 6\mathbf{k})$$

respectively, where a is a scalar constant.

(a) Find the vectors $\overrightarrow{ML}$ and $\overrightarrow{MN}$.

(b) Prove that $\cos \angle LMN = \dfrac{9}{10}$

10 Relative to an origin O, points A and B have position vectors $2\mathbf{i} + 9\mathbf{j} - 6\mathbf{k}$ and $6\mathbf{i} + 3\mathbf{j} + 6\mathbf{k}$ respectively, $\mathbf{i}$, $\mathbf{j}$ and $\mathbf{k}$ being orthogonal unit vectors. Find the angle AOB correct to the nearest degree.

11 Show by using a vector method that the diagonals of a rhombus intersect at right-angles.

12 In $\triangle ABC$, E lies on BC, with $BE/EC = \frac{2}{3}$, F lies on CA, with $CF/FA = \frac{1}{4}$, and G lies on AB produced, with $GB/GA = \frac{1}{6}$. Relative to the origin O the position vectors of A, B, C are respectively $\mathbf{a}$, $\mathbf{b}$, $\mathbf{c}$. Determine the position vectors of E, F, G in terms of $\mathbf{a}$, $\mathbf{b}$, $\mathbf{c}$ and deduce that E, F, G lie on a straight line.

13 O, A and B are three non-collinear points; the position vectors of A and B with respect to O are **a** and **b** respectively. M is the mid-point of OB, T is the point of trisection of AB nearer B, $AMTX$ is a parallelogram and OX cuts AB at Y. Find, in terms of **a** and **b**, the position vectors of

(a) M (b) T (c) X (d) Y.

14 The points A, B, P, Q have position vectors **a**, **b**, $\frac{1}{3}$**b**, $\frac{1}{4}$**a** with respect to an origin O, where **a** and **b** are non-parallel vectors. The mid-points of the sides OB, OA, AB of the triangle OAB are D, E, F respectively. Show that ED is parallel to AB. AP meets EF at L. Prove that the position vector of L is $\frac{1}{2}$**a** + $\frac{1}{6}$**b**.

15 Write down, in vector form an equation of the line l which passes through L $(-3, 1, -7)$ and M $(5, 3, 5)$.

Find the position vector of the point P on the line for which OP is perpendicular to l, where O is the origin.

Hence find the shortest distance from O to the line l.

16 The vectors **u** and **v** are given by:

u = 5**i** − 4**j** + s**k**, **v** = 2**i** + t**j** − 3**k**.

(a)   Given that the vectors **u** and **v** are perpendicular, find a relation between the scalars s and t.

(b)   Given instead that the vectors **u** and **v** are parallel, find the values of the scalars s and t.

17 Vectors **r** and **s** are given by:

$\mathbf{r} = \lambda\mathbf{i} + (2\lambda - 1)\,\mathbf{j} - \mathbf{k}$,

$\mathbf{s} = (1 - \lambda)\,\mathbf{i} + 3\lambda\mathbf{j} + (4\lambda - 1)\,\mathbf{k}$,

where λ is a scalar.

(a)   Find the values of λ for which **r** and **s** are perpendicular.

When $\lambda = 2$, **r** and **s** are the position vectors of the points A and B respectively, referred to an origin O.

(b)   Find $\overrightarrow{AB}$.

(c)   Use a scalar product to find the size of $\angle BAO$, giving your answer to the nearest degree.

18 With respect to an origin O, the position vectors of the points L and M are $2\mathbf{i} - 3\mathbf{j} + 3\mathbf{k}$ and $5\mathbf{i} + \mathbf{j} + c\mathbf{k}$ respectively, where c is a constant.

The point N is such that $OLMN$ is a rectangle.

(a) Find the value of c.

(b) Write down the position vector of N.

(c) Find, in the form $\mathbf{r} = \mathbf{p} + t\mathbf{q}$, an equation of the line MN.

19 Referred to a fixed origin O, the points A and B have position vectors:

$5\mathbf{i} + \mathbf{j} + 2\mathbf{k}$ and $-\mathbf{i} + 7\mathbf{j} + 8\mathbf{k}$.

The line l_1 passes through A and the line l_2 passes through B.

The lines l_1 and l_2 intersect at the point C whose position vector is $\mathbf{i} + 2\mathbf{j} + \mathbf{k}$.

(a) Find equations for the lines l_1 and l_2, giving each in the form
   $\mathbf{r} = \mathbf{a} + t\mathbf{b}$.

(b) Find the size of $\angle OAB$, giving your answer to the nearest degree.

20 Referred to an origin O, the points A and B have position vectors given by:

$\overrightarrow{OA} = 7\mathbf{i} + 3\mathbf{j} + 8\mathbf{k},$

$\overrightarrow{OB} = 5\mathbf{i} + 4\mathbf{j} + 6\mathbf{k}.$

(a) Show that the point P with the position vector given by:

$\overrightarrow{OP} = (5 - 2\lambda)\,\mathbf{i} + (4 + \lambda)\,\mathbf{j} + (6 - 2\lambda)\,\mathbf{k},$

where λ is a parameter, lies on the straight line L passing through the points A and B.

(b) Find the value of λ for which OP is perpendicular to L.

With centre O and radius OA, a circle is drawn to cut the line L at the points A and C.

(c) Determine the position vector of C.

SUMMARY

You should now be able to:

- use the result $\overrightarrow{PQ} = \overrightarrow{OQ} - \overrightarrow{OP}$

- write down the vector equation of a line through points A and B. (It is $\mathbf{r} = \mathbf{a} + \lambda\,(\mathbf{b} - \mathbf{a})$, where $\mathbf{a}$ and $\mathbf{b}$ are the position vectors of A and B respectively.)

- use either $\mathbf{r} = \begin{pmatrix} x \\ y \\ z \end{pmatrix}$ or $\mathbf{r} = x\mathbf{i} + y\mathbf{j} + z\mathbf{k}$ for a general position vector.

- recall that coordinates are written sideways (x, y, z), whereas vectors are written downwards $\begin{pmatrix} x \\ y \\ z \end{pmatrix}$.

- deduce from a vector equation of a line the corresponding parametric and cartesian equations

- use the result $\mathbf{a} = \begin{pmatrix} x \\ y \\ z \end{pmatrix} \Rightarrow |\mathbf{a}| = \sqrt{x + y^2 + z^2}$

- use the scalar product of vectors $\mathbf{a}$ and $\mathbf{b}$ which is given by both $\mathbf{a} \cdot \mathbf{b} = |\mathbf{a}|\,|\mathbf{b}|\cos\theta$, where θ is the angle between $\mathbf{a}$ and $\mathbf{b}$ and $\mathbf{a} \cdot \mathbf{b} = a_1 b_1 + a_2 b_2 + a_3 b_3$, where

$$\mathbf{a} = \begin{pmatrix} a_1 \\ a_2 \\ a_3 \end{pmatrix} \text{ and } \mathbf{b} = \begin{pmatrix} b_1 \\ b_2 \\ b_3 \end{pmatrix}$$

- recall that for non-zero vectors $\mathbf{a}$ and $\mathbf{b}$

  $\mathbf{a} \cdot \mathbf{b} = 0 \iff \mathbf{a}$ is perpendicular to $\mathbf{b}$

- use the 'two routes approach' to solve problems involving ratio geometry.

7

Complex numbers

INTRODUCTION   In this section we're going to extend our normal ideas of numbers to Include those formed by multiples of an 'impossible' number, the square root of −1. These so-called *complex* numbers are very important in more advanced mathematics. In this section we'll be looking at their basic properties and how they can be represented visually.

Powers of i

When we apply the formula for solving quadratic equations to

$$x^2 + 2x + 5 = 0$$

we find that:

$$x = \frac{-2 \pm \sqrt{4 - 20}}{2}$$

$$= \frac{-2 \pm \sqrt{-16}}{2}$$

$$= \frac{-2 \pm \sqrt{16 \times -1}}{2}$$

$$= \frac{-2 \pm 4 \times \sqrt{-1}}{2}$$

$$= -1 \pm 2\sqrt{-1}$$

Of course we know that if we square any 'ordinary' number we're going to end up with something positive, so for these numbers, the term $\sqrt{-1}$ doesn't make sense. However, mixtures of these new numbers (called *imaginary* numbers) and the old numbers (the *real* numbers) which together make *complex* numbers have proved extremely useful. Let's have a look at some of their properties.

An alternative notation for $\sqrt{-1}$ is i. Using this notation:

$$i^2 = (\sqrt{-1})^2 \quad = -1$$
$$i^3 = (\sqrt{-1})^3 \quad = (\sqrt{-1})^2\,\sqrt{(-1)} \quad = -1 \times i = -i$$
$$i^4 = (\sqrt{-1})^4 \quad = (\sqrt{-1})^2\,(\sqrt{-1})^2 \quad = -1 \times -1 = 1$$

and then it starts the cycle again:

$$i^5 = i; \qquad i^6 = i^2 = -1; \qquad i^7 = i^3 = -i; \qquad i^8 = i^4 = 1$$

and so on.

Similarly

$$i^{-1} \;=\; \frac{1}{i} \;=\; \frac{i}{i^2} \;=\; -i$$

$$i^{-2} \;=\; \frac{1}{i^2} \;=\; \frac{1}{-1} \;=\; -1$$

$$i^{-3} \;=\; \frac{1}{i^3} \;=\; \frac{i}{i^4} \;=\; i$$

$$i^{-4} \;=\; \frac{1}{i^4} \;=\; \frac{1}{1} \;=\; 1$$

and so on.

Addition, subtraction and equations

When we have mixtures of real and imaginary numbers, usually the real part is written first, for example:

   2 + 3i.   Here 2 is the real part and 3 the imaginary part.

This can be written:

   Re $(2 + 3i) = 2$

and

   Im $(2 + 3i) = 3$

The real parts and the imaginary parts are treated as if they are completely separate: if we are adding any two numbers we add the real parts and then add the imaginary parts, for example:

$$(2 + 3i) + (-4 + i) \;=\; (2 - 4) + (3i + i)$$
$$= -2 + 4i$$

Similarly, when we're subtracting two complex numbers we subtract the real parts and subtract the imaginary parts separately, for example:

$$(2 + 3i) - (-4 + i) \;=\; (2 + 4) + (3i - i)$$
$$= 6 + 2i$$

This property can be quite useful; it means that sometimes from one equation we can find two unknowns. Suppose we had:

$$x - 2 + i(y - 5) \;=\; 3 + 2i$$

where x and y are real numbers. There is no mixing of the two parts – the real parts must be equal to each other and the imaginary parts must be equal to each other, i.e.

$$x - 2 = 3 \quad \text{and} \quad y - 5 = 2$$
$$x = 5 \quad \text{and} \quad y = 7$$

You should now be able to answer Exercises 1–3 on page 126.

Multiplication of complex numbers

This is the same as algebraic multiplication, except that the term with i^2 becomes real, for example:

$$(3 + 4i)\,(1 - 2i) \quad = 3 - 6i + 4i - 8i^2$$
$$= 3 - 2i + 8 \qquad (\text{using } i^2 = -1)$$
$$= 11 - 2i$$

Let's introduce z^*, which is called the *conjugate* of z. This z^* has the same real part as z but has an imaginary part opposite in sign although equal in magnitude, so that:

if $\quad z = a + bi \quad$ then $\quad z^* = a - bi$

The interesting thing about the conjugate is that the product zz^* is always real:

$$zz^* \quad = (a + bi)\,(a - bi) = a^2 - b^2\,i^2$$
$$= a^2 + b^2 \;(= |z|^2)$$

and this fact will be important in the next topic.

You should now be able to answer Exercises 4–5 on page 126.

Fractions

When we multiply two linear factors together, the product gives an indication of what the original factors were. For example, with

$$(2 - x)\,(3 + 4x) = 6 + 5x - 4x^2$$

we would, with a bit of practice, be able to work back from the right-hand side to find what the contents of the brackets on the left-hand side must have been.

The situation is a little different with complex numbers because of the fact that $i^2 = -1$. If we take the same example with i instead of x,

$$(2 - i)\,(3 + 4i) \quad = 6 + 5i - 4i^2$$
$$= 10 + 5i$$

the original factors are disguised because the $-4i^2$ has merged with the other real number. This means that we can't divide expressions as we could in earlier algebra. We can find:

$$\frac{6 + 5x - 4x^2}{2 - x}$$

easily enough, but the same method doesn't work for:

$$\frac{10 + 5i}{2 - i}$$

For fractions with complex denominators we multiply top and bottom by the conjugate of the denominator. This means that the denominator will be real and we can divide through more simply.

Let's try that with this one,

$$\frac{10 + 5i}{2 - i} = \frac{10 + 5i}{2 - i} \times \frac{2 + i}{2 + i} = \frac{20 + 10i + 10i + 5i^2}{4 - i^2}$$

$$= \frac{15 + 20i}{5}$$

$$= 3 + 4i$$

which was the other factor of $10 + 5i$.

You should now be able to answer Exercises 6–8 on page 126.

Finding square roots

The method that we used for finding partial fractions and for combining trigonometric curves also works very well in this case: we assume the answer and work back from there.

Let's suppose we want to find the square roots of $7 - 24i$. Obviously the square roots themselves must be complex numbers otherwise we wouldn't end up with an expression containing i when we squared it. So if they are complex numbers we can write them as $a + bi$, for some real numbers a and b, and put:

$$\sqrt{7 - 24i} = a + bi$$

Square both sides:

$$7 - 24i = (a + bi)^2 = a^2 + 2abi + b^2i^2$$

$$= (a^2 - b^2) + (2ab)i$$

The real parts on both sides must be equal, and so must the imaginary parts:

$$7 = a^2 - b^2 \qquad \qquad \ldots ①$$

$$-24 = 2ab \qquad \qquad \ldots ②$$

Taking ② and rearranging:

$$b = \frac{-12}{a} \qquad \qquad \cdots ③$$

We can put this into ① :

$$7 = a^2 - \left(\frac{-12}{a}\right)^2 \quad \text{(careful with signs)}$$

$$= a^2 - \frac{144}{a^2}$$

Multiply by a^2:

$$7a^2 = a^4 - 144$$

Rearrange:

$$a^4 - 7a^2 - 144 = 0$$

Factorise:

$$(a^2 - 16)(a^2 + 9) = 0$$

i.e.: $a^2 = 16$ or $a^2 = -9$ (impossible, because a is real)

$$\Rightarrow a = \pm 4$$

If $a = +4$, from [3], $b = \dfrac{-12}{4} = -3$

If $a = -4$, $\quad b = \dfrac{-12}{-4} = 3$

i.e. the two square roots of $7 - 24i$ are

$$4 - 3i \text{ and } -4 + 3i \ \left(\text{i.e. } \pm (4 - 3i)\right)$$

You should now be able to answer Exercises 9–10 on page 127.

The Argand diagram

Now we will go on to look at a way of representing complex numbers on some axes.

We'll let the real numbers take values along what would normally be the x-axis:

Figure 7.1

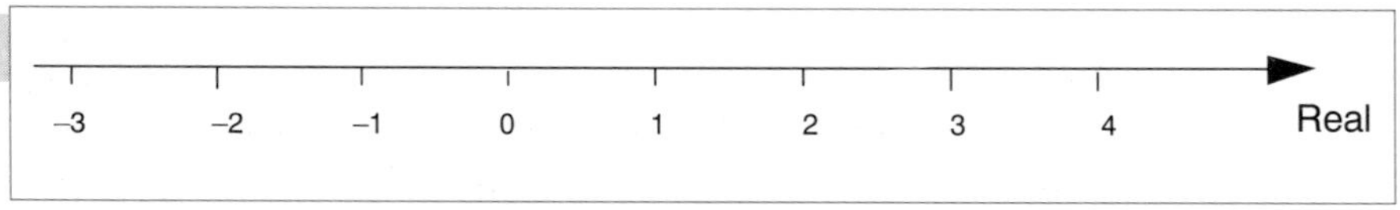

Normal addition, subtraction, multiplication and division take place entirely on this line – the imaginary numbers add another dimension to this:

Figure 7.2

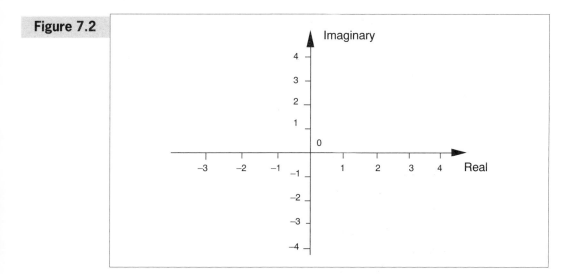

This is called an 'Argand diagram', after the mathematician of the same name. Complex numbers are represented by lines on the Argand diagram. For example, the line joining the origin to the point (3, 2) represents the complex number 3 + 2i. Similarly, the line joining the origin to (–2, –1) represents the complex number –2 –i.

Figure 7.3

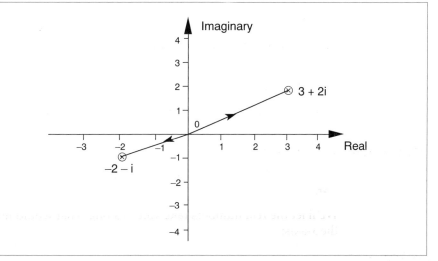

Suppose we have a line *OP* on an Argand diagram representing the complex number $a + bi$. The length of *OP* is called the *modulus* of $a + bi$, written $|\, a + bi\, |$, and the angle *OP* makes with the positive *x*-axis is called the *argument* of $a + bi$, written arg $(a + bi)$.

Figure 7.4

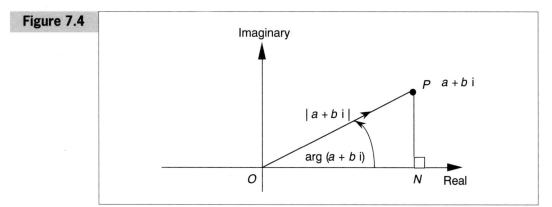

We can calculate the values of $| a + bi |$ quite easily by using Pythagoras's theorem, since $\triangle ONP$ is right-angled:

$$| a + bi | = \sqrt{ON^2 + PN^2}$$
$$= \sqrt{a^2 + b^2}$$

and, from the same triangle:

$$\tan \left[\arg (a + bi) \right] = \frac{b}{a}$$

i.e.: $\qquad \arg (a + bi) = \tan^{-1} \frac{b}{a}$

The argument needs careful consideration, for example:

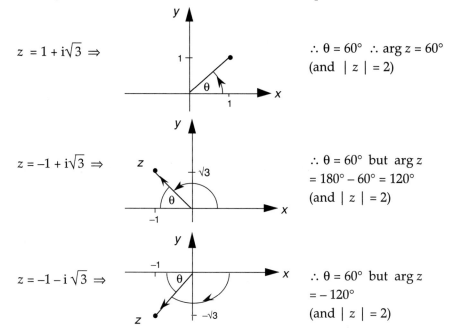

$z = 1 + i\sqrt{3} \Rightarrow$ $\qquad$ $\therefore \theta = 60° \;\; \therefore \arg z = 60°$
(and $| z | = 2$)

$z = -1 + i\sqrt{3} \Rightarrow$ $\qquad$ $\therefore \theta = 60°$ but $\arg z$
$= 180° - 60° = 120°$
(and $| z | = 2$)

$z = -1 - i\sqrt{3} \Rightarrow$ $\qquad$ $\therefore \theta = 60°$ but $\arg z$
$= -120°$
(and $| z | = 2$)

116

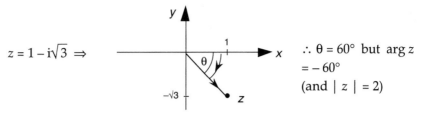

$z = 1 - i\sqrt{3} \Rightarrow$

$\therefore \theta = 60°$ but arg z
$= -60°$
(and $|z| = 2$)

You need to remember that:

- arg z is between $+180°$ and $-180°$ (or between $+\pi$ and $-\pi$)
- arg z is measured from the positive x axis.

Example Find the modulus and argument of:

(a) $1 + i$
(b) $-1 + i$
(c) $-\sqrt{3} - i$
(d) $1 - i$

Solution

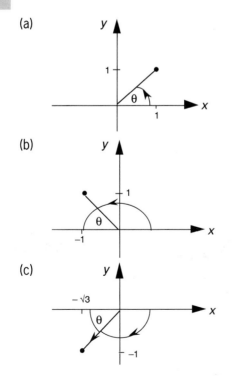

(a)

$\therefore |1 + i| = \sqrt{1^2 + 1^2} = \sqrt{2}$

$\text{Tan } \theta = 1 \therefore \theta = \dfrac{\pi}{4}$

$\therefore \arg z = \dfrac{\pi}{4}$

(b)

$\therefore |-1 + i| = \sqrt{1^2 + 1^2} = \sqrt{2}$

$\text{Tan } \theta = 1 \therefore \theta = \dfrac{\pi}{4}$

$\therefore \arg z = \pi - \dfrac{\pi}{4} = \dfrac{3\pi}{4}$

(c)

$\therefore |-\sqrt{3} - i| = \sqrt{(-\sqrt{3})^2 + (-1)^2} = 2$

$\text{Tan } \theta = \dfrac{1}{\sqrt{3}} \therefore \theta = \dfrac{\pi}{6}$

$\therefore \arg z = \dfrac{-5\pi}{6}$

117

(d)

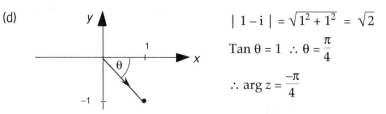

$$| 1-i | = \sqrt{1^2 + 1^2} = \sqrt{2}$$

$$\text{Tan } \theta = 1 \therefore \theta = \frac{\pi}{4}$$

$$\therefore \arg z = \frac{-\pi}{4}$$

So whenever you have to give the argument of a complex number, draw a diagram so that you locate it in the correct quadrant. Giving the angle in the wrong quadrant is a very common error.

Remember also that the argument of a complex number varies between π and $-\pi$ (or 180° and −180°, if you are working in degrees).

You should now be able to answer Exercise 11 on page 127.

The modulus of products and quotients

We will now look at the properties of products and quotients of complex numbers.

Suppose we have two complex numbers:

$$z_1 = a + bi, \quad z_2 = c + di$$

Then

$$
\begin{aligned}
| z_1 z_2 | &= | (a + bi)(c + di) | \\
&= | ac + bdi^2 + bci + adi | \\
&= | (ac - bd) + i(bc + ad) | \\
&= \sqrt{(ac - bd)^2 + (bc + ad)^2} \\
&= \sqrt{a^2c^2 - 2abcd + b^2d^2 + b^2c^2 + 2abcd + a^2d^2} \\
&= \sqrt{a^2c^2 + b^2d^2 + b^2c^2 + a^2d^2} \\
&= \sqrt{a^2(c^2 + d^2) + b^2(c^2 + d^2)} \\
&= \sqrt{(a^2 + b^2)(c^2 + d^2)} \\
&= \sqrt{a^2 + b^2}\sqrt{c^2 + d^2} \\
&= | a + bi | | c + di | \\
&= | z_1 | | z_2 |
\end{aligned}
$$

Although the process was lengthy it has provided a very useful result. Suppose:

$$z_1 = 1 - i \quad \text{and} \quad z_2 = \sqrt{3} + i$$

If we want the modulus of the product z_1z_2, we *could* work out:

$$
\begin{aligned}
z_1 z_2 &= (1-i)(\sqrt{3}+i) \\
&= \sqrt{3} + i - i\sqrt{3} - i^2 \\
&= (\sqrt{3}+1) + i(1-\sqrt{3})
\end{aligned}
$$

Then:

$$
\begin{aligned}
|z_1 z_2| &= \sqrt{(\sqrt{3}+1)^2 + (1-\sqrt{3})^2} \\
&= \sqrt{3 + 2\sqrt{3} + 1 + 1 - 2\sqrt{3} + 3} \\
&= \sqrt{8} = 2\sqrt{2}
\end{aligned}
$$

Instead, we work out:

$$
|z_1| = \sqrt{1^2 + (-1)^2} \quad \text{and} \quad |z_2| = \sqrt{(\sqrt{3})^2 + 1^2}
$$
$$
= \sqrt{2} \qquad\qquad\qquad\qquad\quad = 2
$$

and then:

$$
|z_1 z_2| = |z_1||z_2| = \sqrt{2} \times 2 = 2\sqrt{2}
$$

which is the same as before, but quicker.

A similar result holds for quotients, i.e.

$$
\left| \frac{z_1}{z_2} \right| = \frac{|z_1|}{|z_2|}
$$

The proof follows the same general lines as for products.

The argument of products and quotients

Taking the two complex numbers $z_1 = a + bi$, $z_2 = c + di$ and remembering that $z_1 z_2 = (ac - bd) + i(bc + ad)$, we find that:

$$
\tan \arg(z_1 z_2) = \frac{bc + ad}{ac - bd}
$$

$$
\text{divide by } ac = \frac{\dfrac{bc}{ac} + \dfrac{ad}{ac}}{\dfrac{ac}{ac} - \dfrac{bd}{ac}}
$$

$$
= \frac{\dfrac{b}{a} + \dfrac{d}{c}}{1 - \left(\dfrac{b}{a}\right)\left(\dfrac{d}{c}\right)} = \frac{\tan p + \tan q}{1 - \tan p \tan q}
$$

$$
= \tan(p+q) \qquad \text{where} \quad \tan p = \frac{b}{a}, \quad \tan q = \frac{d}{c}
$$

$$
= \tan\left(\arg(z_1) + \arg(z_2)\right) \quad \text{since} \quad p = \tan^{-1}\frac{b}{a}
$$

$$
= \arg z_1 \text{ etc.}
$$

i.e. $\arg(z_1 z_2) = \arg(z_1) + \arg(z_2)$

(assuming $\arg z_1$ and $\arg z_2$ in the correct range).

The proof might seem a little long and complicated but you're unlikely to be asked to reproduce it. However, the result is important, and you'll be using it quite a few times. Again, there's a similar result for quotients:

$$\arg\left(\frac{z_1}{z_2}\right) = \arg(z_1) - \arg(z_2)$$

which means that arguments behave in much the same way as logs. Let's derive some more results and then collect them all together:

(a) $|z^n| = \underbrace{|z| |z| |z| \dots |z|}_{n \text{ of these}}$

$= |z|^n$

(b) $\left|\dfrac{1}{z}\right| = \dfrac{|1|}{|z|} = \dfrac{1}{|z|}$

(c) $\arg(z^n) = \underbrace{\arg(z) + \arg(z) + \arg(z) + \dots + \arg(z)}_{n \text{ of these}}$

$= n \arg(z)$

(d) $\arg\left(\dfrac{1}{z}\right) = \arg(1) - \arg(z)$

$= 0 - \arg(z)$

$= -\arg z$

Let's box this collection now:

If z and w are two complex numbers,		
$\lvert zw \rvert = \lvert z \rvert \lvert w \rvert$:	$\arg(zw)$	$= \arg(z) + \arg(w)$
$\left\lvert\dfrac{z}{w}\right\rvert = \dfrac{\lvert z \rvert}{\lvert w \rvert}$:	$\arg\dfrac{z}{w}$	$= \arg(z) - \arg(w)$
$\lvert z^n \rvert = \lvert z \rvert^n$:	$\arg(z^n)$	$= n \arg(z)$
$\left\lvert\dfrac{1}{z}\right\rvert = \dfrac{1}{\lvert z \rvert}$:	$\arg\left(\dfrac{1}{z}\right)$	$= -\arg(z)$

The results in (a) and (c) will be studied in more detail in P4.

Example   Find the modulus and argument of:

$$\frac{(1+i)^5}{(1-i)^7}$$

Solution Let $z = 1 + i$ and $w = 1 - i$

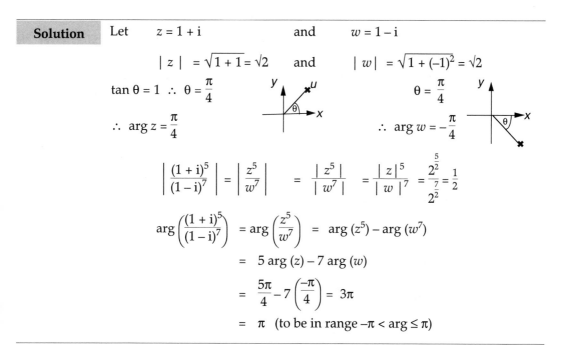

$$|z| = \sqrt{1+1} = \sqrt{2} \qquad \text{and} \qquad |w| = \sqrt{1+(-1)^2} = \sqrt{2}$$

$$\tan\theta = 1 \therefore \theta = \frac{\pi}{4} \qquad\qquad\qquad \theta = \frac{\pi}{4}$$

$$\therefore \arg z = \frac{\pi}{4} \qquad\qquad\qquad\qquad \therefore \arg w = -\frac{\pi}{4}$$

$$\left|\frac{(1+i)^5}{(1-i)^7}\right| = \left|\frac{z^5}{w^7}\right| = \frac{|z^5|}{|w^7|} = \frac{|z|^5}{|w|^7} = \frac{2^{\frac{5}{2}}}{2^{\frac{7}{2}}} = \frac{1}{2}$$

$$\arg\left(\frac{(1+i)^5}{(1-i)^7}\right) = \arg\left(\frac{z^5}{w^7}\right) = \arg(z^5) - \arg(w^7)$$

$$= 5\arg(z) - 7\arg(w)$$

$$= \frac{5\pi}{4} - 7\left(\frac{-\pi}{4}\right) = 3\pi$$

$$= \pi \quad \text{(to be in range } -\pi < \arg \le \pi)$$

You should now be able to answer Exercises 12–15 on page 127.

The $r(\cos\theta + i\sin\theta)$ form for any complex number

Given any complex number z it is conventional to call the modulus of z either $|z|$ or r. Similarly, the argument of z is conventionally written $\arg z$ or θ. Hence, if $z = x + iy$, it follows that $x = r\cos\theta$ and $y = r\sin\theta$.

$$\therefore \quad z = x + iy = r\cos\theta + ir\sin\theta = r(\cos\theta + i\sin\theta)$$

$\therefore$ *Any complex number z of modulus r and argument θ can be put in the form* $z = r(\cos\theta + i\sin\theta)$.

Example   Put $z = 1 - i\sqrt{3}$ in the form $r(\cos\theta + i\sin\theta)$.

Solution

$z = 1 - i\sqrt{3} \Rightarrow$

$$\therefore \quad r = \sqrt{1^2 + (-\sqrt{3})^2} = 2$$

$$\tan\theta = \frac{\sqrt{3}}{1} \quad \therefore \quad \theta = \frac{\pi}{3}$$

$$\therefore \quad \arg z = \frac{-\pi}{3}$$

$$\therefore \quad z = 2\left(\cos\left(\frac{-\pi}{3}\right) + i\sin\left(\frac{-\pi}{3}\right)\right) \quad \therefore \quad z = 2\left(\cos\left(\frac{\pi}{3}\right) - i\sin\frac{\pi}{3}\right)$$

Example   If z_1 and z_2 are complex numbers, prove that

(a) $|z_1 z_2| = |z_1| |z_2|$ (b) $\arg(z_1 z_2) = \arg z_1 + \arg z_2$

(c) $\left| \dfrac{z_1}{z_2} \right| = \dfrac{|z_1|}{|z_2|}$ (d) $\arg\left(\dfrac{z_1}{z_2}\right) = \arg z_1 - \arg z_2$

Solution   Let $z_1 = r_1(\cos\theta_1 + i\sin\theta_1)$ and $z_2 = r_2(\cos\theta_2 + i\sin\theta_2)$

$\therefore$ $z_1 z_2 = r_1 r_2 (\cos\theta_1 + i\sin\theta_1)(\cos\theta_2 + i\sin\theta_2)$

$\therefore$ $z_1 z_2 = r_1 r_2 \left[(\cos\theta_1 \cos\theta_2 - \sin\theta_1 \sin\theta_2) + i(\sin\theta_1 \cos\theta_2 + \sin\theta_2 \cos\theta_1)\right]$

$\therefore$ $z_1 z_2 = r_1 r_2 \left[\cos(\theta_1 + \theta_2) + i\sin(\theta_1 + \theta_2)\right]$ ... (*)

(a)   The identity (*) above gives $|z_1 z_2| = r_1 r_2$

But $|z_1| = r_1$ and $|z_2| = r_2$ $\therefore$ $|z_1 z_2| = |z_1| |z_2|$

(b)   The identity (*) above gives $\arg(z_1 z_2) = \theta_1 + \theta_2$

But $\arg z_1 = \theta_1$ and $\arg z_2 = \theta_2$ $\therefore$ $\arg(z_1 z_2) = \arg z_1 + \arg z_2$

It also follows that

$$\frac{z_1}{z_2} = \frac{r_1(\cos\theta_1 + i\sin\theta_1)}{r_2(\cos\theta_2 + i\sin\theta_2)}$$

$\therefore$ $$\frac{z_1}{z_2} = \frac{r_1(\cos\theta_1 + i\sin\theta_1)(\cos\theta_2 - i\sin\theta_2)}{r_2(\cos\theta_2 + i\sin\theta_2)(\cos\theta_2 - i\sin\theta_2)}$$

$\therefore$ $$\frac{z_1}{z_2} = \frac{r_1}{r_2}\left[\frac{(\cos\theta_1 \cos\theta_2 + \sin\theta_1 \sin\theta_2) + i(\sin\theta_1 \cos\theta_2 - \sin\theta_2 \cos\theta_1)}{(\cos^2\theta_2 + \sin^2\theta_2)}\right]$$

$\therefore$ $$\frac{z_1}{z_2} = \frac{r_1}{r_2}\left[\cos(\theta_1 - \theta_2) + i\sin(\theta_1 - \theta_2)\right]$$ ... (**)

(c)   The identity (**) above gives $\left| \dfrac{z_1}{z_2} \right| = \dfrac{r_1}{r_2}$

But $|z_1| = r_1$ and $|z_2| = r_2$ $\therefore$ $\left| \dfrac{z_1}{z_2} \right| = \dfrac{|z_1|}{|z_2|}$

(d)   The identity (**) above gives $\arg\left(\dfrac{z_1}{z_2}\right) = \theta_1 - \theta_2$.

But $\arg z_1 = \theta_1$ and $\arg z_2 = \theta_2$ $\therefore$ $\arg\left(\dfrac{z_1}{z_2}\right) = \arg z_1 - \arg z_2$

You may prefer this approach to the purely algebraic one previously adopted.

Addition and subtraction of complex numbers in an Argand diagram

The lines representing complex numbers $z_1 z_2$ and $z_1 + z_2$ give a parallelogram, with the diagonal representing $z_1 + z_2$.

Figure 7.5

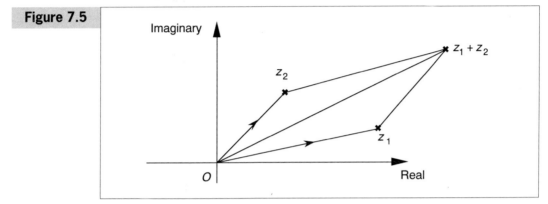

Can you see the similarity with vectors here?

If we took the difference between the two numbers z_1 and z_2, we could get either of two different parallelograms, according to which number was being subtracted from the other.

Figure 7.6

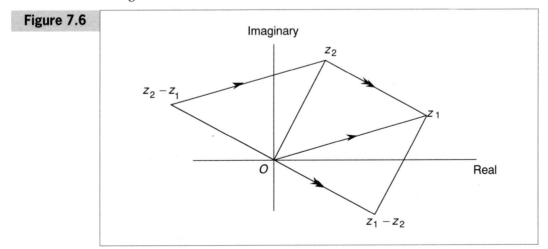

You should be able to work out the two different parallelograms.

Multiplying a complex number by a real number in an Argand diagram

If we take a complex number w such that:

$$w \quad = \quad a + bi$$

and multiply w by some real number p, what is the relationship between w and the new number pw?

We'll look at the modulus first:

$$| pw | \quad = | p | | w |$$
$$= p | w | \qquad \text{since } p \text{ is real}$$

So the length of the line joining the origin to pw is p times as long as that joining the origin to w.

Now we'll see what happens with the argument:

$$\arg(pw) \quad = \arg(p) + \arg(w)$$
$$= 0 + \arg(w) \qquad \text{because } p \text{ is real}$$
$$= \arg(w)$$

so the arguments are the same. We'll put these onto an Argand diagram:

Figure 7.7

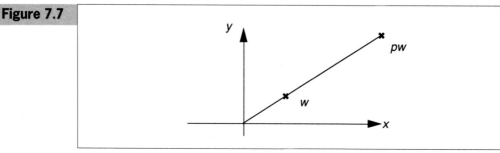

We can see that the point pw is on the same straight line from the origin as w but p times further away. Since p could be a fraction, pw is closer to the origin if $0 \leq p < 1$.

Products and quotients of complex numbers in an Argand diagram

We have seen on page 122 that if:

$$z_1 = r_1 (\cos \theta_1 + i \sin \theta_1) \quad \text{and} \quad z_2 = r_2 (\cos \theta_2 + i \sin \theta_2)$$

then $\quad z_1 z_2 = r_1 r_2 (\cos (\theta_1 + \theta_2) + i \sin (\theta_1 + \theta_2))$

and $\quad \dfrac{z_1}{z_2} = \dfrac{r_1}{r_2} (\cos (\theta_1 - \theta_2) + i \sin (\theta_1 - \theta_2))$

Therefore:

- When we multiply complex numbers, we multiply the moduli and add the arguments.
- When we divide complex numbers, we divide the moduli and subtract the arguments.

Example If z is a complex number, how are z and iz related in an Argand diagram?

Solution Let z have modulus r and argument θ.

Since i has modulus 1 and argument $\frac{\pi}{2}$, it follows that iz has modulus $r \times 1 = r$ and argument $\theta + \frac{\pi}{2}$.

And so the lines representing z and iz in the Argand diagram both have the same length but the z-line has been rotated anti-clockwise through $\frac{\pi}{2}$ to give the iz-line.

Figure 7.8

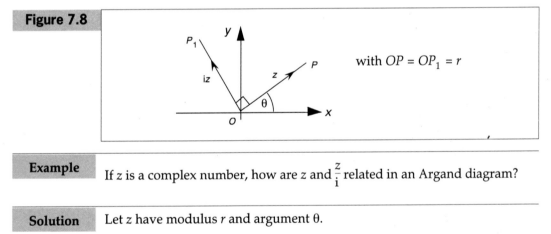

with $OP = OP_1 = r$

Example If z is a complex number, how are z and $\frac{z}{i}$ related in an Argand diagram?

Solution Let z have modulus r and argument θ.

Since i has modulus 1 and argument $\frac{\pi}{2}$, it follows that $\frac{z}{i}$ has modulus $\frac{r}{1} = r$ and argument $\theta - \frac{\pi}{2}$.

And so the lines representing z and $\frac{z}{i}$ in the Argand diagram both have the same length but the z line has been rotated *clockwise* through $\frac{\pi}{2}$ to give the $\frac{z}{i}$ line.

Figure 7.9

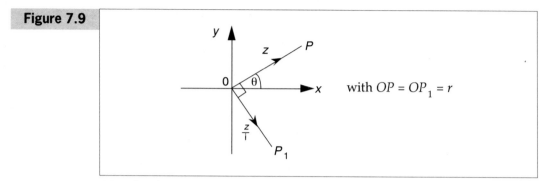

You should now be able to answer Exercises 16–18 on page 128.

EXERCISES

1 Express the following as ±1 or ±i only:

(a) i^3 (b) i^8 (c) i^{10} (d) $\dfrac{1}{i}$ (e) $-i^2$ (f) $\dfrac{-1}{i^3}$ (g) $\dfrac{1}{i^7}$ (h) $(i^3)^2$

2 Find the sum and difference of the following pairs of complex numbers (take the second from the first):

(a) $2 - 3i$, $3 + i$ (b) $1 - i$, $1 + i$

(c) $-3 - i$, $5 + 6i$ (d) $-2i$, $4i$

3 Find the unknowns in the following equations:

(a) $2p + iq$ $= 4 - 7i$

(b) $x + y + i(x - y)$ $= 6 + 2i$

(c) $u + 3i$ $= 2 - vi$

(d) $rs + rs^2i$ $= 4 + 4i$

4 If $z_1 = 2 + 3i$ and $z_2 = 3 - i$, find:

(a) $z_1 z_2$ (b) z_2^2 (c) $z_1 z_1{}^*$ (d) $z_2 z_2{}^*$ (e) $(z_1{}^*)^2$

5 Find, in the form $a + bi$ with $b > 0$ the complex number z satisfying simultaneously the equations $zz^* = 25$, $z + z^* = 6$.

6 Find, in the form $a + bi$, $\dfrac{19 + 4i}{5 - 2i}$

7 Given that $z_1 = 3 + 2i$ and $z_2 = 4 - 3i$

(a) find $z_1 z_2$ and $\dfrac{z_1}{z_2}$, each in the form $a + bi$

8 Express $\dfrac{i}{4 + 3i}$ in the form $a + ib$, where a and b are real

9 Find the two square roots of $3 - 4i$ in the form $a + bi$, where a and b are real.

10 Find the roots, z_1 and z_2, of the equation

$$z^2 - 5 + 12i = 0$$

in the form $a + bi$, where a and b are real, and give the value of $z_1 z_2$.

11 Find the modulus and argument of:

(a) $1 + i\sqrt{3}$　　(b) $2 - 2i$　　(c) $-\sqrt{2} - \sqrt{2}i$　　(d) $2i$

(e) 4　　　　　　(f) $-\sqrt{3} + i$　　(g) $-3i$　　　　(h) -5

12 If $z_1 = 1 + i$ and $z_2 = -\sqrt{3} + i$, find the modulus and argument of:

(a) $z_1{}^3$　　(b) $z_1 z_2$　　(c) $\dfrac{z_2}{z_1}$　　(d) $\dfrac{1}{z_2}$　　(e) $z_1 + z_2$　　(f) $z_2 - z_1$

13 Given that $z_1 = \sqrt{2} - \sqrt{2}i$ and $z_2 = 1 + \sqrt{3}i$ and $z_3 = \dfrac{\sqrt{2} - \sqrt{2}i}{1 + \sqrt{3}i}$, find the modulus and argument of both z_1 and z_2. Hence:

(a) find the modulus of z_3

(b) show that the argument of z_3 is $-\dfrac{7\pi}{12}$

14 Given that $z_1 = 1 - i$ and $z_2 = -1 + i\sqrt{3}$, mark on an Argand diagram the points p_1 and p_2 which represent z_1 and z_2 respectively.

Find $|z_1|$ and $|z_2|$ and write $|z_1 z_2|$ in surd form. Find also arg z_1 and arg z_2 and write down arg $z_1 z_2$ giving each argument (in terms of π) between $-\pi$ and π. Use the given forms of z_1 and z_2 to find $z_1 z_2$ in the form $a + ib$. Deduce that:

$$\cos \frac{5\pi}{12} = \frac{\sqrt{3} - 1}{2\sqrt{2}}$$

15 The complex number z is given by:

$$z = \frac{3 + i}{2 - i}$$

(a) Show that arg $z = 45°$ and find $|z|$.

The complex number z is represented by the point P in an Argand diagram, origin O. The complex number $-5 + ki$ is represented by the point Q and $\angle POQ$ is $90°$.

(b) Find the value of k.

(c) Find the complex number w, represented by the mid-point M of PQ.

(d) Calculate arg w, giving your answer in degrees to 1 decimal place.

16 Express $1 + i\sqrt{3}$ in the form $r\,(\cos\theta + i\sin\theta)$. Hence express $(1 + i\sqrt{3})^6$ in the form $a + ib$

17 Express $\sqrt{10i - 24}$ in the form $a + ib$

18 Express $\sqrt{i}$ in the form $a + ib$.

SUMMARY

You should now be able to:

- recall that $i = \sqrt{-1}$, so that $i^2 = -1$, $i^3 = -i$ and $i^4 = 1$ etc.

- add and subtract complex numbers

- multiply complex numbers. For example $(2 + i)(3 + i) = 5 + 5i$

- divide complex numbers by using the complex conjugate of the denominator. For example

$$\frac{2 + i}{3 + i} = \frac{(2 + i)(3 - i)}{(3 + i)(3 - i)} = \frac{7 + i}{10} = 0.7 + 0.1i$$

- represent any complex number by a line in the Argand diagram

- find the modulus $|z|$ of any complex number z

- find the argument arg z of any complex number z. Remember that $-\pi < \arg z \le \pi$

- express any complex number z in the form $r\,(\cos\theta + i\sin\theta)$, where $|z| = r$ and arg $z = \theta$

- recall that when addition or subtraction is represented in an Argand diagram, then the algebra is that of vectors

- recall that when complex numbers are multiplied, the moduli are multiplied and the arguments added

- recall that when complex numbers are divided, the moduli are divided and the arguments subtracted.

Differential equations

INTRODUCTION In this section we revise separable differential equations and then introduce methods for dealing with different cases, both first and second order.

Differential equations with variables separable: a reminder

You first met differential equations in Module P2. They are essential to a great many areas of science and technology. They can be used to describe all manner of natural and man-made phenomena – from the trajectories of space craft to the growth of human populations, and from the spread of heat through solid bodies to the motion of waves in liquids.

You will have guessed, of course, that there is a great deal more to differential equations than you have seen so far. This section takes the next step, introducing several vitally important new methods for tackling problems of two commonly occurring types. First, let's remind ourselves of earlier work by trying an example or two.

$$\frac{dy}{dx} = x(y^2 + y)$$

Differential equations of this form are said to have 'variables separable' because they can be rearranged in such a way that all mention of y appears on the left and all mention of x on the right. In this case, we have:

$$\frac{dy}{y^2 + y} = x\,dx$$

Integrating the left-hand side gives:

$$\int \frac{dy}{y^2 + y} = \int \left[\frac{1}{y} - \frac{1}{y+1}\right] dy = \ln\,(y) - \ln\,(y+1) = \ln\left[\frac{y}{(y+1)}\right]$$

(provided $y > 0$)

while on the right:

$$\int dx = \frac{1}{2}x^2 + C$$

So: $\ln\left[\frac{y}{(y + 1)}\right] = \frac{1}{2}x^2 + C$

$$\frac{y}{(y + 1)} = e^{\frac{1}{2}x^2 + C} = Ae^{\frac{x^2}{2}}$$

where $A = e^C$

Therefore:

$$y = (y + 1)Ae^{\frac{x^2}{2}}$$

$$y\left(1 - Ae^{\frac{x^2}{2}}\right) = Ae^{\frac{x^2}{2}}$$

so that finally:

$$y = \frac{Ae^{\frac{x^2}{2}}}{1 - Ae^{\frac{x^2}{2}}}$$

Notice the way in which this method separates the two variables, integrates the resulting expressions and then applies a little algebra to produce the final answer. Always be on the lookout for problems that can be solved in this way – even when you have mastered more sophisticated methods.

Example   Solve the differential equation:

$$\frac{1}{x}\frac{dy}{dx} + \frac{x^2 + \sin^2 y}{1 + x^2} = 1$$

given that $y = 0$ when $x = 1$

Solution   The solution is summarised as follows:

At first sight this problem looks an unpromising subject for the variables separable technique. The variables don't appear to be separable! However, note that:

$$\frac{x^2 + \sin^2 y}{1 + x^2} - 1 = \frac{\sin^2 y - 1}{1 + x^2} = \frac{-\cos^2 y}{1 + x^2}$$

So the equation becomes:

$$\frac{1}{x}\frac{dy}{dx} - \frac{\cos^2 y}{1 + x^2} = 0 \quad \Rightarrow \frac{1}{x}\frac{dy}{dx} = \frac{\cos^2 y}{1 + x^2}$$

$$\Rightarrow \frac{dy}{\cos^2 y} = \frac{x\, dx}{1 + x^2}$$

Noticing that the integrand on the left is $\sec^2 y$, we can now integrate to produce:

$$\tan y = \frac{1}{2} \ln (1 + x^2) + C$$

But $y = 0$ when $x = 1$, and so:

$$0 = \frac{1}{2} \ln (1 + 1) + C$$

Therefore

$$C = -\frac{1}{2} \ln 2$$

and

$$\tan y = \frac{1}{2} \ln \left(\frac{1 + x^2}{2} \right)$$

which gives:

$$y = \tan^{-1} \left(\frac{1}{2} \ln \left(\frac{1 + x^2}{2} \right) \right)$$

This is quite a difficult problem, and is deliberately so to emphasise the fact that, although the method of variables separable is straightforward in principle, you may find yourself involved in some tricky mathematics when you use it.

You should now be able to answer Exercise 1 on page 148.

Equations of the form: $\frac{dy}{dx} + Py = Q$

We now introduce a new method which allows us to deal with a broader class of problems, namely those that can be written in the form:

$$\frac{dy}{dx} + Py = Q$$

where both P and Q are functions of x. As an example, consider the following equation.

$$\frac{dy}{dx} + \frac{y}{x} = x$$

Here $P = \frac{1}{x}$ and $Q = x$. Notice right away that – no matter how hard you try – it is impossible to separate the variables in such a way that the previous technique may be used. However, notice also that if we multiply through by x we produce the equation:

$$x \frac{dy}{dx} + y = x^2$$

whose left-hand side can be written as:

$$\frac{d}{dx}(xy)$$

Thus, integrating both sides, we have:

$$xy \quad = \frac{x^3}{3} + C$$

i.e. $\quad y \quad = \frac{x^2}{3} + \frac{C}{x}$

Of course, it was an inspired move to multiply the original equation by x. It was only then that we were able to integrate the left-hand side and solve the problem. In general, you might think, it won't be quite so simple. In a sense, though, you would be wrong. There is a straightforward technique that will allow us to take the same approach to every equation of this form. For example, consider the following equation.

$$\frac{dy}{dx} - 2xy = e^{x^2}$$

In this case the trick is to multiply by e^{-x^2}, giving:

$$e^{-x^2}\frac{dy}{dx} - 2xe^{-x^2}y = 1$$

Once again, we can now recognise the left-hand side as the derivative of a function of x and y, namely:

$$\frac{d}{dx}(e^{-x^2}y)$$

Integration therefore gives: $\qquad e^{-x^2}y = x + C$

so that: $\qquad\qquad\qquad\qquad y = (x + C)e^{x^2}$

This time the choice of multiplier seems even more inspired – a little like pulling a rabbit out of a hat. How could we possibly spot the required trick without a good deal of luck? The answer is quick and simple – there is a fool-proof way of selecting exactly the right multiplier in every case. In fact, the multiplier is always:

$$e^{\int Pdx}$$

This is called the **integrating factor**. Let us apply it to the general equation, and see just what effect it has. On multiplying, we have:

$$e^{\int Pdx}\frac{dy}{dx} + Pe^{\int Pdx}y = Qe^{\int Pdx}$$

But the left-hand side is simply:

$$\frac{d}{dx}(e^{\int Pdx}y)$$

and so integrating gives:

$$e^{\int Pdx} y = \int Qe^{\int Pdx} dx + C$$

from which:

$$y = \frac{\int Qe^{\int Pdx} dx + C}{e^{\int Pdx}}$$

Of course, we may still be left with an awkward integral in $\int Qe^{\int Pdx} dx$, but we have clearly taken a very large step towards the solution.

Examples	**1**	Solve the differential equations:

        (a) $\dfrac{dy}{dx} + 3y = e^{-5x}$ given that $y = 0$ when $x = 0$.

        (b) $(x + 2)\dfrac{dy}{dx} - 2y = 5$

  2 Find the general solution of the differential equation

$$x^2 \frac{dy}{dx} + 4xy = \sqrt{1 + x^3}$$

Solutions	**1**	(a) The integrating factor is $e^{\int 3dx} = e^{3x}$ and so the equation becomes:

$$e^{3x}\frac{dy}{dx} + 3e^{3x} y = e^{-2x}$$

i.e. $\dfrac{d}{dx}(e^{3x} y) = e^{-2x}$

from which:

$$e^{3x}y = -\frac{1}{2}e^{-2x} + C$$

Since $y = 0$ when $x = 0$, we have:

$$0 = -\frac{1}{2} + C$$

and so $C = \dfrac{1}{2}$

Finally therefore $y = \dfrac{1}{2}(e^{-3x} - e^{-5x})$

    (b) The equation can be rewritten as

$$\frac{dy}{dx} - \frac{2}{x + 2}y = \frac{5}{x + 2}$$

The integrating factor $= e^{\int \frac{-2}{x+2} dx}$

$$= e^{-2\ln(x+2)} = e^{-\ln(x+2)^{-2}} = \frac{1}{(x+2)^2}$$

133

The equation becomes:

$$\frac{1}{(x+2)^2} \frac{dy}{dx} - \frac{2}{(x+2)^3} y = \frac{5}{(x+2)^3}$$

$$\therefore \quad \frac{d}{dx}\left[\frac{y}{(x+2)^2}\right] = \frac{5}{(x+2)^3}$$

$$\therefore \quad \frac{y}{(x+2)^2} = \frac{-5}{2(x+2)^2} + C$$

$$\therefore \quad y = C\,(x+2)^2 - 2.5$$

2 First divide through by x^2 to give

$$\frac{dy}{dx} + \frac{4}{x}y = \frac{1}{x^2}\sqrt{1+x^3}.$$

The integrating factor is

$$e^{\int \frac{4}{x}\, dx} = e^{4\ln x} = e^{\ln x^4} = x^4$$

and so the equation becomes

$$x^4\frac{dy}{dx} + 4x^3 y = x^2\sqrt{1+x^3}$$

$$\therefore \quad \frac{d}{dx}(x^4 y) = x^2\sqrt{1+x^3}$$

$$\therefore \quad x^4 y = \frac{2}{9}(1+x^3)^{1\frac{1}{2}} + C$$

$$\therefore \quad y = \frac{2(1+x^3)^{1\frac{1}{2}}}{9x^4} + \frac{C}{x^4}$$

You should now be able to answer Exercise 2 on page 148.

The differential equations we have just investigated are said to be **first order** and **linear** – first order because they contain only first derivatives like $\frac{dy}{dx}$, and linear because they contain no derivatives raised to powers other than one. You will naturally suspect that equations which are of a higher order or non-linear will demand more complicated solution techniques. Although this is true, such problems need not be difficult if you know how to approach them.

We shall now look at a particular type of **second order linear** differential equation and see that there is a systematic way of solving it.

Equations of the form: $a\dfrac{d^2y}{dx^2} + b\dfrac{dy}{dx} + cy = f(x)$

In the special form of equation we shall study, that is:

$$a\frac{d^2y}{dx^2} + b\frac{dy}{dx} + cy = f(x) \qquad \dots \text{①}$$

We shall assume that a, b and c **are all constants**, but that $f(x)$ is any function of x.

Before we actually solve an equation of this type, let us speculate on the form the solution will take. (In fact, we shall find that our speculation will make the job very much easier when we do attempt a solution.)

Suppose that, by whatever method, we have managed to find a function $P(x)$ such that $y = P(x)$ satisfies equation ①. We call this a **particular integral** in line with standard terminology.

Now suppose that $y = G(x)$ is *any* other solution of the equation – a **general solution** in other words. Then, defining:

$$C(x) = G(x) - P(x)$$

we have:

$$a\frac{d^2}{dx^2}C(x) + b\frac{d}{dx}C(x) + cy$$

$$= a\frac{d^2}{dx^2}G(x) + b\frac{d}{dx}G(x) + cy - \left[a\frac{d^2P(x)}{dx^2} + b\frac{d}{dx}P(x) + cy\right]$$

$$= f(x) - f(x) \quad \text{since both } G(x) \text{ and } P(x) \text{ are solutions of the differential equation (1)}$$

$$= 0$$

This means that we can express the general solution as:

$$G(x) = C(x) + P(x)$$

where $C(x)$ is a solution of the differential equation:

$$a\frac{d^2y}{dx^2} + b\frac{dy}{dx} + cy = 0 \qquad \dots \text{②}$$

In the terminology of differential equations, $C(x)$ is called the **complementary function**.

In case you are a little bewildered by this, we have shown that the solution of equation ① can be found in two stages. First we discover a particular integral – any solution of ① will do the trick – then we add a complementary function found by solving ②.

The problem of finding a particular integral is best left to specific examples. We shall consider this later. However, there is a great deal we can say about complementary functions without knowing the values of a, b and c, so we next turn our attention to these.

Complementary functions

(The next two pages describe *why* the method for finding the complementary function C(x) actually works. However, you may prefer to simply know *how* to find C(x) – after all, that is all that is required for this module. In that case, you should now go straight to the Summary at the end of the section.

The complementary function C(x) is a solution of the equation:

$$a\frac{d^2y}{dx^2} + b\frac{dy}{dx} + cy = 0 \qquad \dots \textcircled{2}$$

In order to solve ②, we first do a little lateral thinking. (You will see the reason for this shortly, but for the moment just take it on trust.) Consider the quadratic equation produced from the coefficients of ②, i.e.

$$am^2 + bm + c = 0$$

i.e. $\quad a\left(m^2 + \frac{b}{a}m + \frac{c}{a}\right) = 0$

This is known as the **auxiliary equation**.

If the two roots are m_1 and m_2, then this gives us

$$a(m - m_1)(m - m_2) = 0$$

i.e. $\quad a\left[m^2 - (m_1 + m_2)m + m_1 m_2\right] = 0$

Notice therefore that ② can be rewritten as:

$$a\left[\frac{d^2y}{dx^2} - (m_1 + m_2)\frac{dy}{dx} + m_1 m_2 y\right] = 0$$

Dividing by a and rearranging, we have:

$$\frac{d^2y}{dx^2} - m_2\frac{dy}{dx} - m_1\left[\frac{dy}{dx} - m_2 y\right] = 0$$

That is $\quad \dfrac{dY}{dx} - m_1 Y = 0 \qquad \dots \textcircled{3}$

where $\quad Y = \dfrac{dy}{dx} - m_2 y$

It follows from [3] that:

$$Y = Ke^{m_1 x} \quad \text{for some constant } K.$$

(This is a fact that you met several times in your earlier work, and can be verified using the method of separating the variables.)

Therefore:

$$\frac{dy}{dx} - m_2 y = Ke^{m_1 x}$$

Recognising a familiar form, we can now multiply by the integrating factor:

$$e^{\int -m_2 dx} = e^{-m_2 x}$$

so that:

$$\frac{d}{dx}\left[e^{-m_2 x} y \right] = K e^{(m_1 - m_2) x} \qquad \dots \textcircled{4}$$

We must now consider two different cases: m_1 and m_2 unequal, and m_1 and m_2 equal. In the first of these the right-hand side of ④ retains the exponential function, but in the second it is reduced to K. This makes a significant difference to the rest of the analysis, and so we treat the two cases separately.

m_1 and m_2 unequal

Integrating ④ we produce:

$$e^{-m_2 x} y = \frac{K}{m_1 - m_2} e^{(m_1 - m_2) x} + K'$$

for some constant K'.

Multiplying by $e^{m_2 x}$ and replacing the coefficients on the right-hand side by appropriate constants A_1 and A_2, we are left with:

$$y = A_1 e^{m_1 x} + A_2 e^{m_2 x}$$

This is the complementary function that we wanted. In other words:

$$C(x) = A_1 e^{m_1 x} + A_2 e^{m_2 x}$$

If m_1 and m_2 are real, we are happy to leave $C(x)$ as it is. However, since the two m's are the roots of a quadratic equation, it is quite possible that they are complex numbers. In such a case it is more convenient to express $C(x)$ in trigonometrical form. m_1 and m_2 are conjugates and so we can write:

$$m_1 = \alpha + i\beta \qquad m_2 = \alpha - i\beta$$

$$\text{Thus} \quad C(x) = A_1 e^{(\alpha + i\beta)x} + A_2 e^{(\alpha - i\beta)x}$$

$$= [A_1 e^{i\beta x} + A_2 e^{-i\beta x}] e^{\alpha x}$$

$$= [A_1\{\cos (\beta x) + i\sin (\beta x)\} + A_2\{\cos (\beta x) - i\sin (\beta x)\}] e^{\alpha x}$$

(This step will become clear if and when you study Module P4. For the moment, take it on trust!)

Collecting terms and replacing $(A_1 + A_2)$ and $i (A_1 - A_2)$ by B_1 and B_2, we have:

$$C(x) = [B_1\cos (\beta x) + B_2\sin (\beta x)] e^{\alpha x}$$

m_1 and m_2 equal

Replace the two roots by m. This time integrating ④ produces:

$$e^{-mx}y = Kx + K'$$

for some constant K'.

Multiplying by e^{mx} and replacing K and K' by A_1 and A_2, we conclude that the complementary function we seek is:

$$C(x) = (A_1x + A_2)e^{mx}$$

The method, then, for finding the complementary function $y = C(x)$ for the second order differential equation $a\,\dfrac{d^2y}{dx^2} + b\,\dfrac{dy}{dx} + cy = 0$ is as follows:

- Solve the (auxiliary) equation $am^2 + bm + c = 0$ to find the roots m_1 and m_2

- If m_1 and m_2 are real and unequal, then $C(x) = A_1e^{m_1x} + A_2e^{m_2x}$

- If m_1 and m_2 are equal, then $C(x) = (A_1x + A_2)\,e^{mx}$, where m is the (equal) value of m_1 and m_2

- If m_1 and m_2 are complex, then these roots will be of the form $\alpha \pm \beta i$. In that case $C(x) = (B_1 \cos \beta x + B_2 \sin \beta x)\,e^{\alpha x}$.

It's now time to try using these results. When attempting problems, remember that you need only quote the facts listed above – it's not necessary to repeat the arguments that led to them.

Examples   Find complementary functions for the following differential equations.

1 $\quad 2\dfrac{d^2y}{dx^2} - 8\dfrac{dy}{dx} + 6y = 0$ **3** $\quad \dfrac{d^2y}{dx^2} + 6\dfrac{dy}{dx} + 25y = 0$

2 $\quad \dfrac{d^2y}{dx^2} + 6\dfrac{dy}{dx} + 9y = 0$

Solutions   **1**   The auxiliary equation is:

$$2m^2 - 8m + 6 = 0$$

i.e. $2(m-1)(m-3) = 0$ so that $m = 1$ or 3

From the table the complementary function is therefore:

$$C(x) = A_1e^x + A_2e^{3x} \qquad \therefore y = A_1e^x + A_2e^{3x}$$

2   The auxiliary equation is:

$$m^2 + 6m + 9 = 0$$

i.e. $(m + 3)^2 = 0$ and $m = -3$

This is a case where the two roots are equal, and so the complementary function is:

$$C(x) = (A_1x + A_2)\,e^{-3x} \qquad \therefore\, y = (A_1x + A_2)\,e^{-3x}$$

3   Using the quadratic formula, we find that the auxiliary equation:

$$m^2 + 6m + 25 = 0$$

has complex roots:

$$\alpha + i\beta = -3 + 4i \text{ and} \qquad \alpha - i\beta = -3 - 4i$$

so that $\alpha = -3$, $\beta = 4$ and the complementary function is:

$$C(x) = [B_1\cos(4x) + B_2\sin(4x)]\,e^{-3x} \therefore y = [B_1\cos(4x) + B_2\sin(4x)]\,e^{-3x}$$

Notice how helpful it is to quote the facts in the list. Learn these by heart and be ready to use them when needed.

Note: In each of these equations the right-hand side is 0, i.e. $f(x) = 0$ in the notation of equation ①. Thus $y = 0$ is a particular integral, and the complementary function that we seek is also the general solution.

If this statement still baffles you, look back at the way in which each of these terms is defined. What it means is that, in each of these cases, when we have found the complementary function we will also have solved the differential equation.

You should now be able to answer Exercise 3 on page 149.

Having dealt with complementary functions, we now turn our attention to the other part of general solutions.

Particular integrals

Recall the task we face when we need to find a particular integral. The function we seek can be *any specific* solution of the differential equation:

$$a\,\frac{d^2y}{dx^2} + b\,\frac{dy}{dx} + cy = f(x) \qquad\qquad ... ①$$

In general, particular integrals are found by inspection – that is, by experience and inspiration – or by trial and error. If you followed our earlier treatment of the complementary function, you may also see that a very similar method, based on the roots of the auxiliary equation and involving the solution of two first-order differential equations (using two integrating factors), would probably work – but only given considerable time and effort. (You can try it for yourself if you enjoy this sort of thing – and most mathematicians do.)

The approach we take, however, is not one of these. We shall restrict ourselves to a small number of cases of f(x), and note the corresponding particular integrals. In practice, the cases we consider are the only ones that ever arise in examinations – except in instances where the particular integral is given.

f(x) = pe^qx

Here, p and q are constants.

In such a case it is usually possible to find a particular integral of the form

$$P(x) = Ce^{qx} \text{ or } P(x) = (Bx + C)\,e^{qx}$$

If this fails, however, the form

$$P(x) = (Ax^2 + Bx + C)e^{qx}$$

will guarantee success.

f(x) = p

Here p is a constant.

In such a case it is usually possible to find a particular integral of the form

$$p(x) = C$$

If this fails, however, the form

$$p(x) = Ax^2 + Bx + C$$

will guarantee success.

f(x) = px + q

Again, p and q are constants.

In such a case it is usually possible to find a particular integral of the form

$$P(x) = Cx + D.$$

If this fails, however, the form

$$P(x) = Ax^3 + Bx^2 + Cx + D$$

will guarantee success.

f(x) = pcos(rx) + qsin(rx)

Here, p, q and r are constants.

In such a case it is usually possible to find a particular integral of the form

$$P(x) = A\cos(rx) + B\sin(rx)$$

If this fails, however, the form

$$P(x) = [A\cos(rx) + B\sin(rx)\,]\,(1 + Cx + Dx^2)$$

will guarantee success – provided the rather messy working is undertaken with care.

To illustrate the use of these helpful facts, we will now take a look at three examples based on the previous examples.

Examples

Find particular integrals for the following differential equations:

1 $2\dfrac{d^2y}{dx^2} - 8\dfrac{dy}{dx} + 6y = e^x$ **3** $\dfrac{d^2y}{dx^2} + 6\dfrac{dy}{dx} + 25y = 195 \sin(2x)$

2 $\dfrac{d^2y}{dx^2} + 6\dfrac{dy}{dx} + 9y = 18x + 21$

Hence write down formulae for their general solutions.

Solutions

1   Try $P(x) = Ce^x$

Setting $y = P(x)$ we have

$$\dfrac{dy}{dx} = Ce^x \text{ and } \dfrac{d^2y}{dx^2} = Ce^x$$

Substitution in $2\dfrac{d^2y}{dx^2} - 8\dfrac{dy}{dx} + 6y = e^x$

gives $2Ce^x - 8Ce^x + 6Ce^x = e^x$ $\therefore$ $0 = e^x$.

Clearly this doesn't work!

So now we'll try $P(x) = (Bx + C)e^x$

Setting $y = P(x)$ we have:

$$\dfrac{dy}{dx} = (Bx + C)e^x + e^xB = (Bx + C + B)e^x$$

and $\dfrac{d^2y}{dx^2} = (Bx + C + B)e^x + e^xB = (Bx + C + 2B)e^x$

Substitution in $2\dfrac{d^2y}{dx^2} - 8\dfrac{dy}{dx} + 6y = e^x$

gives $2(Bx + C + 2B)e^x - 8(Bx + C + B)e^x + 6(Bx + C) = e^x$

So, equating coefficients, we have:

$2B - 8B + 6B = 0$ (a great help!)

and $2C + 4B - 8C - 8B + 6C = 1$

$\therefore$ $B = -\dfrac{1}{4}$ and C can be anything.

$\therefore$ Choosing C as zero we get the particular integral as

$$P(x) = -\dfrac{1}{4}xe^x.$$

2   Try $P(x) = Cx + D$

Setting $y = P(x)$ we have

$$\frac{dy}{dx} = C \quad \text{and} \quad \frac{d^2y}{dx^2} = 0$$

Substitution in $\frac{d^2y}{dx^2} + 6\frac{dy}{dx} + 9y = 18x + 21$

gives $0 + 6C + 9\,(Cx + D) = 18x + 21$.

So, equating coefficients, we have:

$$9C = 18 \text{ and } 6C + 9D = 21$$

$$\therefore \quad C = 2 \quad \text{and} \quad D = 1$$

and therefore $P(x) = 2x + 1$ is the required particular integral.

3   Following our earlier advice, set:

$$y \quad = P(x) = A\cos 2x + B\sin 2x$$

Then $\quad \dfrac{dy}{dx} \quad = -2A\sin 2x + 2B\cos 2x$

and $\quad \dfrac{d^2y}{dx^2} \quad = -4A\cos 2x - 4B\sin 2x$

Therefore:

$$\frac{d^2y}{dx^2} + 6\frac{dy}{dx} + 25y = (21A + 12B)\cos 2x + (-12A + 21B)\sin 2x$$

Equating this with $\sin 2x$ gives:

$$21A + 12B = 0$$

$$-12A + 21B = 195$$

which may be solved to produce:

$$A = -4 \quad B = 7 \quad \text{and therefore:}$$

$$P(x) = \quad -4\cos 2x + 7\sin 2x$$

These results may now be combined with the complementary functions that we found earlier to produce the required general solutions. Remember that:

$$G(x) = C(x) + P(x)$$

so that, for the three examples:

1 $y = A_1 e^x + A_2 e^{3x} - \frac{1}{4}xe^x$

2 $y = (A_1 x + A_2)\,e^{-3x} + 2x + 1$

3 $y = [B_1\cos 4x + B_2\sin 4x]e^{-3x} - 4\cos 2x + 7\sin 2x$

Now that we've got the general solution to question 1, we can see why our attempt to find a particular solution of the form $P(x) = Ce^x$ failed. It was because this already formed part of the complementary function.

In all cases, then, *the simpler form for the particular solution will fail if it forms part of the complementary function.*

You now have all the details of the technique for finding general solutions. As you can see, there is a good deal to learn – but you may be surprised how easily it can be mastered if approached in the right frame of mind.

In fact, solving differential equations is a topic that many people thoroughly enjoy.

Let's try some different questions from scratch.

Examples

Solve the differential equations below, making use of any hints that are given:

1 $\dfrac{d^2y}{dx^2} + 2\dfrac{dy}{dx} + y = 2\cos x$

[Hint: Try a particular integral of form $k\sin x$.]

2 $\dfrac{d^2y}{dx^2} - \dfrac{dy}{dx} - 2y = e^{5x}$

where $y = \dfrac{dy}{dx} = \dfrac{1}{6}$ when $x = 0$

[Hint: Try a particular integral of form ke^{5x}.]

3 $\dfrac{d^2y}{dx^2} + 4y = \sin 2x$

where $y = 0$ when $x = 0$ and $\dfrac{1}{4}\pi$

[Hint: Try a particular integral of form $kx\cos 2x$.]

Solutions

The solutions are summarised as follows:

1 The auxiliary equation $m^2 + 2m + 1 = 0$ has equal roots. In fact, $m = -1$. The complementary function is therefore:

$$C(x) = (A_1x + A_2)\,e^{-x}$$

For the particular integral, we take $y = P(x) = k\sin x$, so that:

$$\dfrac{d^2y}{dx^2} + 2\dfrac{dy}{dx} + y = -k\sin x + 2k\cos x + k\sin x$$

$$= 2\,k\cos x$$

This must equal $2\cos x$ and so $k = 1$.

The general solution is therefore:

$$y = G(x) = (A_1x + A_2)\,e^{-x} + \sin x$$

2 The auxiliary equation $m^2 - m - 2 = 0$ has roots $m_1 = -1$ and $m_2 = 2$, and so:

$$C(x) = A_1 e^{-x} + A_2 e^{2x}$$

Now take the particular integral to be:

$$y = P(x) = k e^{5x} \quad \text{so that:}$$

$$\frac{d^2 y}{dx^2} - \frac{dy}{dx} - 2y = (25k - 5k - 2k) e^{5x} = 18k e^{5x}$$

Comparing coefficients with the original equation gives:

$$k = \frac{1}{18} \quad \text{and therefore} \quad P(x) = \frac{e^{5x}}{18}$$

So the general solution is:

$$y = G(x) = A_1 e^{-x} + A_2 e^{2x} + \frac{e^{5x}}{18}$$

Since $y = \frac{1}{6}$ and $\frac{dy}{dx} = \frac{1}{6}$ when $x = 0$, we have:

$$A_1 + A_2 + \frac{1}{18} = \frac{1}{6} \qquad -A_1 + 2A_2 + \frac{5}{18} = \frac{1}{6}$$

simply by setting $x = 0$ in the formulae for y and $\frac{dy}{dx}$.

These equations can be solved simultaneously to show that:

$$A_1 = \frac{1}{9} \quad A_2 = 0 \text{ and so:} \qquad y = \frac{2e^{-x} + e^{5x}}{18}$$

3 The auxiliary equation $m^2 + 4 = 0$ has complex roots $\pm 2i$. So:

$$C(x) = B_1 \cos 2x + B_2 \sin 2x$$

Taking as particular integral $y = P(x) = kx \cos 2x$ gives:

$$\frac{d^2 y}{dx^2} + 4y = -4k [x\cos 2x + \sin 2x] + 4kx\cos 2x = -4k\sin 2x$$

Comparing coefficients,

$$k = -\frac{1}{4} \quad \text{and} \quad P(x) = -\frac{1}{4} x\cos 2x$$

so that $y = G(x) = B_1 \cos 2x + B_2 \sin 2x - \frac{1}{4} x\cos 2x$

We also know that $y = 0$ when $x = 0$ and $\frac{1}{4}\pi$.

$$x = 0 \text{ implies:} \quad B_1 = 0$$

$$x = \frac{1}{4}\pi \text{ implies: } B_2 = 0 \text{ and so:} \quad y = -\frac{1}{4} x\cos 2x$$

In this case, the final solution is the particular integral we found earlier.

You should now be able to answer Exercise 4 on page 149.

Using substitution to solve differential equations

Sometimes you will need to use a substitution to solve a differential equation; in this case you will always be given a substitution which, when applied to the differential equation, will lead to a solution. Let's look at some examples.

Example

Use the substitution $y = vx$, where v is a function of x, to solve the differential equation

$$xy \frac{dy}{dx} = x^2 + y^2 .$$

Solution

The substitution $y = vx$ is the most common of all. It's almost certain that this is the one that you will meet in your examination.

We are told that $y = vx$.

Differentiate and get $\dfrac{dy}{dx} = v \times 1 + x \times \dfrac{dv}{dx}$

(i.e. differentiating vx as a product).

$$\therefore \qquad \frac{dy}{dx} = v + x \frac{dv}{dx}$$

Now substitute for y and $\dfrac{dy}{dx}$ in the given equation.

$$\therefore \qquad xy \frac{dy}{dx} = x^2 + y^2$$

$$\Rightarrow x \times vx \times \left(v + x\frac{dv}{dx} \right) = x^2 + v^2 x^2$$

$$\Rightarrow x^2 v^2 + x^3 v \frac{dv}{dx} = x^2 + v^2 x^2$$

$$\Rightarrow x^3 v \frac{dv}{dx} = x^2 \qquad \Rightarrow x v \frac{dv}{dx} = 1.$$

And so we've now got a differential equation that we recognise – it's separable.

$$\therefore \qquad v\,dv = \frac{dx}{x} \qquad \Rightarrow \frac{v^2}{2} = \ln x + c$$

(Don't forget the $+ c$ at this stage.)

But $y = vx$ $\left(\text{i.e. } v = \dfrac{y}{x} \right)$

$$\therefore \qquad \text{Substituting for } v \text{ we get}$$

$$\frac{y^2}{2x^2} = \ln x + c \Rightarrow y^2 = 2x^2 \ln x + Ax^2 \qquad \text{(where } A = 2c\text{).}$$

And as the general solution of the given differential equation is

$$y = x \sqrt{2 \ln x + A} .$$

Example   Use the substitution $\dfrac{dy}{dx} = p$ to solve the differential equation:

$$(1 + x^2)\frac{d^2y}{dx^2} = 2x\frac{dy}{dx}.$$

Solution $\dfrac{dy}{dx} = p \Rightarrow \dfrac{d^2y}{dx^2} = \dfrac{dp}{dx}.$

$\therefore$ Substituting for $\dfrac{dy}{dx}$ and $\dfrac{d^2y}{dx}$ in the given equation, we get:

$$(1 + x^2)\frac{dp}{dx} = 2xp$$

Once again this is separable.

$\therefore$ $\dfrac{dp}{p} = \dfrac{2xdx}{1 + x} \Rightarrow \ln p = \ln (1 + x^2) + c$

(Don't forget that $+ c$!)

$\therefore$ $p = A(1 + x^2)$ (using the properties of natural logarithms)

But $p = \dfrac{dy}{dx}.$

$\therefore$ $\dfrac{dy}{dx} = A (1 + x^2) \quad \Rightarrow y = A\left(x + \dfrac{x^3}{3}\right) + B.$

Example   Use the substitution $u = \ln y$ to solve the differential equation

$$\frac{1}{y}\frac{dy}{dx} + \frac{\ln y}{x} = 1$$

Solution   Using $u = \ln y$, we have:

$$\frac{du}{dx} = \frac{1}{y}\frac{dy}{dx}$$

and so the differential equation can be written:

$$\frac{du}{dx} + \frac{u}{x} = 1$$

This is now in the familiar form, and we may thus apply the integrating factor:

$$e^{\int \frac{1}{x}\, dx} = e^{\ln x} = x$$

You should now be able to answer Exercise 5 on page 149.

Families of solution curves to differential equations

If we were asked to solve the differential equation $\dfrac{dy}{dx} = 2x$, then we would separate the variables to give $dy = 2x \, dx$ so that, on integration, we would get $y = x^2 + c$. Every value of the constant c gives us a different solution.

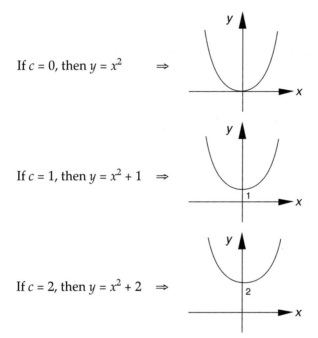

If $c = 0$, then $y = x^2$ $\Rightarrow$

If $c = 1$, then $y = x^2 + 1$ $\Rightarrow$

If $c = 2$, then $y = x^2 + 2$ $\Rightarrow$

And so, as we vary c the graph of $y = x^2 + c$ is translated up and down the y-axis. We get what is called *a family of solutions* to the differential equation.

Example   Describe the family of solution curves to the differential equation

$$\frac{dy}{dx} = -\frac{x}{y}.$$

Find the particular member of the family that passes through the point $(3, 4)$.

Solution $\dfrac{dy}{dx} = -\dfrac{x}{y}$ separates to give $y \, dy = -x \, dx$ and, on integrating, this becomes

$\dfrac{1}{2} y^2 = -\dfrac{1}{2} x^2 + c$ i.e. $x^2 + y^2 = k$.

But $x^2 + y^2 = k$ is the equation of a circle whose centre is $(0, 0)$ and whose radius is $\sqrt{k}$.

∴ the family of solution curves is the set of circles centred at the origin.

Figure 8.1

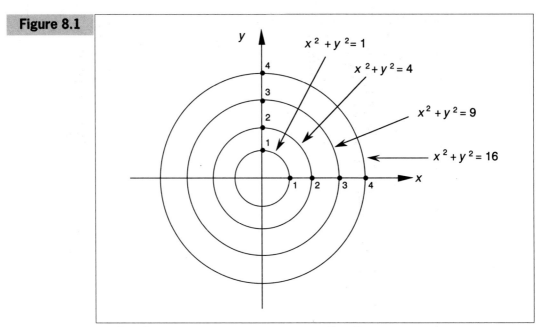

If $x^2 + y^2 = k$ passes through (3, 4), then $3^2 + 4^2 = k$ i.e. $k = 25$

∴ The particular member that passes through the point (3, 4) is the circle $x^2 + y^2 = 25$ i.e. the circle, centre the origin and radius 5.

You should now be able to answer Exercises 6–7 on page 150.

EXERCISES

1 Find the general solutions of the following differential equations:

(a) $\dfrac{dy}{dx} + y = 4$ (b) $\dfrac{dy}{dx} + xy = 4x$ (c) $e^x \dfrac{dy}{dx} = x(y^2 + 4)$

2 Solve the following differential equations:

(a) $\dfrac{dy}{dx} + y = x$ (b) $x\dfrac{dy}{dx} - y = x^2$

(c) $\dfrac{dy}{dx} + y \cot x = \cos x$ (d) $(x^2 - 1)\dfrac{dy}{dx} + 2xy = x$

(e) $\dfrac{dy}{dx} + 3y = e^{2x}$

3 Solve the following differential equations:

(a) $\dfrac{d^2y}{dx^2} - 4y = 0$

(b) $\dfrac{d^2y}{dx^2} - \dfrac{dy}{dx} - 2y = 0$

(c) $\dfrac{d^2y}{dx^2} - \dfrac{2dy}{dx} + y = 0$

(d) $\dfrac{d^2y}{dx^2} + y = 0$

(e) $4\dfrac{d^2y}{dx^2} + 4\dfrac{dy}{dx} + y = 0$

(f) $\dfrac{d^2y}{dx^2} + \dfrac{dy}{dx} + y = 0$

4 Find the general solutions of the following differential equations:

(a) $\dfrac{d^2y}{dx^2} - 3\dfrac{dy}{dx} + 2y = e^{4x}$

(b) $\dfrac{d^2y}{dx^2} - 3\dfrac{dy}{dx} + 2y = e^{x}$

(c) $\dfrac{d^2y}{dx^2} - 2\dfrac{dy}{dx} + y = 2\sin x$

(d) $\dfrac{d^2y}{dx^2} - y = x^2$

(e) $\dfrac{d^2y}{dx^2} - 9y = 2e^{2x}$

(f) $4\dfrac{d^2y}{dx^2} - 3\dfrac{dy}{dx} - y = 2$

(g) $\dfrac{d^2y}{dx^2} + y = 3\cos 2x$

(h) $\dfrac{d^2y}{dx^2} - 2\dfrac{dy}{dx} + 5y = 80e^{3x}$

(i) $\dfrac{d^2y}{dx^2} + 9y = 3\cos 2x - \sin 2x$.

5 (a) Solve the differential equation $xy\dfrac{dy}{dx} = y^2 + x^2 e^{\frac{y}{x}}$, by means of the substitution $y = vx$.

(b) Transform the equation $\dfrac{d^2y}{dx^2} + x^2 + y + 2 = 0$ by means of the substitution $y = t - x^2$, and hence obtain the general solution of the equation.

(c) Transform the equation $v\dfrac{dv}{dx} + \dfrac{v^2}{2a} = -\mu x$, where a and μ are constants, by the substitution $y = v^2$, and hence find the general solution.

If $v = 0$ when $x = a$, show that $v^2 = 2\mu a^2$ when $x = 0$.

(d) Show that if $z = \tan y$, the equation

$\dfrac{dy}{dx} + x\sin 2y = x^3\cos^2 y$, reduces to $\dfrac{dz}{dx} + 2xz = x^3$.

Hence solve the given equation.

(e) By writing $u = \dfrac{1}{y}$, reduce the equation $\dfrac{dy}{dx} + \dfrac{y}{x} = y^2$ to a linear form and hence obtain its general solution

6 Describe the family of solution curves to the differential equation

$$\frac{dy}{dx} + e^x = 0.$$

Find the equation of the particular member that passes through the origin.

7 Given that $x = e^t$, show that

$$\frac{d^2y}{dx^2} = e^{-2t}\left(\frac{d^2y}{dt^2} - \frac{dy}{dt}\right)$$

Hence show that the substitution $x = e^t$ transforms the differential equation

$$x^2\frac{d^2y}{dx^2} - 4x\frac{dy}{dx} + 6y = 3 \qquad \qquad \text{... ①}$$

into

$$\frac{d^2y}{dt^2} - 5\frac{dy}{dt} + 6y = 3. \qquad \qquad \text{... ②}$$

Hence find the general solution of the differential equation ① .

SUMMARY

You should now be able to:

- apply the method of separable variables to appropriate differential equations

- use the integrating factor $e^{\int P\,dx}$ to solve equations of the form $\frac{dy}{dx} + Py = Q$ (where P and Q are functions of x)

- find complementary functions and particular integrals for equations of the form:
  $a\frac{d^2y}{dx^2} + b\frac{dy}{dx} + cy = f(x)$ where a, b and c are constants and use them to determine general solutions.

- use given substitutions to solve differential equations.

- describe what is meant by a family of solution curves to a differential equation.

Numerical methods:
Roots of equations

We have already touched upon some numerical techniques in Module P1. In this section we will revise what we know already and then extend the procedure further.

There are really two steps in solving an equation – the first is to find a very approximate value for the root and the second is to refine this value to the required degree of accuracy.

Finding an approximate root

We will now look at some of the ways in which we can do this.

Method 1: Algebraic

We want to find a root of the equation $f(x) = 0$ and here we do this by looking for a sign change in the value of the function. We'll try this with:

$$f(x) = x^3 - x - 12$$

We substitute different values for x

$f(0) = -12$

$f(1) = -12$

$f(2) = -6$

$f(3) = 12$

and we find there's a change of sign in between $x = 2$ and $x = 3$. If this is expressed as a sketch graph we can see what's happening more easily:

Figure 9.1

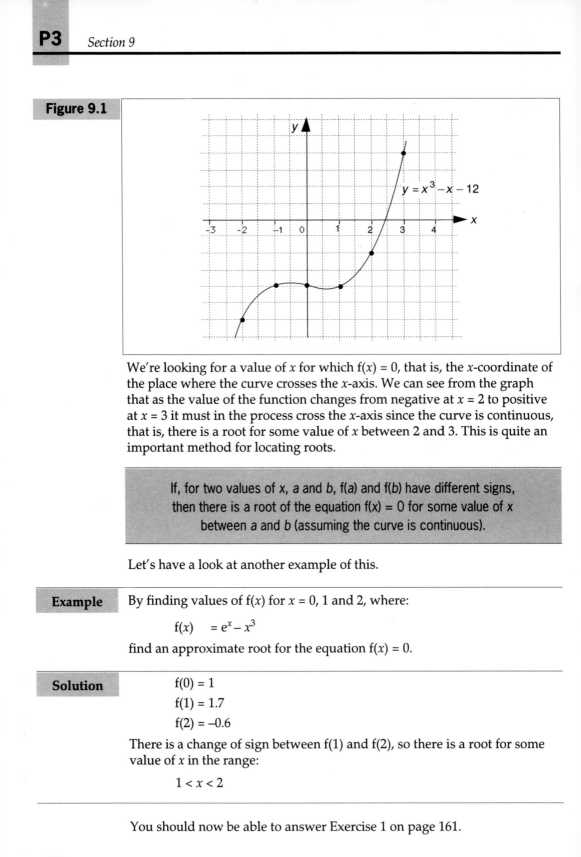

We're looking for a value of x for which $f(x) = 0$, that is, the x-coordinate of the place where the curve crosses the x-axis. We can see from the graph that as the value of the function changes from negative at $x = 2$ to positive at $x = 3$ it must in the process cross the x-axis since the curve is continuous, that is, there is a root for some value of x between 2 and 3. This is quite an important method for locating roots.

> If, for two values of x, a and b, $f(a)$ and $f(b)$ have different signs, then there is a root of the equation $f(x) = 0$ for some value of x between a and b (assuming the curve is continuous).

Let's have a look at another example of this.

Example   By finding values of $f(x)$ for $x = 0$, 1 and 2, where:

$$f(x) \quad = e^x - x^3$$

find an approximate root for the equation $f(x) = 0$.

Solution
$$f(0) = 1$$
$$f(1) = 1.7$$
$$f(2) = -0.6$$

There is a change of sign between $f(1)$ and $f(2)$, so there is a root for some value of x in the range:

$$1 < x < 2$$

You should now be able to answer Exercise 1 on page 161.

There are two general points which arise.

Note 1: Whenever there is a trigonometric function, the calculation must be in *radians*.

Note 2: If the equation is spread over two sides, one side must be taken to the other. The side involving x is then the function whose sign you want to test.

Method 2: Sketching

Here we do exactly the reverse of the procedure suggested in Note 2 – we split an equation $f(x) = 0$ into two sides with simpler functions. Suppose the original function is $f(x) = e^x - x - 2$ and we want to solve $f(x) = 0$ for $x > 0$, i.e.

$$e^x - x - 2 = 0$$

We rearrange this to

$$e^x = x + 2$$

The reason we do this is because we are going to sketch the curves $y = e^x$ and $y = x + 2$, both of which being standard functions are relatively straightforward to plot. The points of intersection of these curves will be exactly the root(s) that we are looking for. Of course, the more accurately we draw the curves, the closer we shall be to the exact root(s): here we're only concerned with finding a very approximate value so a quick sketch using just a few values is sufficient.

Figure 9.2

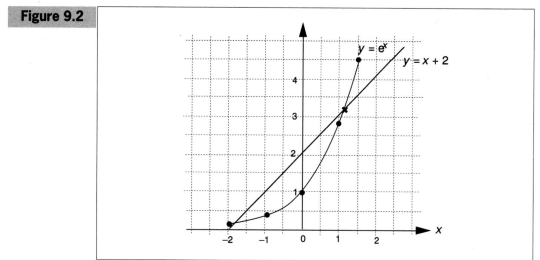

Even with this sketch we can see that the root we're after is between $x = 1$ and $x = 2$ and probably somewhere around $x = 1.2$.

If you can use a graphics calculator, then you can take full advantage of this method.

You should now be able to answer Exercises 2–4 on page 161.

Method 3: Linear interpolation

Suppose we've found two values of x that give a change of sign in the value of a function $f(x)$, say:

$$f(3) \quad = -5$$
$$f(4) \quad = 11$$

We'll sketch this to illustrate the method:

Figure 9.3

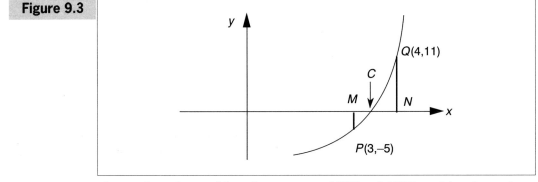

Approximately speaking, the two areas MPC and CNQ are triangles and also are (more or less) similar $\therefore$ assuming that the curve is linear from M to Q:

i.e. $\quad \dfrac{MC}{CN} = \dfrac{MP}{QN} = \dfrac{5}{11} \Rightarrow CN = \dfrac{11\,MC}{5}$

But $\quad MC + CN = 1$, so $\quad MC + \dfrac{11\,MC}{5} = 1$

$$MC\left(1 + \dfrac{11}{5}\right) = 1$$

$$MC\left(\dfrac{16}{5}\right) = 1$$

$$MC = \dfrac{5}{16} \sim 0.3$$

This gives our approximation to the root as:

$$x = 3 + 0.3 = 3.3$$

We've split MN up in the ratio $5 : 11$, which in fractions is $\dfrac{5}{16}$ and $\dfrac{11}{16}$.

Now we will look at another example.

Example	Find an approximation to the root of f(x) = 0, given that:

$$f(2.7) = 8 \qquad f(2.8) = -6$$

Solution	We split the difference between the two x values, which is 0.1, in the ratio $8 : 6$. In fractions this is:

$$\frac{8}{8+6} = \frac{8}{14} = \frac{4}{7} \text{ and } \frac{6}{8+6} = \frac{6}{14} = \frac{3}{7}, \quad \text{both of 0.1}$$

i.e. the two sections are $\frac{4}{7} \times 0.1 = 0.06$ and $\frac{3}{7} \times 0.1 = 0.04$ (approximately)

Figure 9.4

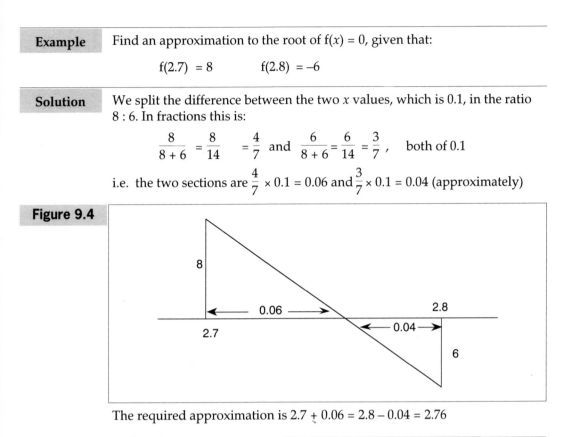

The required approximation is $2.7 + 0.06 = 2.8 - 0.04 = 2.76$

You should now be able to answer Exercises 5–6 on pages 161–62.

Improving an approximate root

Method 1: Newton-Raphson process

This is the first of three methods we have to help us find a better approximate value of the root of an equation. Figure 9.5 illustrates the problem.

Figure 9.5

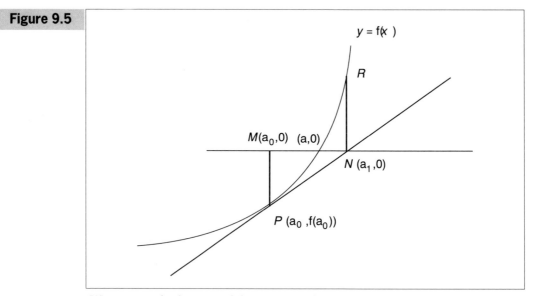

We want to find a root of the equation $f(x) = 0$, in other words where the graph crosses the x-axis. Suppose this is actually at $x = a$ and our first approximation is a little less than this, at $x = a_0$, which we call the point M.

Now we draw in the tangent to the curve at the point P and call the point where this tangent crosses the x-axis N, with coordinates $(a_1, 0)$. We say that, since this tangent is a reasonable approximation to the curve between P and N, a better approximation to the root $x = a$ is $x = a_1$.

To find an expression for a_1, we put:

Gradient of curve at $P = f'(a_0) = \dfrac{MP}{MN} = \dfrac{0 - f(a_0)}{a_1 - a_0}$

i.e. $a_1 - a_0 = \dfrac{-f(a_0)}{f'(a_0)}$

$\Rightarrow$ $a_1 = a_0 - \dfrac{f(a_0)}{f'(a_0)}$

This is a very important result, called the 'Newton–Raphson' method, or sometimes 'Newton's method'.

The 'Newton–Raphson' method:

If a_0 is an approximation to a root of $f(x) = 0$
then a (generally) better approximation is given by

$$a_1 = a_0 - \frac{f(a_0)}{f'(a_0)}$$

'Generally' because if the first approximation is not close enough, or the gradient at the first approximation is not great enough, the crossing point of the tangent is even further from the real crossing point. In Figures 9.6 and 9.7 the first approximation is too far away from the actual root which has resulted in a second approximation even further away from the actual root than the first approximation:

Figure 9.6

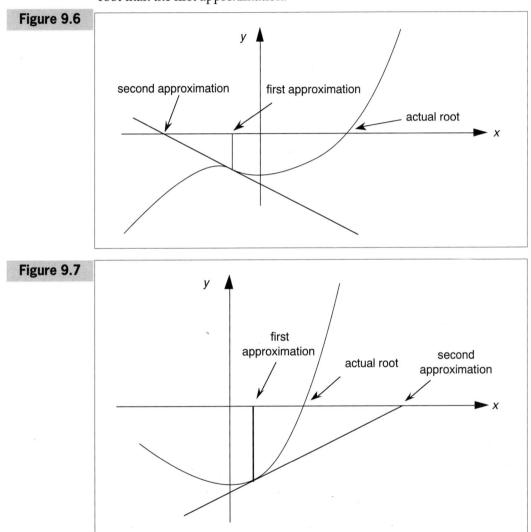

Figure 9.7

As with most of these methods for improving the approximation it is an *iterative process*. This means that we put our first approximation into a formula and this gives us our second approximation. We then put this approximation into the formula to get a third approximation and so on, the result getting closer and closer to the actual root – *converging* to the root in mathematical terms.

And the iterative process that we shall be using is

$$a_{n+1} = a_n - \frac{f(a_n)}{f'(a_n)}.$$

If you look back at the original diagram for the Newton–Raphson process (Figure 9.5) and imagine drawing in a second tangent at the point R, you can see that it would cut the axis quite close to the desired value, $x = a$; then a tangent from this new point and so on.

We can see how this works out in the following example.

Example

Taking $\frac{\pi}{2}$ as a first approximation to a root of the equation $3 \sin x - 2x = 0$, apply the Newton–Raphson procedure to find two further approximations, giving your answer to three decimal places.

Solution

Of course, since there are trigonometric functions involved, we shall use radians.

Write $f(x) = 3 \sin x - 2x$

Then $f'(x) = 3 \cos x - 2$

$$a_0 = \frac{\pi}{2}; \quad a_1 = a_0 - \frac{f(a_0)}{f'(a_0)} = \frac{\pi}{2} - \frac{3 \sin\left(\frac{\pi}{2}\right) - 2\left(\frac{\pi}{2}\right)}{3 \cos\frac{\pi}{2} - 2}$$

$$= \frac{\pi}{2} - \frac{3 - \pi}{-2}$$

$$= 1.5 \leftarrow \text{second approximation}$$

$$a_1 = 1.5; \quad a_2 = a_1 - \frac{f(a_1)}{f'(a_1)} = 1.5 - \frac{3 \sin (1.5) - 2(1.5)}{3 \cos (1.5) - 2}$$

$$= 1.5 - \frac{-0.00752}{-1.788} \quad \leftarrow \quad \begin{array}{l}\text{this should be getting close to}\\ \text{zero if the process is successful}\end{array}$$

$$= 1.5 - 0.0042$$

$$= 1.496 \text{ to three decimal places}$$

You'll find that you have to be careful with the signs.

If the second approximation comes out worse than the first, check first of all that you're using radians for trigonometric functions. If that's correct, check that you've copied and differentiated the original function correctly, and inserted minus signs where appropriate.

We're trying to find the value of a for which $f(a)$ is zero, so successive approximations to a should leave $f(a_i)$ diminishing in size. If this is not the case, it's an early warning that something's awry.

| **Example** | Show that the equation $x^3 - 5x + 1 = 0$ has a root between 0 and 1. Use linear interpolation to estimate this root correct to 2 d.p. Hence use the Newton-Raphson process to find this root correct to 3 d.p. |

| **Solution** | Let $f(x) = x^3 - 5x + 1$ |

Since $f(0) = 1 > 0$ and $f(1) = -3 < 0$, there is a root between 0 and 1.

Linear interpolation gives us an estimated root of 0.25 (see Figure 9.8).

| **Figure 9.8** |

Finally set $f(x) = x^3 - 5x + 1$ and $f'(x) = 3x^2 - 5$.

Taking $x = 0.25$ as our first approximation, a second approximation is given by

$$0.25 - \frac{f(0.25)}{f'(0.25)} = 0.25 - \left[\frac{-0.23}{-4.8}\right] = 0.201$$

[*Use the memories on your calculator* but always write down some rounded figures so that your method is clear. For example, in the above, –0.23 represents – 0.234375, which then goes in the memory. Similarly 0.201 represents 0.201298701.]

A third approximation is given by

$$0.201 - \frac{f(0.201)}{f'(0.201)} = 0.201 - \left[\frac{1.66 \times 10^{-3}}{-4.88}\right] = 0.202$$

A fourth approximation also rounds to 0.202, so we conclude that $x = 0.202$ (3 d.p.)

You should now be able to answer Exercises 7–12 on page 162.

Now we will consider in turn two alternative methods of improving approximations: bisection and rearranging.

Method 2: Bisection

The method of improving an approximate root is called *interval bisection* and it is quite straightforward, although too slow to be of much practical use. It works on the principle of halving the area in which the root lies. The following example illustrates this.

Example   Find the root of the equation:

$$x^3 - x - 12 = 0$$

which lies between $x = 2$ and $x = 3$.

Solution   Let $f(x) = x^3 - x - 12,$

then $f(2) = -6$

$f(3) = 12$

and we can see that there is a solution because of the change in sign in the given interval $2 < x < 3$. Now bisect this interval to give the point $x = 2.5$ and find:

$f(2.5) = 1.125$

This is positive, so the root must lie between the values, giving a change of sign, i.e. in the interval $2 < x < 2.5$. We now bisect this interval, giving the boundary point $x = 2.25$, and find:

$f(2.25)$	=	-2.86	
$f(2)$	$f(2.25)$		$f(2.5)$
-6	-2.86		1.125

We can narrow down the possible area further, and say that the root must lie in the region $2.25 < x < 2.5$ ... and we could go on and on. Using this method we shall always find the answer to whatever degree of accuracy we require – eventually. Now we will look at another method for solving the same equation.

Method 3: Rearranging

This is a method in which we isolate a single variable on one side of an equation and then use this formula to find the solution by iteration.

Rearrange the equation to give:

$$x^3 = x + 12$$

Take cube root $x = (x + 12)^{\frac{1}{3}}$

and use $x_{n+1} = (x_n + 12)^{\frac{1}{3}}$ ...①

This equation ① gives the iterative procedure (you won't be required to find it yourself, it will always be given you). Let's take our first approximation as 2.5.

$$x_0 = 2.5 \qquad \Rightarrow x_1 = (2.5 + 12)^{\frac{1}{3}} = (14.5)^{\frac{1}{3}} \qquad = 2.4385$$

$$x_1 = 2.4385 \qquad \Rightarrow x_2 = (14.4385)^{\frac{1}{3}} \qquad\qquad = 2.4350$$

Similarly:

$$x_3 = 2.4349$$
$$\left.\begin{matrix} x_4 = 2.4348 \\ x_5 = 2.4348 \end{matrix}\right\} \text{ agreement so we stop the procedure}$$

In only five steps we have found the root correct to four decimal places. This would have taken a bit longer with the interval bisection process.

The difficulty with this rearranging process is that you need a different rearrangement for a different root. For example the equation $e^x = 4x$ can be shown to have 2 roots. One can be found using the iterative formula $x_{n+1} = \frac{1}{4}e^{x_n}$ whilst the other has to be found from $x_{n+1} = \ln(4x_n)$. It is for that reason that, in your examination, you'll be given the precise form of the iterative procedure to be used.

You should now be able to answer Exercises 13–16 on pages 162–63.

EXERCISES

1 Show that the equation $e^{-x} = \tan x$ has a root between 0.5 and 0.6.

[Hint: begin by rewriting the equation as $e^{-x} - \tan x = 0$.]

2 Sketch on the same diagram the graphs of $y = 3\cos x$ and $y = \dfrac{x}{\pi} - 1$

for the interval:

$0 \le x \le 2\pi.$

Hence state the number of solutions in this interval of the equation

$x - \pi = 3\pi \cos x.$

3 Show that the equation $e^x - 4\sin x = 0$ has two roots between $x = 0$ and $x = 1.5$ by evaluating $e^x - 4\sin x$ for at least three appropriate values of x.

4 By sketching the graphs of $y = x(2\pi - x)$ and $y = 16\sin x$ on the same diagram, show that the equation $x(2\pi - x) = 16\sin x$ has three roots in the interval $-\pi \le x \le \pi$.

5 Find an approximation to the root of f(x) = 0, given that:

(a) f(2) = 1.7   (b) f(1.1) = –4.2

   f(3) = –6.7   f(1.2) = 0.6

6 A function $y = f(x)$ is tabulated for various values of x as shown below:

x	1.0	1.2	1.4	1.6	1.8
y	3.70	3.82	4.15	4.51	5.07

Estimate: (a) the value of y at $x = 1.15$,

            (b) the value of x for which $y = 4.40$.

7 Using Newton's method once, starting with the approximation $x = 2$, to obtain a second approximation x_1 for a root of the equation:

$$x^5 = x^3 + 25$$

8 Find by trial the two consecutive integers between which the solution of the equation $x + 2e^x = 0$ lies.

Of these two integers, take as a first approximation the one which makes the absolute value of the left side smaller. Then find a second approximation to the solution by a single application of the Newton–Raphson method. Give two decimal places in your answer.

9 Prove that the real root of the equation $x^3 + x^2 + x + (x - 1)^2 = 0$ lies between –2 and –3. Taking $x = -3$ as a first approximation to the root, use Newton's method once to find, to one decimal place, a second estimate of the root.

10 Sketch, in the same diagram, the graphs for $x > 0$ of $y = \ln x$ and $y = \dfrac{2}{x}$

Use the Newton–Raphson process to find, correct to two decimal places, the x-coordinate of the point where the two graphs meet.

11 Show that $y = x^3 + x + 1$ is an increasing function. Hence deduce that the equation $x^3 + x + 1 = 0$ has only one real root. Use the Newton-Raphson method to find this root correct to 1 d.p.

12 Show that the equation $x + \ln x = 3$ has a root between 2 and 3. Use linear interpolation to estimate this root correct to 1 d.p. Now use the Newton-Raphson process to find this root correct to 1 d.p.

13 Use sketch graphs to show that the equation $\frac{1}{3}e^x = x$ has two solutions.

(a) Taking $x = 1$ as your first approximation, use the iterative formula $x_{n+1} = \frac{1}{3}e^{x_n}$ to find one of these solutions, correct to 1 d.p.

(b) Explain how the equation can be rewritten as $x = \ln(3x)$. Taking $x = 2$ as your first approximation, use the iterative formula $x_{n+1} = \ln(3x_n)$ to find the other solution, correct to 1 d.p.

14 Use sketch graphs to show that the equation $x = 4e^{-x}$ has only one solution. Show that the equation can be rewritten as $x = 2\sqrt{xe^{-x}}$.

Now use the iterative formula $x_{n+1} = 2\sqrt{x_n e^{-x_n}}$ to find this solution correct to 1 d.p.

15 (a) Show that there is a root of the equation $8 \sin x - x = 0$ lying between 2.7 and 2.8.

(b) Taking 2.8 as a first approximation to this root, apply the Newton-Raphson procedure once to $f(x) \equiv 8 \sin x - x$ to obtain a second approximation, giving your answer to 3 decimal plces.

(c) Evaluate $f\left(\dfrac{5\pi}{2}\right)$, and hence, by sketching suitable graphs, determine the number of roots of the equation $8 \sin x = x$ in the range $x > 0$.

16 (a) Show that the equation $x^3 + 3x^2 - 3 = 0$ may be rearranged to give

$$x = \sqrt{\left(\frac{3}{x+3}\right)}$$

(b) Hence, using the iteration formula

$$x_{n+1} = \sqrt{\left(\frac{3}{x_n + 3}\right)}$$

with $x_0 = 1$, find the approximate solution x_2 of the equation $x^3 + 3x^2 - 3 = 0$, giving your answer to 2 d.p.

SUMMARY

In this Section we have looked at various methods for finding approximate solutions to equations. This is a two-stage process. First we find an approximate root:

- by the sign test: e.g. f(a) < 0, f(b) > 0 ⇒ there is a root between x = a and x = b, or
- by sketching (and looking for intersecting points), or
- by linear interpolation

Then we find a better approximation by using one or more of the following:

- the Newton-Raphson process
- interval bisection
- any other given iterative procedure.

This completes your work on the nine sections covering the ULEAC syllabus for Module P3. Sections 10–16 of this book concentrate on the topics contained in the syllabus for Module P4.

Coordinate systems

INTRODUCTION This is the first of seven sections that cover topics contained in the ULEAC syllabus for Module P4. Many of these sections will build on the work you have completed in the nine sections that covered Module P3. In this section we begin by looking at the equation of a circle and then go on to consider conic sections in general: the parabola, the ellipse and the hyperbola. We'll then introduce polar coordinates and use them in sketching and the finding of areas. Finally we'll study the radius of curvature.

The equation of a circle

If a circle has centre (a, b) and radius r,

Figure 10.1

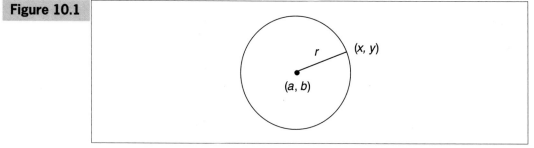

and if then (x, y) is any point on the circle, we have, using Pythagoras' theorem,

$$(x - a)^2 + (y - b)^2 = r^2$$

This is the equation of the circle.

Example A circle has centre $(1, 3)$ and radius 5. Write down and simplify its equation.

Solution $(x - 1)^2 + (y - 3)^2 = 5^2$

Multiplying out the brackets we get:

$$x^2 - 2x + 1 + y^2 - 6y + 9 = 25$$
$$\therefore \qquad x^2 + y^2 - 2x - 6y - 15 = 0.$$

Example	Write down the coordinates of the centre and the radius of the circle whose equation is $(x - 3)^2 + (y + 4)^2 = 36$.

Solution	Centre is $(3, -4)$. Radius $= \sqrt{36} = 6$.

Example	A circle has equation $x^2 + y^2 - 6x + 8y - 24 = 0$. Find its centre and radius.

Solution	Begin by rewriting the equation:

$$x^2 - 6x + y^2 + 8y = 24$$

Now complete the square for each section:

$$(x - 3)^2 - 9 + (y + 4)^2 - 16 = 24$$

Finally, rewrite:

$$(x - 3)^2 + (y + 4)^2 = 49$$

$\therefore$ Centre is $(3, -4)$ and radius $= \sqrt{49} = 7$.

That was an important example.

You should now be able to answer Exercises 1–4 on page 198.

The equation of a circle can also be given in parametric form.

Example	Describe the curve given by the parametric equations: $x = 3 + \cos\theta$, $y = 1 + \sin\theta$.

Solution	Rewrite as:

$$x - 3 = \cos\theta \text{ and } y - 1 = \sin\theta$$

Using the trigonometric identity $\cos^2\theta + \sin^2\theta = 1$, this becomes:

$$(x - 3)^2 + (y - 1)^2 = 1$$

$\therefore$ We have a circle centre $(3, 1)$ and radius 1.

You should now be able to answer Exercises 5–6 on page 198.

We also need to be able to find the equation of a tangent to the circle.

Example   Show that the point $P(-2, -2)$ lies on the circle $x^2 + y - 2x - 4y - 20 = 0$. What is the equation of the tangent at P?

Solution $(-2)^2 + (-2)^2 - 2(-2) - 4(-2) - 20 = 0$

∴ P lies on the circle.

Rewriting the circle as

$$(x - 1)^2 + (y - 2)^2 = 25$$

we see that it has centre $C(1, 2)$ and radius 5.

Figure 10.2

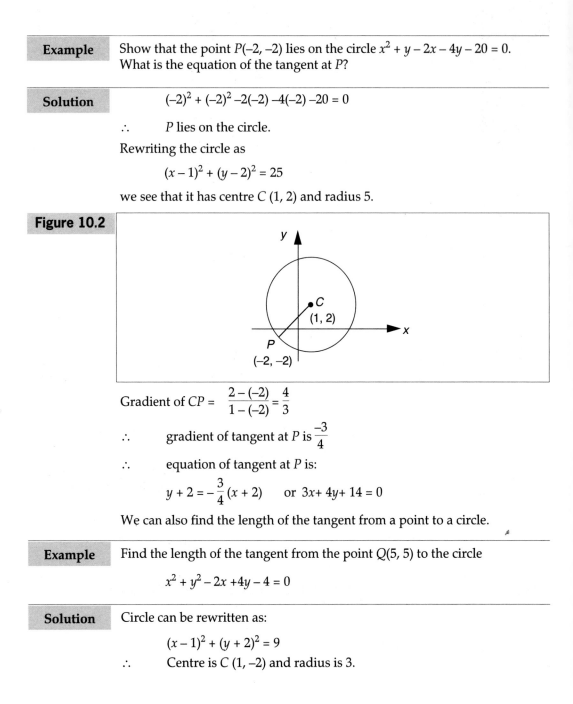

Gradient of CP = $\dfrac{2 - (-2)}{1 - (-2)} = \dfrac{4}{3}$

∴   gradient of tangent at P is $\dfrac{-3}{4}$

∴   equation of tangent at P is:

$$y + 2 = -\frac{3}{4}(x + 2) \quad \text{or} \quad 3x + 4y + 14 = 0$$

We can also find the length of the tangent from a point to a circle.

Example   Find the length of the tangent from the point $Q(5, 5)$ to the circle

$$x^2 + y^2 - 2x + 4y - 4 = 0$$

Solution   Circle can be rewritten as:

$$(x - 1)^2 + (y + 2)^2 = 9$$

∴   Centre is $C(1, -2)$ and radius is 3.

Figure 10.3

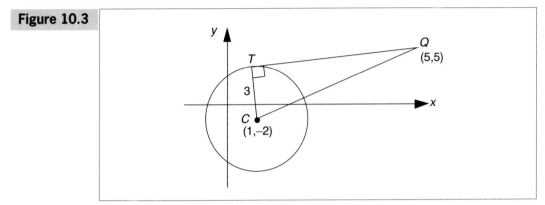

Now $CQ^2 = (5-1)^2 + (5+2)^2 = 65$

∴   Pythagoras on triangle CTQ gives

        $TQ^2 = 65 - 3^2$

∴   length of tangent $= TQ = \sqrt{56}$.

You should now be able to answer Exercises 7–8 on page 198.

In general, a line will meet a circle at two distinct points, which we find by solving the equations simultaneously. For example, the line $y = x + 1$ meets the circle $x^2 + y^2 = 25$ at points whose x-values are given by

$$x^2 + (x + 1)^2 = 25, \quad \text{i.e. } x^2 + x - 12 = 0$$

This last quadratic has distinct roots $x = 3$ and $x = -4$ and so the distinct intersection points are $(3, 4)$ and $(-4, -3)$.

However, if a line is a tangent to a circle, then the resulting quadratic will have repeated roots. Since the general solution of a quadratic is given by

$x = \dfrac{-b \pm \sqrt{b^2 - 4ac}}{2a}$, the condition for repeated roots is $b^2 - 4ac = 0$

or $b^2 = 4ac$. A line is therefore a tangent to a circle if the resulting quadratic has repeated roots, i.e. $b^2 = 4ac$.

Example

The line $y = mx$ is a tangent to the circle $x^2 + y^2 - 2x + 6y + 5 = 0$.
Find the values of m and the possible contact points.

Solution

Substituting for y we get:

        $x^2 + (mx)^2 - 2x + 6(mx) + 5 = 0$

∴ $(1 + m^2) x^2 + (6m - 2) x + 5 = 0$

Repeated roots   ∴ $(6m - 2)^2 = 4 (1 + m^2) 5$

               ∴ $2m^2 - 3m - 2 = 0$ ∴ $m = 2$ or $-\dfrac{1}{2}$

Now $m = 2$ $\Rightarrow$ $5x^2 + 10x + 5 = 0 \Rightarrow x = -1 \Rightarrow y = -2$

$\therefore$ Contact point is $(-1, -2)$

and $m = -\frac{1}{2}$ $\Rightarrow$ $1\frac{1}{4}x^2 - 5x + 5 = 0$ $\Rightarrow x = 2$ $\Rightarrow y = -1$

$\therefore$ other contact point is $(2, -1)$.

You should now be able to answer Exercises 9–13 on page 198.

We are now going to take a look at conic sections in general.

A special family of curves

You will have drawn these curves without knowing that they are all connected by a property that makes them all members of a single large family of curves – the conic sections. Conic sections are so called because they can all be formed by cutting a slice or section through an infinitely large cone, as shown in Figure 10.4.

Figure 10.4

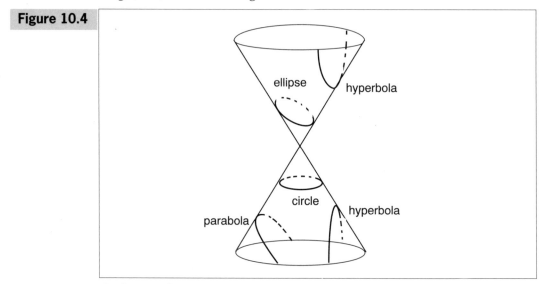

In the next few pages we take a special property of the conic sections as our starting point and develop from it the theory of the family and its individual members. But first the property itself... .

We begin with a point and a line drawn on a plane. To mark them out as special, we give them particular names. In the standard terminology, the point is called the **focus** and the line is called the **directrix**. We now consider the locus of a further point which moves in such a way that its distance from the focus is always proportional to its perpendicular distance from the directrix.

The constant of proportionality is known as the **eccentricity** of the locus and is denoted by e. (Note well: this is not to be confused with the number e = 2.718... which is the base of the natural logarithms.) Because the conic sections appear so different, it is surprising to find that, by varying the value of *e*, we can create any parabola, ellipse or hyperbola in this way, as you will shortly see.

To get to grips with the mathematics of the locus we next attempt to construct its equation in cartesian coordinates *x* and *y*.

The first step, of course, is to position the axes in relation to the focus and directrix. For convenience we shall assume that the focus lies on the *x*-axis at $(\alpha, 0)$, and that the directrix runs parallel to the *y*-axis and passes through the point $(\beta, 0)$. This will allow us to keep the equation of the locus as simple as possible. Since we began with the focus and directrix given, the distance between them is some fixed amount which we shall call *d*. Clearly α and β are related by the formula $\beta = \alpha - d$, but otherwise we may give α and β any values we please. This corresponds to making an appropriate choice for the position of the origin.

All this is shown in Figure 10.5 below.

Figure 10.5

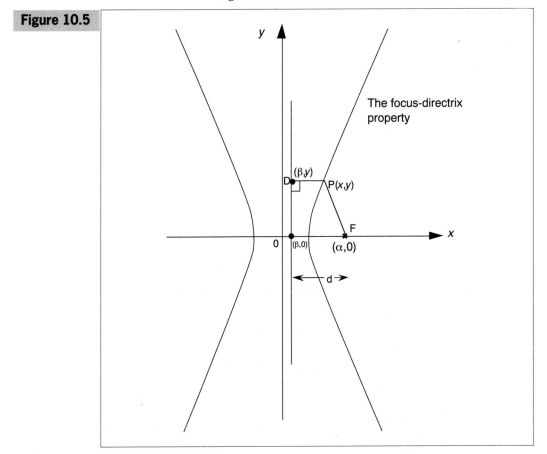

169

Figure 10.5 shows the position of a general point $P(x,y)$ on the locus, together with the focus $F(\alpha,0)$ and the point $D(\beta,y)$ on the directrix which marks the end of the perpendicular from P. By definition of the locus,

$$PF = ePD$$

i.e. $\quad \sqrt{[\,y^2 + (x-\alpha)^2\,]} = e(x-\beta)$

Squaring, this gives:

$$y^2 + (x-\alpha)^2 = e^2(x-\beta)^2$$

and on rearranging:

$$y^2 + x^2(1 - e^2) = 2x(\alpha - \beta e^2) + (\beta^2 e^2 - \alpha^2) \qquad \ldots \text{①}$$

This is the general form of the equation of the locus, but it is of little use as it stands – and you need not try to remember it. However, we shall see it developed in several directions in the next few pages as we investigate the effect of different values of e.

Example

Write down the equation of the locus of a point which is twice as far from the focus as from the directrix, where the focus is at (3,0) and the directrix is the line $x = -1$.

Solution

The solution is summarised as follows:

In this case, $e = 2$, $\alpha = 3$ and $\beta = -1$ and so the equation is:

$$y^2 - 3x^2 = 14x - 5$$

We shall see later that any such locus with $e > 1$ is a hyperbola.

The parabola: $y^2 = 4ax$

The first case we consider is $e = 1$, in other words, that in which the locus is equidistant from the focus and the directrix. From equation ①, this leads to:

$$y^2 = 2x(\alpha - \beta) + (\beta^2 - \alpha^2)$$

Now recall that we can give α and β any values we wish, subject to maintaining $\beta = \alpha - d$. This simply corresponds to an appropriate choice of origin. Here we choose to make $\alpha = \frac{1}{2}d$, so that:

$$\beta = \frac{1}{2}d - d = -\frac{1}{2}d$$

If we also define a new constant a to be $\frac{1}{2}d$, then:

$$\alpha = a \quad \beta = -a$$

and the equation becomes:

$$y^2 = 4ax$$

This is a familiar equation that you have met in your past work, and whose graph you have probably sketched several times. Figure 10.6 will remind you of its shape. This curve is a **parabola** with focus at $(a,0)$ and the line $x = -a$ as directrix.

In addition to the cartesian equation (i.e. the equation in x and y), it is often helpful to specify the parabola in parametric form. For this we define the parameter t as follows:

$$t = \frac{y}{2a} \text{ so that } y = 2at \text{ and}$$

$$x = \frac{y^2}{4a} = \frac{(2at)^2}{4a} = at^2$$

So the parametric form we require is:

$$x = at^2 \quad y = 2at$$

Figure 10.6

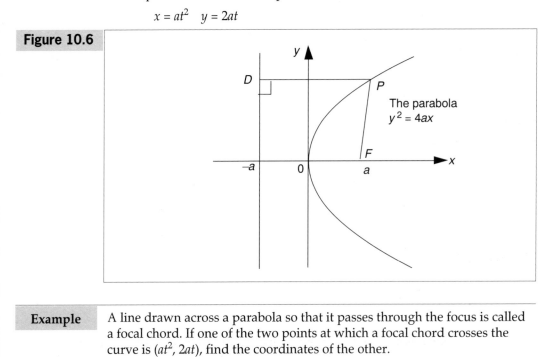

The parabola $y^2 = 4ax$

Example

A line drawn across a parabola so that it passes through the focus is called a focal chord. If one of the two points at which a focal chord crosses the curve is $(at^2, 2at)$, find the coordinates of the other.

Solution

The solution is summarised as follows.

Take $(x_1, y_1) = (a, 0)$ and $(x_2, y_2) = (at^2, 2at)$. The focal chord passes through both of these and so has the equation:

$$\frac{y - 0}{2at - 0} = \frac{x - a}{at^2 - a}$$

i.e. $$y = \frac{2t}{t^2 - 1}(x - a)$$

Now suppose that the second point in which the chord crosses the parabola is $(as^2, 2as)$ for some s. Then s must satisfy:

$$2as = \frac{2t}{t^2 - 1}(as^2 - a)$$

Cancelling $2a$ and multiplying by $(t^2 - 1)$, we see that:

$$s(t^2 - 1) = t(s^2 - 1)$$

so that: $st^2 - ts^2 - s + t = 0$

i.e. $-(s - t)(st + 1) = 0$

However, s is not equal to t, since the point we seek is at the other end of the chord from $(at^2, 2at)$. Therefore:

$$st = -1 \qquad \text{i.e. } s = -\frac{1}{t}$$

and the point is $\left(\dfrac{a}{t^2}, \dfrac{-2a}{t} \right)$

You should now be able to answer Exercise 14 on page 199.

The ellipse: $\dfrac{x^2}{a^2} + \dfrac{y^2}{b^2} = 1$

Now we consider the case $e < 1$, in which the locus is closer to the focus than to the directrix. In order to convert equation (1) into its more convenient and familiar form, we choose α and β so that:

$$\beta = \frac{\alpha}{e^2}$$

Again, this simply corresponds to a convenient choice of origin. The equation then becomes:

$$y^2 + x^2(1 - e^2) = \alpha^2 \frac{1 - e^2}{e^2}$$

If we now define $a = \dfrac{\alpha}{e}$, the equation is transformed to:

$$y^2 + x^2(1 - e^2) = a^2(1 - e^2)$$

Dividing by the right-hand side and defining $b^2 = a^2(1 - e^2)$, we have:

$$\frac{x^2}{a^2} + \frac{y^2}{b^2} = 1$$

The graph of this equation is shown below. This curve is an **ellipse**. Note that, by definition of a, we have:

$$\alpha = ae \qquad \text{and} \qquad \beta = \frac{\alpha}{e^2} = \frac{a}{e}$$

So its focus is at $(ae, 0)$ and its directrix is the line $x = \dfrac{a}{e}$. Notice, however, that exactly the same equation results if we use $-a$ in place of a. In fact, we draw exactly the same curve if we take the focus to be $(-ae, 0)$ and the directrix to be $x = -\dfrac{a}{e}$. In other words an ellipse has two foci and two directrices, as Figure 10.7 shows.

Figure 10.7

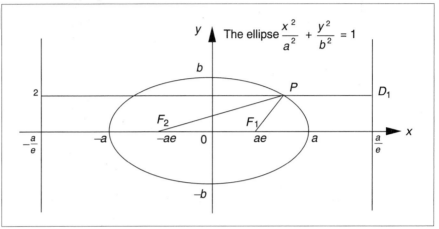

Like the parabola, the ellipse can be presented in parametric form.

First put $x = a \cos\theta$.

This is possible because, by the equation of the curve, $\dfrac{x^2}{a^2}$ and $\dfrac{x}{a}$ are therefore both at most 1. It follows that:

$$\frac{y^2}{b^2} = 1 - \cos^2\theta = \sin^2\theta \text{ and so } y = b\sin\theta$$

The required parametric equations are therefore:

$$x = a\cos\theta, \ y = b\sin\theta$$

Example

Let P be any point on an ellipse. Show that the sum of the distances of P from the two foci is a constant.

Solution

The solution is summarised as follows:

Label the two foci F_1 and F_2, and denote by D_1 and D_2 the points on the directrices at the ends of the perpendiculars from P. By the focus-directrix property of the ellipse,

$$PF_1 = ePD_1 \text{ and } PF_2 = ePD_2$$

Thus: $PF_1 + PF_2 = e(PD_1 + PD_2)$

$$= \frac{e\,2a}{e} = 2a$$

since $PD_1 + PD_2$ is the perpendicular distance between the two directrices. Therefore the sum is just $2a$ and constant.

If you tried this problem using any other method you would find that it rapidly became very complicated. As a general rule in problems of this sort, always think about the *geometry* before trying other approaches.

You should now be able to answer Exercises 15–16 on page 199.

The hyperbola: $\dfrac{x^2}{a^2} - \dfrac{y^2}{b^2} = 1$

The remaining case is that in which $e > 1$, i.e. the locus is further from the focus than from the directrix. Despite the very different curves that result, the analysis here is almost identical to that of the ellipse.

We first choose $\beta = \dfrac{\alpha}{e^2}$, so removing the term in x from equation (1).

Next we introduce the constant a by defining: $a = \dfrac{\alpha}{e}$

Further, we define: $\qquad b^2 = a^2(e^2 - 1)$

(This is the only change from our previous analysis and is forced on us by the fact that $e > 1$.) Finally, dividing equation (1) by $a^2(1 - e^2)$, we have:

$$\frac{x^2}{a^2} - \frac{y^2}{b^2} = 1$$

The resulting curve is a **hyperbola** and is shown in Figure 10.8.

Figure 10.8

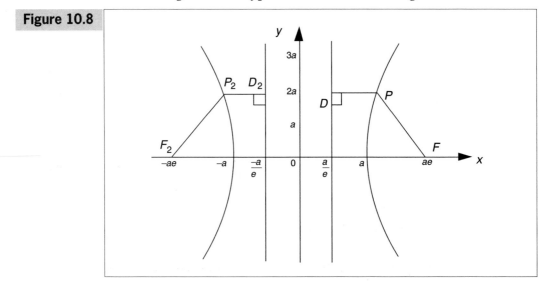

Now notice, that in the special case where $b = a$, the two asymptotes are the lines $y = \pm x$ which make angles of $\pm \frac{1}{4}\pi$ with the x-axis and are therefore at right angles to each other. The corresponding curve is known as a **rectangular hyperbola** for obvious reasons, and is a very common example of its type. Since $b = a$, the equation of a rectangular hyperbola may be written: $\frac{x^2}{a^2} - \frac{y^2}{a^2} = 1$ or $x^2 - y^2 = a^2$

However, in the case of the rectangular hyperbola it is much more usual to express the equation in relation to axes along the asymptotes. This is relatively easy if you refer to the Figure 10.10.

Figure 10.10

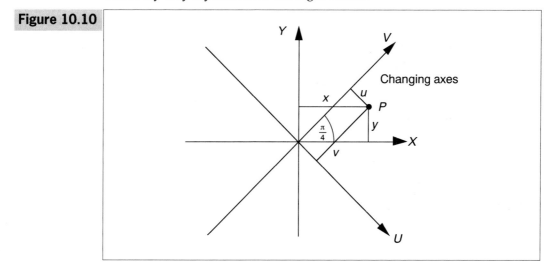

Changing axes

If we call the coordinates of P on the new axes (i.e. the asymptotes) u and v, then we can express the old coordinates x and y as:

$$x = \frac{u}{\sqrt{2}} + \frac{v}{\sqrt{2}} \qquad y = \frac{v}{\sqrt{2}} - \frac{u}{\sqrt{2}}$$

Thus $x + y = v\sqrt{2}$ and $x - y = u\sqrt{2}$

Therefore the hyperbola's equation can be transformed as follows:

$$2uv = u\sqrt{2} \times v\sqrt{2} = (x - y)(x + y) = x^2 - y^2 = a^2$$

i.e. $uv = \frac{1}{2}a^2$

Since it may appear unnatural to use u and v as coordinates, we rename them x and y. (Of course, they are a different x and y from those we used previously, but there is no further danger of confusion.) If we also define a constant $c^2 = \frac{1}{2}a^2$, then the equation becomes:

$$xy = c^2$$

which is the best-known form for the rectangular hyperbola (see Figure 10.11).

Figure 10.11

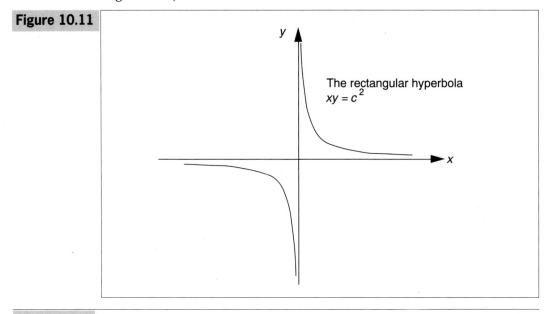

The rectangular hyperbola $xy = c^2$

Example

The rectangular hyperbola may be represented parametrically by the equations:

$$x = ct, \qquad y = \frac{c}{t}$$

Using this representation, find the equation of the tangent at a general point on the curve, and find the intersection of the tangents at the points $\left(ct, \frac{c}{t} \right)$ and $\left(cs, \frac{c}{s} \right)$.

Solution

From the equation $xy = c^2$ we have:

$$y + x \frac{dy}{dx} = 0$$

Thus: $\quad \dfrac{dy}{dx} = \dfrac{-y}{x} = \dfrac{-\frac{c}{t}}{ct} = -\dfrac{1}{t^2}$

The equation of the tangent is therefore:

$$y = -\frac{1}{t^2} x + \left(\frac{c}{t} + \frac{1}{t^2} ct \right) = -\frac{1}{t^2} x + \frac{2c}{t}$$

Multiplying by t^2 gives:

$$t^2 y + x = 2ct$$

The tangent to the point $\left(cs, \dfrac{c}{s}\right)$ is therefore:

$$s^2y + x = 2cs$$

and so the two tangents intersect where the last two equations hold simultaneously. Solving quickly leads to the point of intersection:

$$x = \frac{2cst}{s+t} \qquad y = \frac{2c}{s+t}$$

Example

Tangents are drawn from the point (–3, 3) to the rectangular hyperbola with equation $xy = 16$. Find the coordinates of the point of contact of these tangents with the hyperbola.

Solution

A general line through (–3, 3) is given by

$$y - 3 = m(x + 3)$$

This will be a tangent to the rectangular hyperbola $xy = 16$

$$\text{if } x[m(x + 3) + 3] = 16$$

has repeated roots. (Refer back to page 167 if necessary.)

i.e. if $mx^2 + 3(1 + m)\,x - 16 = 0$ has repeated roots

$\therefore\ 9(1 + m)^2 = 4\,(m)\,(-16)$ i.e. $9m^2 + 82m + 9 = 0$

$\therefore\ m = \dfrac{-1}{9}$ or $-9 \Rightarrow x = 12$ or $\dfrac{-4}{3} \Rightarrow y = \dfrac{4}{3}$ or -12

The required coordinates are $\left(12, \dfrac{4}{3}\right)$ and $\left(\dfrac{-4}{3}, 12\right)$

You should now be able to answer Exercises 27–29 on page 201.

We'll now move on to define and investigate polar coordinates, draw the curves of certain polar equations, and find their areas.

An alternative system of coordinates

Whenever you have drawn graphs in the past you have always used cartesian coordinates – the familiar x and y. In fact, you may well believe that this is the only way in which points of the plane can be defined. If so, you would be wrong. Other systems of coordinates do exist, and some of them have special properties which make them particularly useful for certain applications.

In this section we shall investigate one such system: **polar coordinates**. The following diagram indicates the way in which we define the polar coordinates of any point.

Figure 10.12

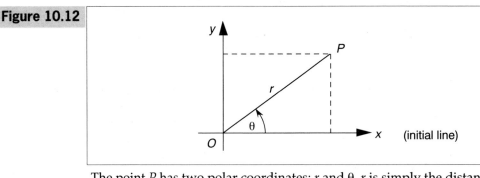

The point P has two polar coordinates: r and θ. r is simply the distance of P from the origin O, i.e. the length of the line OP, and θ is the angle between the x-axis (known as the **initial line** in the terminology of polar coordinates) and OP, measured in an anti-clockwise direction.

If we compare these new coordinates with the x and y we are used to, we see that there is a simple relationship between them. As the diagram shows, a little trigonometry reveals that x and y can be written:

$$x = r\cos\theta \qquad y = r\sin\theta$$

while r and θ can be expressed as:

$$r = \sqrt{(x^2 + y^2)} \qquad \tan\theta = \frac{y}{x}$$

The following triangle summarises these results:

Figure 10.13

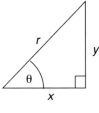

This means, of course, that any locus whose equation is originally given in cartesian coordinates may now be restated in terms of polar coordinates and vice versa.

To illustrate the use of r and θ, and to show some of the surprising shapes which we can easily produce with polar coordinates, we shall now consider a number of loci in polar form.

Examples of loci in polar coordinates

There are several polar equations whose graphs you should know well and be able to sketch almost without thinking. (Almost, but not quite – it is always unwise to do anything without thinking in mathematics.) In the next few pages we shall investigate these one by one and present some of the strangest curves you have seen in your work to date.

Before we do, however, let's give a moment's thought to our approach Unlike our curve sketching before, where we looked for specific features of the curves we drew, here we normally use a simpler, more direct method. Since the range of values of θ is *usually* (though not always) limited to $0 \le \theta \le 2\pi$, it is perfectly feasible to consider only a small sample of values of θ, calculate the corresponding values of r and plot the points that result. If we choose the sample wisely, this will give us enough information to fill the gaps and plot the rest of the curve.

It is also conventional to limit r to positive or zero values only. Whenever r takes a negative value, we say that r is undefined and so don't plot it. But now for some examples.

$\theta = \alpha$ where α is a given constant

In questions involving the drawing of curves in polar coordinates, it is sometimes more helpful to think of the geometry rather than setting up a table of values.

In this case the geometry is fairly clear: any point P for which the angle POx is a constant α must lie on a straight line running through the origin and making an angle α with the initial line Ox. This is easily seen in Figure 10.14. The required locus is therefore the straight line of which OP is a part.

Figure 10.14

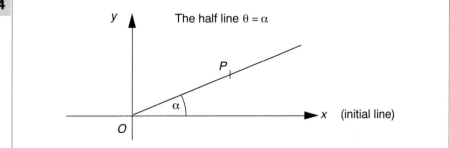

Notice that a sample of θ values was scarcely appropriate for this example – only one was possible.

$r = p\sec(\alpha - \theta)$ where p and α are given constants

In this case you may prefer to choose a sample of θ values and calculate the resulting r's. This is unnecessary, though, if you are willing to think in geometrical terms yet again. Rearranging the equation gives:

$$r\cos(\alpha - \theta) = p$$

The trigonometry of the situation shows that, whatever the position of P, the value of r must be such that the line OQ is of constant length p, where Q is the end of the perpendicular from P to OR. This can only be so if Q is a fixed point, and therefore P always lies on the same perpendicular to OR, as the following diagram shows. In other words, the graph is a straight line drawn at right angles to a given line OR and intersecting it at a distance p from the origin. α is the angle between OR and the initial line.

Figure 10.15

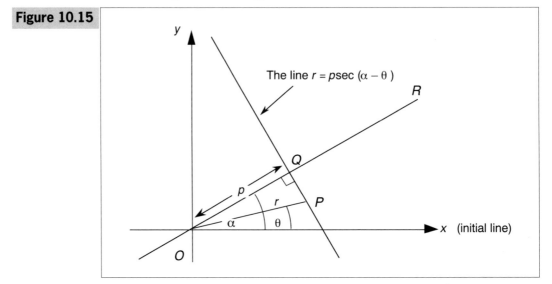

This is a very important result for it allows us to represent almost any straight line in polar coordinates. Be warned by the 'almost', though. Lines through the origin cannot be represented in this way, since the value of p would then be 0 so reducing the equation to $r = 0$. Such lines are always given in the form $\theta = \alpha$.

$r = a$ where a is a constant

It is clear here that the locus is always at a constant distance a from O, and must therefore be a circle of radius a with O as its centre. The diagram is shown in Figure 10.16:

Figure 10.16

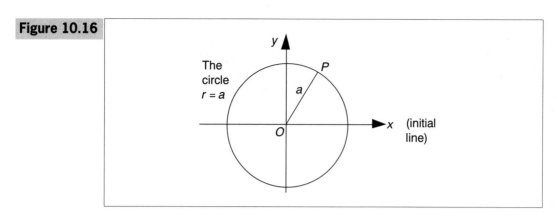

r = 2acos θ where a is a constant

Geometry would help in this case too, but perhaps less obviously than in the previous examples. For this reason we adopt the method we mentioned earlier and consider a small sample of θ values.

θ	0	$\dfrac{\pi}{3}$	$\dfrac{\pi}{2}$	$\dfrac{2\pi}{3}$	π	$\dfrac{4\pi}{3}$	$\dfrac{3\pi}{2}$	$\dfrac{5\pi}{3}$	2π
r	$2a$	a	0	$-a$	$-2a$	$-a$	0	a	$2a$

But since *r* can only take positive or zero values, this table reduces to:

θ	0	$\dfrac{\pi}{3}$	$\dfrac{\pi}{2}$	$\dfrac{2\pi}{3}$	π	$\dfrac{4\pi}{3}$	$\dfrac{3\pi}{2}$	$\dfrac{5\pi}{3}$	2π
r	$2a$	a	0	–	–	–	0	a	$2a$

The curve for $r = 2a\cos\theta$ is shown below in Figure 10.17.

Figure 10.17

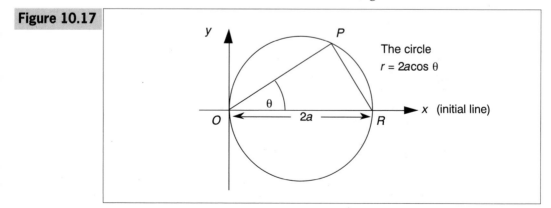

It is (reasonably) clear that the curve is a circle. Returning to the geometry of the equation, you may now see why. The point *P* is always positioned so that the angle *OPR* is a right angle. Your knowledge of the properties of circles will tell you that *P* must therefore lie on a circle with *OR* as its diameter.

r = kθ where k is a constant

Sample values of θ give:

θ	0	$\frac{\pi}{4}$	$\frac{\pi}{2}$	$\frac{3\pi}{4}$	π	$\frac{5\pi}{4}$	$\frac{3\pi}{2}$	$\frac{7\pi}{4}$	2π
r	0	$\frac{k\pi}{4}$	$\frac{k\pi}{2}$	$\frac{3k\pi}{4}$	kπ	$\frac{5k\pi}{4}$	$\frac{3k\pi}{2}$	$\frac{7k\pi}{4}$	2kπ

And so *P's* distance from the origin increases in proportion to θ, and thus the curve spirals out and away from 0 as θ moves from 0 to 2π.

Figure 10.18

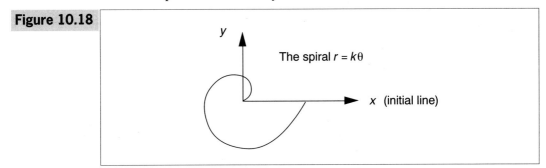

The spiral *r = k*θ

r = a[1 + cos θ] where a is a constant

The relevant values are:

θ	0	$\frac{\pi}{3}$	$\frac{\pi}{2}$	$\frac{2\pi}{3}$	π	$\frac{4\pi}{3}$	$\frac{3\pi}{2}$	$\frac{5\pi}{3}$	2π
r	2a	$\frac{3a}{2}$	a	$\frac{a}{2}$	0	$\frac{a}{2}$	a	$\frac{3a}{2}$	2a

and so the curve is:

Figure 10.19

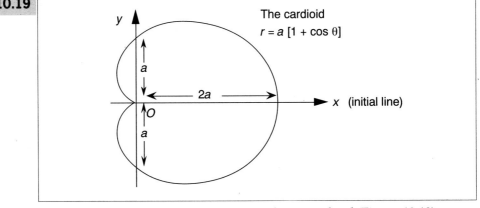

The cardioid
r = a [1 + cos θ]

The result is a heart-shaped curve known as a cardioid (Figure 10.19). Compare the simplicity of the polar treatment with the extremely messy algebra and graph drawing that would be required if cartesian coordinates were used.

$r = a[3 + 2\cos \theta]$ where a is a constant

Using the usual sample of θ values, we have:

θ	0	$\dfrac{\pi}{3}$	$\dfrac{\pi}{2}$	$\dfrac{2\pi}{3}$	π	$\dfrac{4\pi}{3}$	$\dfrac{3\pi}{2}$	$\dfrac{5\pi}{3}$	2π
r	$5a$	$4a$	$3s$	$2a$	a	$2s$	$3a$	$4a$	$5a$

and so:

Figure 10.20

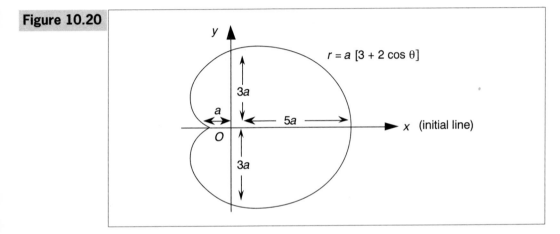

$r = a\cos 2\theta$ where a is a constant

In this case, because of the particularly unusual nature of the curve, we need to expand the sample of θ values to give us additional information.

θ	0	$\dfrac{\pi}{6}$	$\dfrac{\pi}{4}$	$\dfrac{\pi}{3}$	$\dfrac{\pi}{2}$	$\dfrac{2\pi}{3}$	$\dfrac{3\pi}{4}$	$\dfrac{5\pi}{6}$	cont. 1 ...
r	a	$\dfrac{a}{2}$	0	$\dfrac{-a}{2}$	$-a$	$\dfrac{-a}{2}$	0	$\dfrac{a}{2}$	cont. 2 ...

1 ...	π	$\dfrac{7\pi}{6}$	$\dfrac{5\pi}{4}$	$\dfrac{4\pi}{3}$	$\dfrac{3\pi}{2}$	$\dfrac{5\pi}{3}$	$\dfrac{7\pi}{4}$	$\dfrac{11\pi}{6}$	2π
2 ...	a	$\dfrac{a}{2}$	0	$\dfrac{-a}{2}$	$-a$	$\dfrac{-a}{2}$	0	$\dfrac{a}{2}$	a

Ignoring negative values of r we therefore get the following curve (Figure 10.21)

Figure 10.21

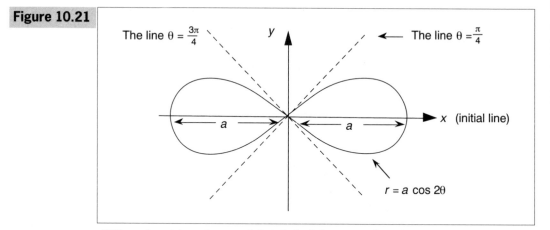

(When sketching the graph it is helpful to note that the lines θ = \f(π,4) and θ = $\frac{3\pi}{4}$ are tangents to the curve at the origin.)

$r^2 = a^2\cos 2\theta$ where a is a constant

For this example we again ignore the negative square root when calculating r, and note that there are some values of θ – those which make cos 2θ negative – for which corresponding parts of the curve cannot exist. For the remaining values of θ, we have:

θ	0	$\frac{\pi}{6}$	$\frac{\pi}{4}$	$\frac{\pi}{2}$	$\frac{3\pi}{4}$	$\frac{5\pi}{6}$	π	$\frac{7\pi}{6}$	$\frac{5\pi}{4}$	$\frac{3\pi}{2}$	$\frac{7\pi}{4}$	$\frac{11\pi}{6}$	2π
r	a	$\frac{a}{\sqrt{2}}$	0	–	0	$\frac{a}{\sqrt{2}}$	a	$\frac{a}{\sqrt{2}}$	0	–	0	$\frac{a}{\sqrt{2}}$	a

Again using the fact that the lines θ = $\frac{\pi}{4}$ and θ = $\frac{3\pi}{4}$ are tangents to the curve at the origin, we get:

Figure 10.22

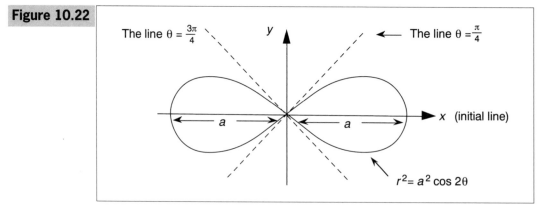

You have now seen a variety of polar curves and should be feeling confident that you can draw them for yourself. Make sure you can recognise the appropriate curve from its equation and vice versa.

You may well find this very helpful in examinations where time is limited and the careful consideration of a large sample of points may not be possible. In the following exercises you are under no such constraint, so take your time and ensure that you spot all the curves' features.

You should now be able to answer Exercises 30–31 on page 201.

Extreme points and tangents

As a check on the accuracy of our graphs, it is occasionally useful to find the points at which the x- and y-coordinates of a curve achieve their maximum and minimum values. This is also a necessary piece of analysis if we wish to determine the equations of tangents to the curve which are parallel or perpendicular to the initial line. To illustrate the method, we consider the following example.

$r = a[1 + \cos \theta]$

We have already drawn the curve for this equation. Let us now confirm its accuracy by checking that we drew its highest point in the correct position. For this, we need to find the values of r and θ which maximise y.

Now $y = r\sin \theta$ and so:

$$\frac{dy}{d\theta} = r\cos \theta + \frac{dr}{d\theta} \sin \theta$$

For maximum y, $\frac{dy}{d\theta} = 0$ and therefore, on rearranging:

$$r = -\frac{dr}{d\theta} \tan \theta$$

For this example, $r = a[1 + \cos \theta]$ and so:

$$\frac{dr}{d\theta} = -a\sin \theta$$

Thus y is maximised when:

$$a[1 + \cos \theta] = a\sin \theta \tan \theta$$

i.e. $\cos \theta [1 + \cos \theta] = \sin^2 \theta$

Rearranging we have:

$$\cos \theta = \sin^2 \theta - \cos^2 \theta = 1 - 2\cos^2 \theta$$

and so cos θ is a solution of the quadratic equation:

$$2X^2 + X - 1 = 0$$

i.e. $\cos \theta = \dfrac{-1 \pm \sqrt{[1^2 - 4 \times 2 \times (-1)]}}{2 \times 2}$

$$= \dfrac{1}{2} \text{ or } -1$$

If we restrict our attention to $0 \le \theta \le \pi$ (which is reasonable, since the lower half of the curve is simply a mirror image of the upper), we conclude:

$$\theta = \dfrac{\pi}{3} \text{ or } \pi$$

From the graph it is clear that, for the upper half-curve, y is maximised when $\theta = \dfrac{\pi}{3}$ and minimised when $\theta = \pi$. It is also clear that the graph positioned both points correctly.

Using this information we can now go on to find the equation of the tangent at the maximum point. At this point:

$$r = a[1 + \cos \dfrac{\pi}{3}] = \dfrac{3a}{2}$$

and so:

$$y = r\sin \dfrac{\pi}{3} = \dfrac{3a\sqrt{3}}{4}$$

Since the tangent we seek is parallel to the initial line, it is perpendicular to the y-axis (i.e. the line $\theta = \dfrac{1}{2}\pi$) and intersects it $\dfrac{3a\sqrt{3}}{4}$ away from the origin.

You will remember that we dealt with lines described in such a way earlier in the section. In fact, the equation of the line is:

$$r = \dfrac{3a\sqrt{3}}{4} \sec \left(\dfrac{1}{2}\pi - \theta \right)$$

Example   Show that the x-value of the curve

$$r = a[1 + \cos \theta]$$

has turning points when $\theta = 0$ and $\theta = \dfrac{2\pi}{3}$. Write down the equations of the tangents to the curve at these two points.

| Solution | We wish to find the extreme values of $x = r\cos\theta$. So, differentiating with respect to θ, we have: |

$$\frac{dx}{d\theta} = -r\sin\theta + \frac{dr}{d\theta}\cos\theta$$

For extreme values of x therefore:

$$r\tan\theta = \frac{dr}{d\theta}$$

Since $r = a[1 + \cos\theta]$, this gives:

$$[1 + \cos\theta]\tan\theta = -\sin\theta$$

Multiplying by $\cos\theta$ and rearranging:

$$\sin\theta + 2\sin\theta\cos\theta = 0$$

i.e. $\sin\theta\,[1 + 2\cos\theta] = 0$

Thus:

$$\text{either } \sin\theta = 0 \text{ or } \cos\theta = -\frac{1}{2}$$

It follows that $\theta = 0$ and $\theta = \dfrac{2\pi}{3}$ produce turning points of x.

The corresponding values of x are $2a$ and $-\dfrac{1}{4}a$.

Now the tangents at such points are perpendicular to the initial line $\theta = 0$, and so have equations:

$$r = 2a\sec(0 - \theta) = 2a\sec\theta$$
$$r = -\frac{1}{4}a\sec(0 - \theta) = -\frac{1}{4}a\sec\theta$$

Finding the areas of polar curves

We close the section by investigating a problem that you have already seen many times in relation to cartesian coordinates – that of calculating the area bounded by a curve whose equation is known. The key to solving this problem is the simple formula:

$$\text{area} = \frac{1}{2}\int_\alpha^\beta r^2\,d\theta$$

which tells us how to work out the area of the region bounded by some general polar curve and the straight lines $\theta = \alpha$ and $\theta = \beta$. The curve itself is assumed to have an equation which expresses r as a function of θ.

To see the truth of this result, consider the diagram below. The arc *PQ* belongs to the curve in question. *P* is the point with polar coordinates *r* and θ, and *Q* is a short distance away with coordinates *r* + δ*r* and θ + δθ.

Figure 10.23

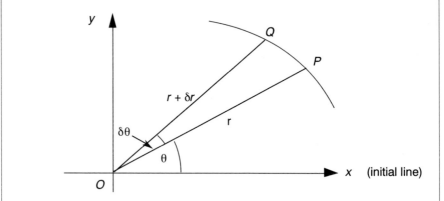

Since *P* and *Q* are close, we can assume that δ*r* and δθ are small and that the region *OPQ* is adequately approximated by a triangle. Because δ*r* is small, the height of this triangle is approximately *r*. Because δθ is small, its base is approximately *r*δθ. Its area is therefore approximately:

$$\frac{1}{2} \times r \times r\delta\theta = \frac{1}{2}r^2\delta\theta$$

Of course, as δ*r* and δθ grow infinitesimally small, the approximations become more and more exact until, in the limit, there is no approximation at all. The area we require is the sum of all such infinitesimal triangles from θ = α to θ = β. In the usual notation of integration, this is now clearly the formula we wished to verify. Remember this – you may find it very useful.

To illustrate the application of the formula, we shall use it to calculate the area enclosed by a curve we saw earlier.

r = a[1 + cos θ]

Figure 10.24

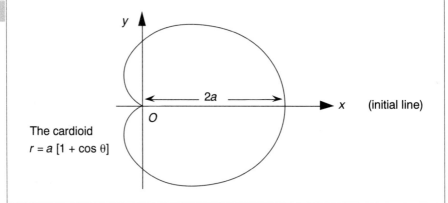

The cardioid
r = *a* [1 + cos θ]

From the diagram it is clear that we need only calculate the area of the upper half of the curve (i.e. between $\theta = 0$ and $\theta = \pi$), then double it. In general, it is often possible to split a polar curve into separate sections of equal area and so simplify the calculation. In this case, the area we require is:

$$2 \times \frac{1}{2} \int_0^\pi r^2 \, d\theta \quad = a^2 \int_0^\pi (1 + \cos\theta)^2 \, d\theta$$

$$= a^2 \int_0^\pi (1 + 2\cos\theta + \cos^2\theta) \, d\theta$$

$$= a^2 \int_0^\pi [1 + 2\cos\theta + \tfrac{1}{2}\{\cos 2\theta + 1\}] \, d\theta$$

$$= a^2 \left[\frac{3\theta}{2} + 2\sin\theta + \frac{1}{4}\sin 2\theta\right]_0^\pi = \frac{3\pi a^2}{2}$$

Examples   Find the areas enclosed by the curves:

1    $r = k\theta$ between $\theta = 0$ and $\theta = \pi$
2    $r = a\cos 2\theta$
3    $r^2 = a^2\cos 2\theta$

Solutions   1   The required area is:

$$\frac{1}{2}\int_0^\pi r^2 \, d\theta = \frac{1}{2}\int_0^\pi k^2\theta^2 \, d\theta = \frac{1}{2}k^2\left[\frac{\theta^3}{3}\right]_0^\pi = \frac{k^2\pi^3}{6}$$

2   From the diagram of this curve (see Figure 10.21), you will notice that we need only integrate between $\theta = 0$ and $\theta = \frac{1}{4}\pi$. The curve as a whole is made up of four such identical regions. Thus the area we want is:

$$4 \times \frac{1}{2}\int_0^{\frac{\pi}{4}} r^2 \, d\theta = 2\int_0^{\frac{\pi}{4}} a^2\cos^2 2\theta \, d\theta$$

$$= 2a^2 \int_0^{\frac{\pi}{4}} \frac{1}{2}[\cos 4\theta + 1] \, d\theta$$

$$= a^2 \left[\frac{\pi}{4}\sin 4\theta + \theta\right]_0^{\frac{\pi}{4}} = \frac{1}{4}\pi a^2$$

3   Again, the diagram of the curve (see Figure 10.22) is useful. The curve is made up of four regions identical in area to that between $\theta = 0$ and $\theta = \frac{\pi}{4}$. The area we need is therefore:

$$4 \times \frac{1}{2}\int_0^{\frac{\pi}{4}} r^2 \, d\theta = 2\int_0^{\frac{\pi}{4}} a^2\cos 2\theta \, d\theta = a^2\left[\sin 2\theta\right]_0^{\frac{\pi}{4}} = a^2$$

As you can see from problems 2 and 3, it is useful to have a sketch of the curve available, but otherwise it's just a matter of (reasonably) straightforward integration. Since sin θ and cos θ turn up frequently in polar problems, it helps to remember one or two trigonometrical techniques – for example, that:

$$\cos^2 \theta = \tfrac{1}{2}\big[\cos 2\theta + 1\big].$$

You should now be able to answer Exercise 32 on page 201.

Intrinsic coordinates

So far we have see how to express curves in:

- cartesian coordinates (x,y)
- polar coordinates (r, θ)
- parameters (usually t)

However, there is a fourth way and this is by means of *intrinsic coordinates*. They involve the length of the curve (s) from some fixed point A to variable point P, together with the angle (ψ) that the tangent at P makes with the positive x-axis.

Figure 10.25

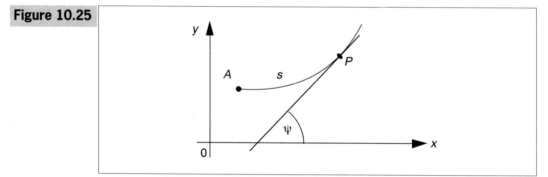

As P moves along the curve, the intrinsic coordinates (s, ψ) specify the position of P.

For example, the curve with intrinsic equation $s = a\tan \psi$ can be shown to be a catenary and looks like the one shown in Figure 10.26.

Figure 10.26

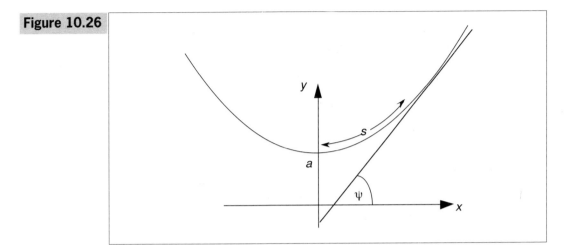

As ψ varies from 0 to $\dfrac{\pi}{2}$ the distance s varies from 0 to infinity. Similarly, as ψ varies from $\dfrac{-\pi}{2}$ to 0, s varies from infinity to 0. You'll be returning to this later in Exercise 37.

If we now take a point Q on the curve very close to P, we can draw in a circle which includes the section PQ of the original curve.

Figure 10.27

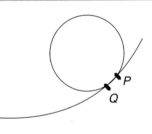

As $Q \rightarrow P$ we get a unique circle at P called the *circle of curvature of the curve at P*.

If the radius of this circle is ρ, then it can be shown that $\rho = \dfrac{ds}{d\psi}$. We call ρ the radius of curvature at P.

You need to learn by heart that $\rho = \dfrac{ds}{d\psi}$.

The radius of curvature in cartesian form

We need now to find an expression for ρ in terms of (x,y), the coordinates of P.

Clearly $\dfrac{dy}{dx} = \tan \psi$ and Pythagoras gives us $dx^2 + dy^2 = ds^2$. All of this combines very nicely to give:

Figure 10.28

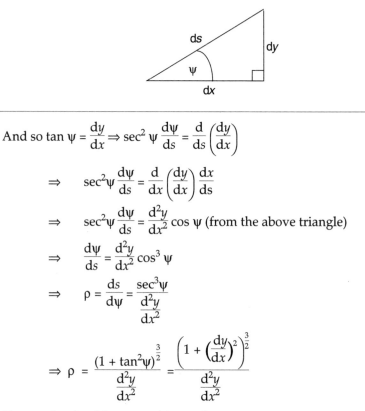

And so $\tan \psi = \dfrac{dy}{dx} \Rightarrow \sec^2 \psi \dfrac{d\psi}{ds} = \dfrac{d}{ds}\left(\dfrac{dy}{dx}\right)$

$\Rightarrow \quad \sec^2\psi \dfrac{d\psi}{ds} = \dfrac{d}{dx}\left(\dfrac{dy}{dx}\right)\dfrac{dx}{ds}$

$\Rightarrow \quad \sec^2\psi \dfrac{d\psi}{ds} = \dfrac{d^2y}{dx^2}\cos\psi$ (from the above triangle)

$\Rightarrow \quad \dfrac{d\psi}{ds} = \dfrac{d^2y}{dx^2}\cos^3\psi$

$\Rightarrow \quad \rho = \dfrac{ds}{d\psi} = \dfrac{\sec^3\psi}{\dfrac{d^2y}{dx^2}}$

$\Rightarrow \rho = \dfrac{(1 + \tan^2\psi)^{\frac{3}{2}}}{\dfrac{d^2y}{dx^2}} = \dfrac{\left(1 + \left(\dfrac{dy}{dx}\right)^2\right)^{\frac{3}{2}}}{\dfrac{d^2y}{dx^2}}$

You need to be able to use this result.

Example   Find the radius of curvature of the curve $y = x + 3x^2 - 4x^3$ at the origin.

Solution $\dfrac{dy}{dx} = 1 + 6x - 12x^2$ and $\dfrac{d^2y}{dx^2} = 6 - 24x$.

$\therefore \qquad \rho = \dfrac{\left[1 + (1 + 6x - 12x^2)^2\right]^{\frac{3}{2}}}{(6 - 24x)}$

$\therefore \qquad$ At $x = 0$, $\rho = \dfrac{2^{\frac{3}{2}}}{6} = 0.47$

You should now be able to answer Exercises 35–38 on pages 201–202.

The radius of curvature in parametric form

$$\tan \psi = \frac{dy}{dx} \Rightarrow \sec^2\psi \frac{d\psi}{ds} = \frac{d}{ds}\left(\frac{\dot{y}}{\dot{x}}\right)$$

$$\left(\text{Using the identity } \frac{dy}{dx} = \frac{dy}{dt} \div \frac{dx}{dt} = \frac{\dot{y}}{\dot{x}}\right)$$

$$\Rightarrow \quad \sec^2\psi \frac{d\psi}{ds} = \frac{d}{dt}\left(\frac{\dot{y}}{\dot{x}}\right) \times \frac{dt}{ds}$$

$$= \left(\frac{\dot{x}\ddot{y} - \dot{y}\ddot{x}}{\dot{x}^2}\right) \times \frac{dt}{dx} \times \frac{dx}{ds} = \left(\frac{\dot{x}\ddot{y} - \dot{y}\ddot{x}}{\dot{x}^3}\right) \cos \psi$$

$$\therefore \quad \rho = \frac{ds}{d\psi} = \frac{\dot{x}^3}{\dot{x}\ddot{y} - \dot{y}\ddot{x}} \sec^3 \psi$$

$$= \frac{\dot{x}^3}{\dot{x}\ddot{y} - \dot{y}\ddot{x}}[1 + \tan^2 \psi]^{\frac{3}{2}}$$

$$= \frac{\dot{x}^3}{\dot{x}\ddot{y} - \dot{y}\ddot{x}}\left[1 + \left(\frac{\dot{y}}{\dot{x}}\right)^2\right]^{\frac{3}{2}}$$

$$\therefore \quad \rho = \frac{[\dot{x}^2 + \dot{y}^2]^{\frac{3}{2}}}{\dot{x}\ddot{y} - \dot{y}\ddot{x}}$$

You need to be able to use this result.

Example   For the curve $x = 2 \sin t$, $y = \sin 2t$, find the radius of curvature at $t = \dfrac{\pi}{6}$.

Solution $\dot{x} = 2 \cos t$, $\ddot{x} = -2 \sin t$

$\dot{y} = 2 \cos 2t$, $\ddot{y} = -4 \sin 2t$

$\therefore$ When $t = \dfrac{\pi}{6}$, $\dot{x} = \sqrt{3}$, $\ddot{x} = -1$, $\dot{y} = 1$, $\ddot{y} = -2\sqrt{3}$

$\therefore$ $\rho = \dfrac{\left[(\sqrt{3})^2 + (1)^2\right]^{3/2}}{\left[\sqrt{3} \times (-2\sqrt{3}) - 1 \times (-1)\right]} = -\dfrac{8}{5}$

But the radius ρ must be positive $\therefore \rho = \dfrac{8}{5}$

You should now be able to answer Exercises 39–41 on page 202.

EXERCISES

1 Find the centre and radius of these circles:

   (a) $x^2 + y^2 - 2x - 6y - 6 = 0$

   (b) $x^2 + y^2 + 8x - 9 = 0$

   (c) $x^2 + y^2 + 4y = 0$

   (d) $x^2 + y^2 + 6x + 8y = 0$

2 Write down and simplify the equation of the circle whose centre is (1, 2) and where radius is 3.

3 Sketch the curve $x^2 + y^2 = 9$

4 Sketch the circle $x^2 + y^2 - 25 = 0$. Find the coordinates of the point of intersection of this circle with the line $y = x + 1$

5 Describe the curves given by the following parametric equations:

   (a) $x = 1 + \cos\theta, y = 5 + \sin\theta$

   (b) $x = 2 + 3\cos\theta, y = 1 + 3\sin\theta$

   (c) $x = a\cos\theta, y = a\sin\theta$ (*a* constant)

6 Write down parametric equations for the circle:

   $(x - 2)^2 + (y + 3)^2 = 25$

7 Show that $P(7, -2)$ lies on the circle $x^2 + y^2 - 6x - 2y - 15 = 0$. What is the equation of the tangent at P?

8 Find the length of the tangent from Q (2, 1) to the circle:
   $x^2 + y^2 + 4x - 4y - 8 = 0$.

9 The line $y = mx$ is a tangent to the circle $x^2 + y^2 + 2x + 14y + 40 = 0$. Find the values of m and the corresponding contact points.

10 The line $y = mx + 3$ is a tangent to the circle $x^2 + y^2 + 2x - 12y + 32 = 0$. Find the values of m and the corresponding contact points.

11 Show that the line $3y - x = 3$ is a tangent to the circle $x^2 + y^2 - 10x - 12y + 51 = 0$ and find the contact point.

12 If the line $y = mx + c$ is a tangent to the circle $x^2 + y^2 = a^2$, prove that $c^2 = a^2 (1 + m^2)$.

13 A, B, C are the points $(-2, -4), (3, 1), (-2, 0)$. Find the equation of the circle passing through A, B, C and show that the tangent at B is parallel to the diameter through C.
   (Hint: let the equation be $x^2 + y^2 + ax + by + c = 0$ and find three simultaneous equations.)

14 Show that the equation of the chord PQ, of the parabola $y^2 = 4ax$, which joins the points $P(at^2, 2at)$ and $Q(as^2, 2as)$, can be written as:

$$y(t + s) = 2x + 2ats$$

By letting $s \rightarrow t$, deduce that the equation of the tangent at P is $yt = x + at^2$.

15 The ellipse $\dfrac{x^2}{a^2} + \dfrac{y^2}{b^2} = 1$ has focus F_1 (ae, o) and $P(a \cos \theta, b \sin \theta)$.

The focal chord $F_1 P$ meets the ellipse again at $Q(a \cos \psi, b \sin \psi)$. Prove that:

$$\cos \left(\frac{\psi - \theta}{2} \right) = e \cos \left(\frac{\psi + \theta}{2} \right)$$

16 The line $y = mx + c$ touches the ellipse $\dfrac{x^2}{a^2} + \dfrac{y^2}{b^2} = 1$.

Prove that $c^2 = a^2m^2 + b^2$.

17 Prove that the tangents to $y^2 = 4ax$ at $T(at^2, 2at)$ and $S(as^2, 2as)$ meet at the point R, where R is $\left(ast, a(s + t) \right)$. If $t = 2s$, prove that the locus of R is the curve $2y^2 = 9ax$.

18 Prove that the equation of the normal to the parabola $y^2 = 4ax$ at the point $P(at^2, 2at)$ is $y + tx = at (2 + t^2)$.

If the normal meets the x and y axes at X and Y respectively, prove that

$$XY = a (2 + t^2) \sqrt{1 + t^2}$$

19 Prove that the equation of the tangent to the parabola $y^2 = 4ax$ at the point $P (at^2, 2at)$ is $yt = x + at^2$. If this tangent meets the axis at X and Y, prove that

$$XY = at \sqrt{1 + t^2}.$$

20 The normals to the parabola $y^2 = 4ax$ at $P(at^2, 2at)$ and $Q(as^2, 2as)$ meet at R. Show that the coordinates of R are:

$$\left(a (2 + t^2 + st + s^2) , - ast (s + t) \right)$$

21 Any tangent to an ellipse meets the tangents at the ends of the major axis in M, M'. Prove that MM' subtends a right angle at either focus.

22 The tangent and normal at any point P on an ellipse meet the major axis at T and G respectively. If PN is the ordinate of P and C the centre, prove that $CT \cdot NG = b^2$.

23 The normal at P, a point on the ellipse $b^2x^2 + a^2y^2 = a^2b^2$, passes through the lower end of the minor axis. Find the eccentric angle of P.

24 Show that the equation of the tangent at (x_1, y_1) to the hyperbola

$$\frac{x^2}{a^2} - \frac{y^2}{b^2} = 1 \text{ is } \frac{xx_1}{a^2} - \frac{yy_1}{b^2} = 1.$$

25 Prove that the triangle formed by the asymptotes and any tangent to the curve $\dfrac{x^2}{4} - \dfrac{y^2}{2} = 1$ is of constant area. [HARD]

26 Show that the locus of the point:

$$x = \frac{a}{2}\left(t + \frac{1}{t}\right), y = \frac{b}{2}\left(t - \frac{1}{t}\right),$$

for varying values of t, is the hyperbola

$$\frac{x^2}{a^2} - \frac{y^2}{b^2} = 1.$$

Derive the equation of the tangent at the point with parameter t.

27 Prove that the equation of the chord joining the points $\left(ct, \dfrac{c}{t}\right), \left(cs, \dfrac{c}{s}\right)$ on the rectangular hyperbola $xy = c^2$, is $x + sty - c(s + t) = 0$.

28 Show that the equation of the normal at $\left(ct, \dfrac{c}{t}\right)$ on the rectangular hyperbola $xy = c^2$, is

$$y - t^2 x = ct^{-1} - ct^3.$$

Deduce that this normal meets the curve again at the point with coordinates $\left(-\dfrac{c}{t^3}, -ct^3\right)$.

29 The tangents at $T\left(ct, \dfrac{c}{t}\right)$ and $S\left(cs, \dfrac{c}{s}\right)$ on the rectangular hyperbola $xy = c^2$, meet at Q. Prove that the coordinates of Q are $\left(\dfrac{2cst}{s + t}, \dfrac{2c}{s + t}\right)$.

If $s = \dfrac{1}{t}$, prove that Q lies on the line $y = x$.

30 Write down the polar equations of the curves in the diagrams below.

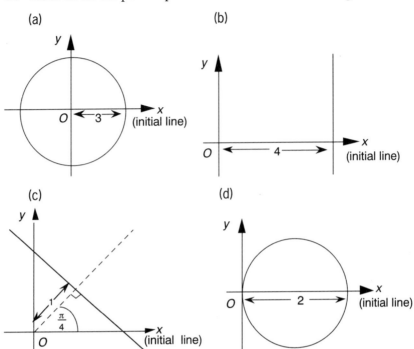

(a)

(b)

(c)

(d)

31 Sketch the curves which correspond to the following polar equations.

(a) $\theta = \dfrac{1}{4}\pi$

(b) $r = 2\sec\left(\dfrac{1}{2}\pi - \theta\right)$

(c) $r = a\,[1 - \cos\theta]$

(d) $r = 9 + 6\cos\theta$

(e) $r = \sin 2\theta$

32 Sketch the curve where polar equation is $r = a\sin 2\theta$.

Find the area of one loop.

33 Find the area of the sector of the curve $r = a(2 + \cos\theta)$ bounded by the lines $\theta = 0,\ \theta = \dfrac{\pi}{2}$.

34 Show that the curve $r = 2a\cos\theta$ is a circle, radius a. Hence obtain the formula for the area of a circle.

35 Find the radius of curvature of $y = \ln x$ at $x = \dfrac{1}{3}$.

36 Prove that the radius of curvature of the catenary $y = c \cosh\left(\dfrac{x}{c}\right)$

at any point (x,y) is $\dfrac{y^2}{c}$.

37 Use the results $\tan \psi = \dfrac{dy}{dx}$, $\dfrac{ds}{dx} = \sqrt{1 + \left(\dfrac{dy}{dx}\right)^2}$, to prove that for the

catenary $y = c \cosh\left(\dfrac{x}{c}\right)$, $s = c \tan \psi$.

38 Find the coordinates of the point on the curve $y = x^2 (3 - x)$ at which the curvature is zero.

39 Find the radius of curvature at $\theta = 0$ on the curve $x = 2 \cosh \theta$, $y = \sinh \theta$.

40 For the cycloid $x = a(\theta + \sin \theta)$, $y = a(1 + \cos \theta)$, show that

$$\rho = 4a \cos\left(\frac{\theta}{2}\right)$$

41 Prove that the radius of curvature at the point $\left(ct, \dfrac{c}{t}\right)$ on the

rectangular hyperbola $xy = c^2$ is $\dfrac{c}{2}\left(t^2 + \dfrac{1}{t^2}\right)^{\frac{3}{2}}$.

SUMMARY
You should now:

- know that the equation of the circle centre (a, b) and radius r is
  $(x - a)^2 + (y - b)^2 = r^2$
- be able to find the centre and radius of a circle from its equation
- be able to find the equation of a tangent to a circle
- be able to find the length of a tangent from a given point to a circle
- be able to tackle problems involving:

  the parabola $y^2 = 4ax$, typical point $(at^2, 2at)$

  the ellipse $\dfrac{x^2}{a^2} + \dfrac{y^2}{b^2} = 1$, typical point $(a\cos \theta, b\sin \theta)$

  the hyperbola $\dfrac{x^2}{a^2} - \dfrac{y^2}{b^2} = 1$, typical point $(a\sec \theta, b\tan \theta)$

  the rectangular hyperbola $xy = c^2$, typical point $\left(ct, \dfrac{c}{t}\right)$

- know how to sketch curves given in polar form
- be able to use the formula $\frac{1}{2}\int r^2 \, d\theta$ for finding areas with polar coordinates
- be able to use the formulae

$$\rho = \frac{ds}{d\psi}, \quad \rho = \frac{\left[1 + \left(\frac{dy}{dx}\right)^2\right]^{\frac{3}{2}}}{\frac{d^2y}{dx^2}},$$

and $\quad \rho = \dfrac{\left[\dot{x}^2 + \dot{y}^2\right]^{\frac{3}{2}}}{(\dot{x}\,\ddot{y} - \dot{y}\,\ddot{x})}$

to find radii of curvature.

11

Further complex numbers

INTRODUCTION In this section we are going to look again at complex numbers which we worked on in Section 7. Maclaurin Series provide the starting point and from there we go on to roots of complex numbers, trigonometric identities and assorted loci and transformation questions.

Cos, sin and the exponential function: a useful relation

Without the Maclaurin Series for e^x, $\sin x$ and $\cos x$ we might never notice an interesting and surpri singly useful relationship between these three functions. Just take a look at the formulae that we have already established for e^x and $\sin x$:

$$e^x = 1 + \frac{x}{1!} + \frac{x^2}{1!} + \frac{x^3}{3!} + \frac{x^4}{4!} + \frac{x^5}{5!} + \ldots$$

$$\sin x = x - \frac{x^3}{3!} + \frac{x^5}{5!} - \frac{x^7}{7!} + \ldots$$

Note that, but for changes of sign, the two *share* identical terms. Much the same is true for $\cos x$ as well, for:

$$\cos x = 1 - \frac{x^2}{2!} + \frac{x^4}{4!} - \frac{x^6}{6!} + \ldots$$

Again with the exception of some of the signs, the terms of $\cos x$ appear to be a subset of e^x.

To understand these relationships fully, we need to make a rather subtle move. Instead of dealing with e^x, let us consider e^{ix}, where, as usual, i is the square root of -1. Using the Maclaurin Series for e^x and substituting ix for x, we see that:

$$\begin{aligned}
e^{ix} &= 1 + ix - \frac{x^2}{2!} - \frac{ix^3}{3!} + \frac{x^4}{4!} + \frac{ix^5}{5!} \ldots \quad (\text{since } i^2 = -1, i^3 = -i \text{ etc.}) \\
&= (1 - \frac{x^2}{2!} + \frac{x^4}{4!} - \ldots) + i(x - \frac{x^3}{3!} + \frac{x^5}{5!} - \ldots) \\
&= \cos x + i \sin x
\end{aligned}$$

This remarkable result is worth highlighting:

$$e^{ix} = \cos(x) + i\sin(x)$$

Remember this. You will find it extremely useful later.

Example Evaluate $e^{i\pi}$

Solution $$e^{i\pi} = \cos \pi + i \sin \pi = -1 + 0$$
$$\therefore \quad e^{i\pi} = -1$$

Now that qualifies as a truly remarkable result. The left hand side of this identity involves two irrational numbers (e and π) and the complex number i and yet, put them all together in this way, and you come up with exactly –1.

Relations between hyperbolic and trigonometrical functions

In Section 4 we met the hyperbolic functions – sinh, cosh and tanh – for the first time. We noticed immediately how similar they were to their trigonometrical counterparts – sin , cos and tan. It wasn't just that their names were almost identical; they had surpri singly similar properties as well. We are now in a position to relate the two sets even more closely.

To make a start, we repeat the result we have just proved.

$$e^{ix} = \cos x + i\sin x$$

Replacing x by $-x$ and using well-known facts about sin and cos, we get

$$e^{-ix} = \cos -x + i\sin -x = \cos x - i\sin x$$

Adding these two equations and dividing by 2 gives

$$\cos x = \frac{1}{2}(e^{ix} + e^{-ix})$$

Similarly, subtracting the second from the first and dividing by 2i gives

$$\sin x = \frac{1}{2i}(e^{ix} - e^{-ix})$$

Now recall the definitions of sinh and cosh. From the two formulae for sin and cos that we have just written down, it is clear that

$$\cos x = \cosh ix$$

and $$\sin x = \frac{1}{i}\sinh ix = -i\sinh ix$$

also $$\tan x = \frac{\sin x}{\cos x} = \frac{-i\sinh ix}{\cosh ix} = -i\tanh ix$$

These relations and their equivalents for sinh, cosh and tanh are summarised in Table 11.1.

Table 11.1

Hyperbolic	Trigonometrical
sinh ix	i sin x
cosh ix	cos x
tanh ix	i tan x

Trigonometrical	Hyperbolic
sin ix	i sinh x
cos ix	cosh x
tan ix	i tanh x

These are well worth remembering. If we use them with care, we can tell almost all we need to know about the properties of hyperbolic functions from those of their trigonometrical equivalents – or vice versa.

For example, one of the best-known trigonometrical identities is:

$$\cos^2 x + \sin^2 x = 1$$

Replacing x by ix and using the table above, we get:

$$\cosh^2 x - \sinh^2 x = 1$$

which is an equally well-known hyperbolic identity.

Examples

Find the hyperbolic counterparts of the following trigonometrical identities.

1 $\sin 3x = 3 \sin x - 4 \sin^3 x$

2 $\cos (x + y) = \cos x \cos y - \sin x \sin y$

3 $\sec^2 x = 1 + \tan^2 x$

4 $\tan (x + y) = \dfrac{\tan x + \tan y}{1 - \tan x \cdot \tan y}$

Solutions

We replace x by ix and y by iy, then use the table above to convert from trigonometrical to hyperbolic.

1 $\sin 3ix$ $\quad = \quad 3 \sin ix - 4 \sin^3 ix \quad$ becomes

$\quad\;\;$ i sinh $3x$ $\quad = \quad 3$ i sinh $x - 4[$i sinh $x]^3$

$\quad\quad\quad\quad\quad\;\, = \quad 3$ i sinh $x + 4$ i sinh$^3 x$

Dividing by i,

$$\sinh 3x \quad = \quad 3 \sinh x + 4 \sinh^3 x$$

2 $\quad \cos(ix + iy) \quad = \quad \cos ix \cos iy - \sin ix \sin iy \qquad$ becomes:

$$\cosh(x + y) \quad = \quad \cosh x \cosh y - i \sinh x \, i \sinh y$$
$$= \quad \cosh x \cosh y + \sinh x \sinh y$$

3 $\quad \dfrac{1}{\cos^2 ix} \quad = \quad 1 + \tan^2 ix \quad$ becomes

$$\dfrac{1}{\cosh^2 x} \quad = 1 + [i \tanh x]^2 = 1 - \tanh^2 x$$

i.e. $\operatorname{sech}^2 x \quad = 1 - \tanh^2 x$

4 $\quad \tan(ix + iy) \quad = \dfrac{\tan ix + \tan iy}{1 - \tan ix \tan iy} \quad$ becomes

$$i \tanh(x + y) \quad = \dfrac{i \tanh x + i \tanh y}{1 - i \tanh x \, i \tanh y}$$

Dividing by i,

$$\tanh(x + y) \quad = \dfrac{\tanh x + \tanh y}{1 + \tanh x \tanh y}$$

You should now be able to answer Exercise 1 on page 227.

De Moivre's Theorem

You are now within easy reach of a very striking result – one which gives a deeper insight into trigonometrical functions and their properties. It is a result that can be used to solve a fundamental mathematical problem: how to find all the nth roots of any number, whatever the value of n.

Once again we start with:

$$e^{ix} = \cos x + i \sin x$$

but this time replace x by nx, where n is any value, giving:

$$e^{inx} = \cos nx + i \sin nx$$

But since

$$e^{inx} = (e^{ix})^n$$

it follows that, for any n:

$$[\cos x + i \sin x]^n = \cos nx + i \sin nx$$

This is **De Moivre's Theorem**. Mark it well. We will find a great deal of use for it.

Examples	Simplify:

1 $[\cos x + i \sin x][\cos y + i \sin y]$

2 $\dfrac{\cos 3\theta + i \sin 3\theta}{\cos 2\theta + i \sin 2\theta}$

3 $[\cos 8\theta - i \sin 8\theta]^{\frac{1}{2}}$

Solutions   In each case, convert the expression(s) to the corresponding power(s) of e, simplify, and then revert to trigonometry.

1 $e^{ix}e^{iy} = e^{i(x+y)} = \cos (x + y) + i \sin (x + y)$

2 $\dfrac{e^{3i\theta}}{e^{2i\theta}} = e^{i\theta} = \cos \theta + i \sin \theta$

3 $\sqrt{(e^{-8i\theta})^{\frac{1}{2}}} = e^{-4i\theta} = \cos 4\theta - i \sin 4\theta$

You should now be able to answer Exercise 2 on page 227.

Roots of any number

As hinted earlier, one of the most impressive uses for De Moivre's Theorem lies in finding the roots of any number. As everybody knows, there are two square roots of 1, and these are +1 and –1. However, the three cube roots of 1 are much less well known, and for most people the nth roots of any number are a complete mystery!

Example   Find the three cube roots of 1.

Solution   We need to discover all the values of z for which $z^3 = 1$

One method would be to notice that z = 1 is a solution of $z^3 - 1 = 0$, and then use the factor theorem and long division, to give

$(z - 1) (z^2 + z + 1) = 0$

$\therefore z = 1$ or $z^2 + z + 1 = 0$ $\therefore z = 1$ or $\dfrac{-1 \pm i\sqrt{3}}{2}$

$\therefore$ the three cube roots of 1 are 1, $\dfrac{-1 + i\sqrt{3}}{2}$ and $\dfrac{-1 - i\sqrt{3}}{2}$

However, *there is a more general method* which goes as follows:

Put $z = \cos\theta + i\sin\theta$ where $z^3 = 1$

$\therefore$ De Moivre's Theorem gives $\cos 3\theta + i\sin 3\theta = 1$

Now equate real and imaginary parts to get $\cos 3\theta = 1$ and $\sin 3\theta = 0$

It follows that $3\theta = 2n\pi$, for any integer n, i.e. $\theta = \dfrac{2n\pi}{3}$

Each of the values $n = 0$, 1 and 2 provides a distinct value for z,

namely, $\cos 0 + i\sin 0 = 1$, $\cos\dfrac{2\pi}{3} + i\sin\dfrac{2\pi}{3} = -\dfrac{1}{2} + \dfrac{i\sqrt 3}{2}$ and

$\cos\dfrac{4\pi}{3} + i\sin\dfrac{4\pi}{3} = -\dfrac{1}{2} - \dfrac{i\sqrt 3}{2}$

And so, once again, we get that the three cube roots of 1 are 1, $\dfrac{-1 + i\sqrt 3}{2}$

and $\dfrac{-1 - i\sqrt 3}{2}$. However, the beauty of this second method is that it can be applied to find the roots of any number.

Example   Find the four distinct solutions of the equation $z^4 = 16$.

Solution   You will recall from our earlier work on complex numbers that any complex number can be expressed in the form $r(\cos\theta + i\sin\theta)$.

$\therefore$ Let $z = r(\cos\theta + i\sin\theta)$ where $z^4 = 16$

De Moivre's Theorem gives $r^4(\cos 4\theta + i\sin 4\theta) = 16$

$\therefore$ $r^4\cos 4\theta = 16$ and $r^4\sin 4\theta = 0$

$\therefore$ $r = 2$, $\cos 4\theta = 1$ and $\sin 4\theta = 0$

It follows that $4\theta = 2n\pi$, for any integer n i.e. $\theta = \dfrac{n\pi}{2}$

Each of the values $n = 0$, 1, 2 and 3 provides a distinct value for z, namely,

$2(\cos 0 + i\sin 0) = 2$, $2(\cos\frac{\pi}{2} + i\sin\frac{\pi}{2}) = 2i$, $2(\cos\pi + i\sin\pi) = -2$

and $2(\cos\dfrac{3\pi}{2} + i\sin\dfrac{3\pi}{2}) = -2i$

$\therefore$ the four distinct solutions of the equation $z^4 = 16$ are 2, 2i, -2 and $-2i$.

Example	Find the three distinct solutions of the equation $z^3 = -27i$.

Solutions	Let $z = r(\cos\theta + i\sin\theta)$ where $z^3 = -27i$

De Moivre's Theorem gives $r^3(\cos 3\theta + i\sin 3\theta) = -27i$

$\therefore r^3 \cos 3\theta = 0$ and $r^3 \sin 3\theta = -27$

Since $r > 0$ it follows that $r = 3$, $\sin 3\theta = -1$ and $\cos 3\theta = 0$

$$\therefore 3\theta = \frac{3\pi}{2}, \frac{7\pi}{2} \text{ or } \frac{11\pi}{2} \text{ i.e. } \theta = \frac{\pi}{2}, \frac{7\pi}{6} \text{ or } \frac{11\pi}{6}$$

Now $\theta = \frac{\pi}{2} \Rightarrow z = 3(\cos\frac{\pi}{2} + i\sin\frac{\pi}{2}) \Rightarrow z = 3i,$

$\theta = \frac{7\pi}{6} \Rightarrow z = 3(\cos\frac{7\pi}{6} + i\sin\frac{7\pi}{6}) \Rightarrow z = \frac{-3}{2}(\sqrt{3} + i),$

$\theta = \frac{11\pi}{6} \Rightarrow z = 3(\cos\frac{11\pi}{6} + i\sin\frac{11\pi}{6}) \Rightarrow z = \frac{3}{2}(\sqrt{3} - i)$

$\therefore$ the three distinct solutions of the equation $z^3 = -27i$ are

$$3i, \quad -\frac{3\sqrt{3}}{2} - \frac{3i}{2} \text{ and } \frac{3\sqrt{3}}{2} - \frac{3i}{2}$$

You should now be able to answer Exercise 3 on page 227.

Trigonometric identities

De Moivre's Theorem can also be used to establish identities of various sorts. In this section we will see two types:

- identities in which $\cos nx$ and $\sin nx$ are expressed in terms of power series in $\cos x$ and $\sin x$

- identities in which $\cos^n x$ and $\sin^n x$ are expressed in terms of the cos's and sin's of multiple angles.

cos nx and sin nx

By De Moivre's Theorem,

$$\cos nx + i\sin nx = [\cos x + i\sin x]^n$$

and so, if we multiply out the expression on the right, we produce a series of terms involving powers of $\cos x$ and $\sin x$. Once this is done, the rest is just a matter of comparing real and imaginary parts on the two sides of the equation. Although the analysis could be done – courtesy of the Binomial

Theorem – for a general value of n, we will keep it reasonably simple by taking a look at what happens for one specific value: $n = 3$.

$$\cos 3x + i \sin 3x = [\cos x + i \sin x]^3$$
$$= \cos^3 x + 3i \cos^2 x \sin x - 3 \cos x \sin^2 x - i \sin^3 x$$
(Using $i^2 = -1$, $i^3 = -i$)

and so it must be true that:

$$\cos 3x = \cos^3 x - 3 \cos x \sin^2 x$$
and $\quad \sin 3x = 3 \cos^2 x \sin x - \sin^3 x$

Examples

1 Prove the following identities.

$$\cos 5x = 16 \cos^5 x - 20 \cos^3 x + 5 \cos x$$
$$\sin 5x = [16 \cos^4 x - 12 \cos^2 x + 1] \sin x$$

2 Express $\tan 5x$ in terms of $\tan x$.

Solutions

By De Moivre's Theorem,

$$\cos 5x + i \sin 5x = [\cos x + i \sin x]^5$$
$$= \cos^5 x + 5 i \cos^4 x \sin x - 10 \cos^3 x \sin^2 x - 10 i \cos^2 x \sin^3 x + 5 \cos x \sin^4 x + i \sin^5 x$$

1 Equating real and imaginary parts, and writing $c = \cos x$ and $s = \sin x$ for ease of presentation,

$$\begin{aligned}
\cos 5x \quad &= c^5 - 10c^3[1 - c^2] + 5c[1 - c^2]^2 \\
&= c^5 - 10c^3 + 10c^5 + 5c - 10c^3 + 5c^5 \\
&= 16c^5 - 20c^3 + 5c \\
&= 16 \cos^5 x - 20 \cos^5 x + 5 \cos x, \text{ as required}
\end{aligned}$$

$$\begin{aligned}
\sin 5x \quad &= s[5c^4 - 10c^2(1 - c^2) + (1 - c^2)^2] \\
&= s[5c^4 - 10c^2 + 10c^4 + 1 - 2c^2 + c^4] \\
&= s[16c^4 - 12c^2 + 1] \\
&= \sin x [16 \cos^4 x - 12 \cos^2 x + 1], \text{ as required.}
\end{aligned}$$

2 Using real and imaginary parts,

$$\tan 5x = \frac{\sin 5x}{\cos 5x} = \frac{5c^4 s - 10c^2 s^3 + s^5}{c^5 - 10c^3 s^2 + 5cs^4}$$

Dividing top and bottom by c^5,

$$= \frac{5 \tan x - 10 \tan^3 x + \tan^5 x}{1 - 10 \tan^2 x + 5 \tan^4 x}$$

You should now be able to answer Exercise 4 on page 227.

211

cos^n x and sin^n x

We use the following four identities:

(a) $\cos x = \dfrac{1}{2}(e^{ix} + e^{-ix})$

(c) $\cos nx = \dfrac{1}{2}(e^{inx} + e^{-inx})$

(b) $\sin x = \dfrac{1}{2i}(e^{ix} - e^{-ix})$

(d) $\sin nx = \dfrac{1}{2i}(e^{inx} - e^{-inx})$

Once again, we illustrate the method for a specific value of n: $n = 4$

$$\cos^4 x = \frac{1}{16}(e^{ix} + e^{-ix})^4$$

$$= \frac{1}{16}(e^{i4x} + 4e^{i2x} + 6 + 4e^{-2ix} + e^{-4ix})$$

$$= \frac{1}{16}\left([e^{i4x} + e^{-i4x}] + 4\,[e^{i2x} + e^{-i2x}] + 6\right)$$

$$= \frac{1}{16}(2\cos 4x + 8\cos 2x + 6)$$

$\therefore$ $$\cos^4 x = \frac{1}{8}(\cos 4x + 4\cos 2x + 3)$$

Similarly

$$\sin^4 x = \frac{1}{16}(e^{ix} - e^{-ix})^4$$

$$= \frac{1}{16}(e^{i4x} - 4e^{i2x} + 6 - 4e^{-i2x} + e^{-i4x})$$

$$= \frac{1}{16}\left([e^{i4x} + e^{-i4x}] - 4\,[e^{-i2x} + e^{-i2x}] + 6\right)$$

$$= \frac{1}{16}(2\cos 4x - 8\cos 2x + 6)$$

$\therefore$ $$\sin^4 x = \frac{1}{8}(\cos 4x - 4\cos 2x + 3)$$

Examples   Prove that:

1 $2^4\cos^5 x = \cos 5x + 5\cos 3x + 10\cos x$

2 $2^4\sin^5 x = \sin 5x - 5\sin 3x + 10\sin x$

Solutions   The solutions are summarised as follows:

1 $\cos^5 x = \dfrac{1}{32}(e^{ix} + e^{-ix})^5$

$$= \frac{1}{32}([e^{i5x} + e^{-i5x}] + 5\,[e^{i3x} + e^{-i3x}] + 10\,[e^{ix} + e^{-ix}])$$

$$= \frac{1}{32}(2\cos 5x + 10\cos 3x + 20\cos x)$$

$$= \frac{1}{16}(\cos 5x + 5\cos x + 10\cos x), \text{ as required.}$$

2 $\sin x^5 \quad = \dfrac{1}{32i}(e^{ix} - e^{-ix})^5$

$\qquad\qquad = \dfrac{1}{32i}\left([e^{i5x} - e^{-i5x}] - 5[e^{i3x} - e^{-i3x}] + 10[e^{ix} - e^{-ix}]\right)$

$\qquad\qquad = \dfrac{1}{16}(\sin 5x - 5 \sin 3x + 10 \sin x)$

as required.

You should now be able to answer Exercises 5–6 on page 228.

Modulus inequalities

The Argand Diagram is particularly helpful in establishing the truth of certain modulus inequalities, which are surpri singly difficult to prove algebraically. (Algebraic proofs do exist – you might like to try them for yourself – but they tend to be rather messy and are often difficult to follow.) We will take a look at three results.

$|z_1 + z_2| \le |z_1| + |z_2|$

This is simply a consequence of the so-called triangle inequality: the sum of the lengths of two sides of a triangle must always be at least as great as the length of the third. The Argand Diagram in Figure 11.1 makes this clear.

Figure 11.1

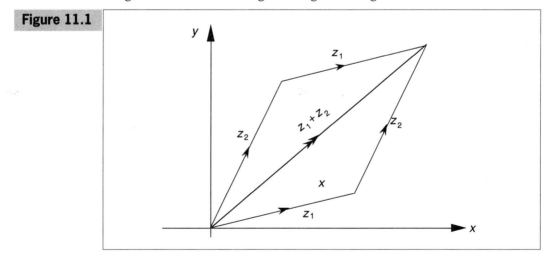

$|z_1 - z_2| \le |z_1| + |z_2|$

In this case the Argand Diagram is as shown in Figure 11.2.

Figure 11.2

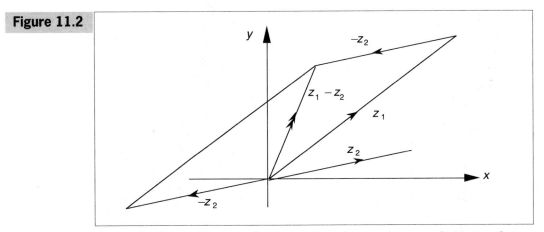

In fact this inequality is really the same as the previous result. Notice that:

$$|z_1 - z_2| = |z_1 + (-z_2)| \leq |z_1| + |-z_2| = |z_1| + |z_2|$$

which follows because the modulus (i.e. length) of any vector is exactly the same as that of its negative.

$|z_1 - z_2| \geq |\,|z_1| - |z_2|\,|$

Again – if you keep a clear head! – this fact is (reasonably) easy to see from the Argand Diagram below.

Figure 11.3

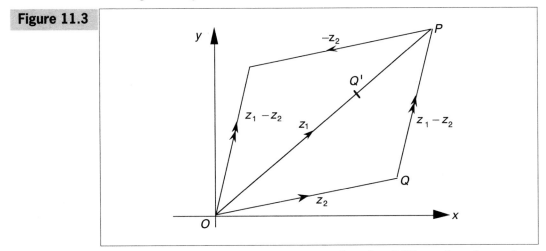

Note that the point Q' has been positioned so that PQ' has a length equal to the difference between the lengths of OP and OQ. In other words the complex number represented by the vector PQ' has a modulus equal to:

$$|\,|z_1| - |z_2|\,|$$

There is no doubt from the diagram that PQ is at least as large as PQ' and so the inequality follows.

Complex conjugates

For each complex number z with:

$$z = x + iy$$

we can define a complex conjugate z^* as follows:

$$z^* = x - iy$$

Unpromi sing as this simple idea may seem, it turns out that z and z^* have many similar properties – properties that, as you will see, we can exploit in a number of ways. Firstly, though, we establish a few basic results about complex conjugates.

The following three identities hold for any complex z, z_1 and z_2.

$$zz^* = |z|^2$$

You will quickly see that this follows immediately from the definition of the conjugate.

$$zz^* = (x + iy)(x - iy) = x^2 + y^2 = |z|^2$$

$(z_1 + z_2)^* = z_1{}^* + z_2{}^*$ and $(z_1 z_2)^* = z_1{}^* z_2{}^*$

To see this, write $z_1 = x_1 + iy_1$ and $z_2 = x_2 + iy_2$

Then

$$
\begin{aligned}
(z_1 + z_2)^* &= [(x_1 + iy_1) + (x_2 + iy_2)]^* \\
&= [(x_1 + x_2) + i(y_1 + y_2)]^* \\
&= [(x_1 + x_2) - i(y_1 + y_2)] \\
&= [(x_1 - iy_1) + (x_2 - iy_2)] \\
&= z_1{}^* + z_2{}^*
\end{aligned}
$$

In words this 'additive rule' may be expressed as follows:

> Given any two complex numbers, it makes no difference
> whether you add them first and then take conjugates,
> or take conjugates first and then add.
> In either case the result is the same.

Also:

$$
\begin{aligned}
(z_1 z_2)^* &= [(x_1 + iy_1)(x_2 + iy_2)] \\
&= [(x_1 x_2 - y_1 y_2) + i(x_1 y_2 + x_2 y_1)]^* \\
&= [(x_1 x_2 - y_1 y_2) - i(x_1 y_2 + x_2 y_1)] \\
&= [(x_1 - iy_1)(x_2 - iy_2)] \\
&= z_1{}^* z_2{}^*
\end{aligned}
$$

To express this 'multiplicative rule' in words, just replace 'add' by 'multiply' in the previous paragraph.

This last pair of facts might appear harmless – even pointless – but they are the beginning of something much more important. We shall come to them again.

Examples

Using the results we have just established, prove that for any complex numbers a, b, z_1, z_2 and z_3

1   $(az_1 + bz_2)^* = a^* z_1^* + b^* z_2^*$

2   $(z_1 + z_2 + z_3)^* = z_1^* + z_2^* + z_3^*$

3   $(z_1 z_2 z_3)^* = z_1^* z_2^* z_3^*$

Solution

1   First apply the additive rule to give:

$$(az_1)^* + (bz_2)^*$$

then apply the multiplicative rule.

2   Rewrite the left-hand side to give:

$$[(z_1 + z_2) + z_3]^* = (z_1 + z_2)^* + z_3^*$$

by the additive rule.

Using the additive rule again leads to the result.

3   Rewrite the left-hand side to give:

$$[(z_1 z_2)z_3]^* = (z_1 z_2)^* z_3^*$$

by the multiplicative rule.

Using the multiplicative rule again leads to the result.

You should now be able to answer Exercise 7 on page 228.

Loci in the Argand Diagram

Just as equations involving x and y lead to loci (i.e. graphs) in the two-dimensional x,y plane, so equations involving the complex number z lead to loci (i.e. graphs) in an Argand Diagram. In fact, certain lines and curves can be described very simply and elegantly in this way. We will now investigate a few of the better-known cases.

arg(z – b) = β

Here b is a given complex constant and $β$ is a given angle.

When dealing with any equation or inequality involving a complex number, it is always worth thinking geometrically and attempting to express the relation **in words** in terms of lengths or angles (or both). You saw how well this worked earlier when we investigated modulus inequalities. In this case, z must lie on a line drawn in such a way that the vector representing $z - b$ makes a constant angle β with the x-axis.

Let us see what this means for the Argand Diagram. First plot a point P to represent the complex number b. Next draw the line passing through P which makes an angle β with the x-axis. Finally notice that there can be no point Q, *not* on this line, such that the angle between PQ and the x-axis is β. Check this in Figure 11.4.

Figure 11.4

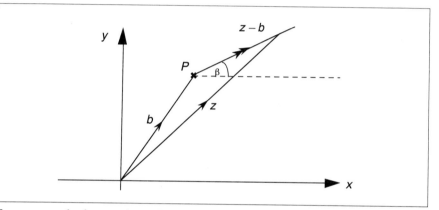

To sum up, the locus of z is the half line which begins at b at an angle β to the x-axis.

$|z - b| = k$

Here b is a given complex constant and k is a given real number. Expressing this formula in words gives the game away almost immediately. The vector which represents $z - b$ has constant length k. This means that the point z is always at a distance k from the point b. The locus of z must therefore be a circle of radius k with b at its centre, as shown in Figure 11.5.

Figure 11.5

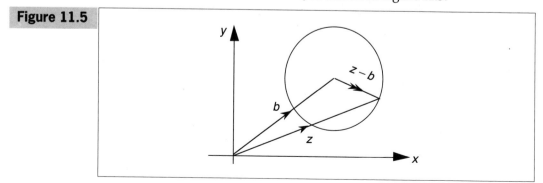

|z − b| = k |z − c|

Here b and c are given complex constants and k is a given real number.

Unfortunately this is one of those awkward cases where it is not enough to express the formula in words. In words, after all, the equation simply tells us that the point z is k times as far from the point b as it is from the point c. If $k = 1$, a little elementary geometry tells us that the locus of z must be the perpendicular bisector of the line joining b and c, because such a line consists of all the points which are equidistant from b and c. The following diagram shows this clearly.

Figure 11.6

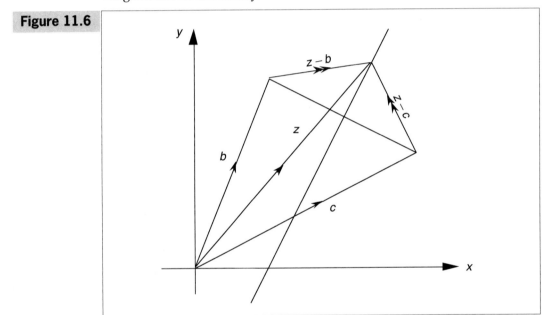

However, if $k > 1$, the locus is not nearly so obvious. In fact, z again lies on a circle – this time with centre at:

$$\frac{k^2 c - b}{k^2 - 1}$$

with radius:

$$\frac{k \,|b - c|}{k^2 - 1}$$

These results can be proved using the sort of co-ordinate geometry that you met in the core course. However, the method is long and messy. To avoid the mess and add a little elegance, define:

$$w = z - c \quad \text{and} \quad d = b - c$$

Then the equation $|z - b| = k \,|z - c|$ becomes:

$$|w - d| = k \,|w|$$

So $\quad |w - d|^2 = k^2 |w|^2$

Using the first of the facts about complex conjugates that we established earlier, we can write this as:

$$(w - d)(w - d)^* = k^2 w w^*$$

Removing brackets and collecting terms,

$$(k^2 - 1)w w^* + w d^* + w^* d - d d^* = 0$$

so that:

$$w w^* + \frac{w d^* + w^* d}{k^2 - 1} - \frac{d d^*}{k^2 - 1} = 0$$

therefore:

$$\left(w + \frac{d}{k^2 - 1}\right)\left(w^* + \frac{d^*}{k^2 - 1}\right) - \frac{d d^*}{(k^2 - 1)^2} - \frac{d d^*}{k^2 - 1} = 0$$

Re-expressing this in terms of moduli,

$$\left|w + \frac{d}{k^2 - 1}\right|^2 = \frac{|d|^2}{(k^2 - 1)^2}\left[1 + (k^2 - 1)\right]$$

i.e. $\quad \left|w + \dfrac{d}{k^2 - 1}\right| = \dfrac{k\,|d|}{k^2 - 1}$

Reverting to $z - c$ and $b - c$ in place of w and d now gives the result we wanted to prove.

Take time to study and understand this proof. It shows how complex conjugates can be used to simplify a mathematical argument.

$\mathbf{arg}\left(\dfrac{z - a}{z - b}\right) = \beta$

Here a and b are given complex constants and β is a given angle. Thinking geometrically, this means that the angle between the vectors representing $z - a$ and $z - b$ must be the constant β. Let us see what this means for the Argand diagram. First plot points A and B to represent the complex numbers a and b respectively. If P now represents a typical position for z, then angle $BPA = \beta$. And so P describes part of a circle through A and B. See Figure 11.7.

Figure 11.7

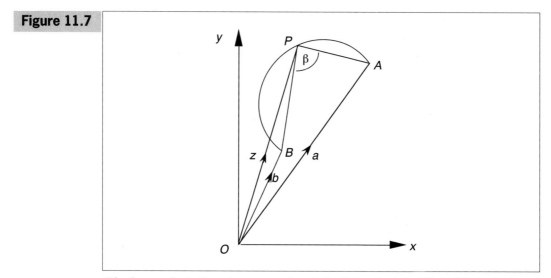

The locus of z is therefore part of a circle through A and B and is such that AB subtends angle β on this circular arc.

Examples If z is a complex number, describe the following loci:

(a) $\arg(z - 3 - 4i) = \dfrac{\pi}{3}$

(b) $|\, z - 1 + i \,| = 2$

(c) $|\, z - 4 \,| = 2 \,|\, z - 1 \,|$

Solutions (a) The Argand Diagram gives us:

Figure 11.8

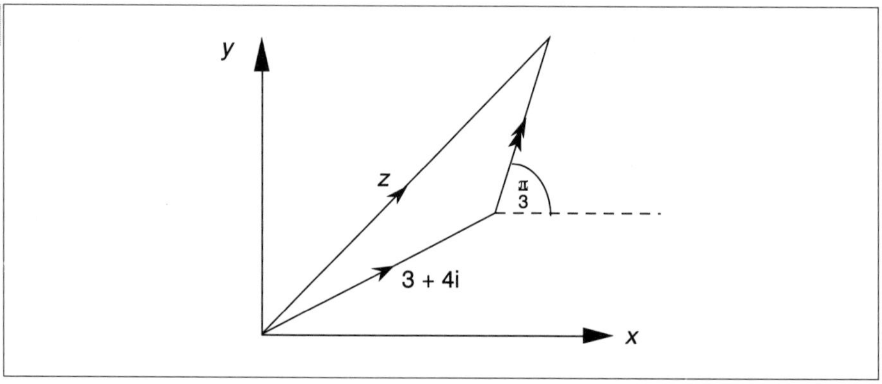

The locus of z is therefore a half line starting at $3 + 4i$ and inclined at $\dfrac{\pi}{3}$ to the x-axis. In cartesian coordinates this locus has equation

$$y - 4 = \tan\frac{\pi}{3}(x - 3), \text{ where } x \geq 3, \text{ i.e. } y = x\sqrt{3} + 4 - 3\sqrt{3}.$$

(b) This is probably best tackled by going back to first principles.

Let $z = x + iy$

$\therefore \ | z - 1 + i | = 2 \qquad \Rightarrow | (x - 1) + i (y + 1) | = 2$

$\Rightarrow \sqrt{(x - 1)^2 + (y + 1)^2} = 2$

$\Rightarrow (x - 1)^2 + (y + 1)^2 = 4$

$\therefore$ the locus of z is a circle of radius 2 centred at $(1, -1)$.

(c) Let $z = x + iy$

$\therefore \ | z - 4 | = 2 | z - 1 | \ \Rightarrow \ | (x - 4) + iy | = 2 | (x - 1) + iy |$

$\Rightarrow \sqrt{(x - 4)^2 + y^2} = 2 \sqrt{(x - 1)^2 + y^2}$

$\Rightarrow (x - 4)^2 + y^2 = 4 \{ (x - 1)^2 + y^2 \}$

This eventually simplifies to give $x^2 + y^2 = 4$

$\therefore$ the locus of z is a circle of radius 2 centre the origin.

You should now be able to answer Exercise 8 on page 228.

Conjugate roots

We now return to the facts about complex conjugates that we met earlier. In particular, recall the results that we proved about the conjugates of the sums and products of complex numbers. A little thought will convince you that similar facts apply to any number of additions and multiplications. For example, making repeated use of the result that the conjugate of a product is the product of the conjugates, we have:

$$(z^3)^* \ = [z \, (z^2) \,]^* = z^* \, (z^2)^* \ = z^* z^* z^* \ = (z^*)^3$$

It is clear that we could go on taking higher and higher powers of z and handling them in the same way. In general, therefore:

$$(z^n)^* = (z^*)^n$$

for any whole number n.

From here it is only a short step, using our knowledge of complex conjugates, to the crucial fact that:

$$[f(z)]^* = f(z^*)$$

for **any** polynomial function $f(z)$ with **real** coefficients.

If you stop to consider this, you will probably find it rather surpri sing. After all, we know that polynomial functions take the form:

$$f(x) = \Sigma a_n x^n$$

If you were to use this definition to seek a direct proof of the result we have just stated, you would find it no easy matter.

Notice the way in which we approached it here, though. We moved towards it in a series of straightforward steps – each of them simple and elegant. This is typical of the way in which mathematics advances.

Example

Using the results about complex conjugates that we established earlier, prove that:

$$[f(z)]^* = f(z^*)$$

for any quadratic function $f(z)$ with real coefficients.

Solution

Let $f(z) = az^2 + bz + c$

where a, b and c are real and z is a complex variable.

Then

$$
\begin{aligned}
[f(z)]^* &= (az^2 + bz + c)^* \\
&= (az^2)^* + (bz)^* + c^* \qquad \text{(see page 215)} \\
&= a^* z^{*2} + b^* z^* + c^* \qquad \text{(see page 215)} \\
&= az^{*2} + bz^* + c
\end{aligned}
$$

since the conjugate of a real number is the same real number.

$$= f(z^*) \text{ as required.}$$

Now we come to the chief purpose of complex conjugates as far as your syllabus is concerned. They can be a great help in finding the roots of equations. To illustrate this we first consider a very simple example.

Suppose you were told that the quadratic equation

$$5z^2 + 8z + 5 = 0$$

had a root $z = 0.8 + 0.6i$

Could you, without doing any algebra or arithmetic, write down the other root? Not yet knowing the trick, of course, you would almost certainly answer: No. However, it could hardly be easier to find the second root. It is just the complex conjugate of the one we already know, i.e.

$$z^* = 0.8 - 0.6i$$

The reason for this is simple. We have seen that the complex conjugate of any polynomial $f(z)$ with real coefficients is exactly the same as $f(z^*)$.

In our example: $5z^2 + 8z + 5$

is certainly a polynomial with real coefficients. It follows that if:

$5z^2 + 8z + 5 = 0$

then $5z^{*2} + 8z^* + 5 = (5z^2 + 8z + 5)^* = 0^* = 0$

In other words, if z is a root, then so is z^*.

Naturally, in the case of a quadratic equation, the roots are easily found anyway. You have only to quote the famous quadratic formula and out they come – both of them. For polynomial equations of higher degree, however, it is a very different matter. Let us now take a look at ways in which complex conjugates can help even here.

Suppose you are told that two of the five roots of:

$3z^5 - 20z^4 + 81z^3 - 148z^2 + 146z - 52 = 0$

are $2 + 3i$ and $1 - i$. Can you factorise this equation and find all its other roots?

Formidable as the equation appears, given this information and your knowledge of complex conjugates, you can solve the problem without too much trouble. Notice first that you are dealing once again with a polynomial in which all the coefficients are real. Therefore, if z is a root, so is z^* by exactly the same argument that we used in the previous example.

This means that we now know four roots:

$2 + 3i$ $2 - 3i$ $1 - i$ $1 + i$

and these must correspond to the four factors:

$[z - (2 + 3i)][z - (2 - 3i)][z - (1 - i)][z - (1 + i)]$

Multiplying these out gives:

$[z^2 - 4z + 13][z^2 - 2z + 2]$

and it is now just a matter of finding the remaining factor and the corresponding root. Clearly this factor must take the form:

$az + b$

to produce a polynomial of degree 5 when multiplied by the two quadratic factors above. However, to give the right z^5 coefficient and constant term, it must be true that:

$a \times 1 \times 1 = 3$ and $b \times 13 \times 2 = -52$

So $a = 3$ and $b = -2$

You can now see that the required factorisation is:

$(3z - 2)(z^2 - 4z + 13)(z^2 - 2z + 2)$

and that the fifth root is $\frac{2}{3}$.

Example Given that 1 + 2i is a root of the equation:

$$z^4 - 4z^3 - 6z^2 + 20z - 75 = 0$$

find the other three roots.

Plot the points representing all four of these roots on an Argand Diagram. Hence, or otherwise, show that these points are the vertices of a rhombus with sides of length $2\sqrt{5}$.

Solution The answer can be summarised as follows:

Since 1 + 2i is a root, so is its complex conjugate 1 – 2i. The left-hand side of the equation must therefore have a factor

$$[z - (1 + 2i)][z - (1 - 2i)]$$
$$= z^2 - 2z + (1 + 2i)(1 - 2i)$$
$$= z^2 - 2z + 5$$

Knowing this, we can factorise fully:

$$(z^2 - 2z + 5)(z^2 - 2z - 15) = 0 \text{ (using long division)}$$

i.e. $(z^2 - 2z + 5)(z + 3)(z - 5) = 0$

The roots are thus:

$$1 + 2i \qquad 1 - 2i \qquad -3 \qquad 5$$

Figure 11.9

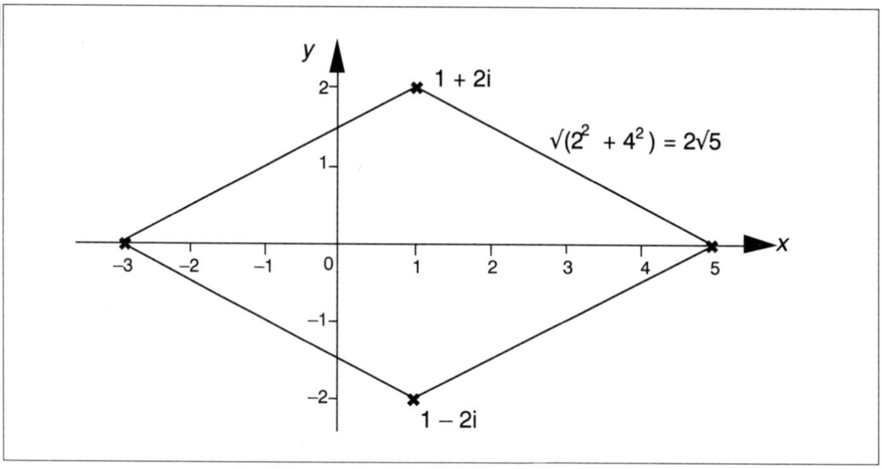

You should now be able to answer Exercises 9–12 on page 228.

Transformations

Earlier in this section we saw that an equation involving z could be plotted as a graph in the Argand Diagram. It is interesting to investigate what happens when we define another complex variable, w, in terms of z and construct the corresponding locus of w in a separate Argand Diagram.

For the rest of this section we refer to z's Argand Diagram as the **z-plane** and to w's as the **w-plane**. This is standard terminology and avoids confusion between the two.

We also term the process of moving from the z-plane to the w-plane a **transformation** or **mapping**. Later in the section we shall investigate two specific transformations, but for the moment we will consider a general approach.

It is almost always the case that, for an equation in z, we can specify the locus in terms of x and y, where as usual,

$$z = x + iy$$

In other words, we can write down an equation for the graph using the coordinate geometry that you learned and practised in modules P1 and P2. Given that w is defined to be some function of z, i.e.

$$w = f(z)$$

we can discover the corresponding locus in the w-plane as follows:

1   Express w as $w = u + iv$.
2   Use the equation:

$$u + iv = f(x + iy)$$

and the equation of the graph in the z-plane to establish a relationship between u and v.

3   Associate this relationship with some well-known graph in the w-plane.

We will now see the method at work for two transformations:

$$w = z^2 \text{ and } w = \frac{z + i}{z - i}$$

considering their effect on simple loci in the z-plane.

W = z²

For this transformation,

$$u + iv = (x + iy)^2 = x^2 - y^2 + 2ixy$$

so that $u = x^2 - y^2 \quad v = 2xy$

Now consider the effect of this on the circle $|z| = k$.

We have:

$$u^2 + v^2 = (x^2 - y^2)^2 + 4x^2y^2 = (x^2 + y^2)^2$$
$$= (|z|^2)^2 = k^4$$

So the locus of w must be a circle of radius k^2 centred at the origin of the w–plane. Notice that this result could have been obtained by observing that

$$|w|^2 = ww^* = z^2 z^{*2} = (zz^*)^2 = (|z|^2)^2$$

As a second example, consider the way in which the x-axis is transformed. Here we have $y = 0$ and so for $x \geq 0$

$$u = x^2 \qquad v = 0$$

at all points on the locus of w. It follows that the required graph is the non-negative portion of the u-axis running from $u = 0$ to $u = +\infty$.

$$w = \frac{z + i}{z - i}$$

This transformation leads to:

$$u + iv = \frac{x + iy + i}{x + iy - i}$$

In a case like this, rather than attempting to take the algebra further in its general form, it usually pays to introduce the equation of the z-locus right away.

For example, suppose once again that we are transforming the x-axis. Putting $y = 0$ in the above equation gives:

$$u + iv = \frac{x + i}{x - i}$$

$$= \frac{(x + i)(x + i)}{(x - i)(x + i)}$$

$$= \frac{x^2 - 1 + 2ix}{x^2 + 1}$$

So $\quad u = \dfrac{x^2 - 1}{x^2 + 1} \quad$ and $v = \dfrac{2x}{x^2 + 1}$

Notice now that:

$$u^2 + v^2 = \frac{(x^2 - 1)^2 + 4x^2}{(x^2 + 1)^2} = 1$$

and so the locus of w is a circle of radius 1 centred on the origin of the w-plane.

Examples

1 Find the locus of w under the transformation $w = z^2$ if the locus of $z = x + iy$ is:

(a) $x^2 - y^2 = 1$ (b) $xy = 1$

2 Find the locus of w under the transformation $w = \dfrac{z - i}{z + i}$ if the locus of z is the y-axis.

Solutions **1** Writing $w = u + iv$, we have:

$$u = x^2 - y^2 \qquad v = 2xy$$

(a) If the locus of z is $x^2 - y^2 = 1$, it follows that $u = 1$

which is a vertical line in the w-plane.

(b) If $xy = 1$, then $v = 2$

which is a horizontal line in the w-plane.

2 $u + iv \ = \ \dfrac{x + iy - i}{x + iy + i} = \dfrac{i(y - 1)}{i(y + 1)}$ when z's locus is $x = 0$

i.e. $u + iv \ = \ \dfrac{y - 1}{y + 1}$

Therefore $u \ = \ \dfrac{y - 1}{y + 1}$ and $v = 0$

which is the u-axis in the w-plane.

You should now be able to answer Exercises 13–15 on pages 228–229.

EXERCISES

1 (a) Prove that $\ln(\cos x + i \sin x) = ix$

Deduce that $\ln(\cos x + i \sin x) + \ln(\cos x - i \sin x) = 0$

(b) Prove that $\cosh(x + iy) = \cosh x \cos y + i \sinh(x) \sin y$

2 Simplify:

(a) $(\cos \theta + i \sin \theta) \div (\cos \theta - i \sin \theta)$

(b) $\left(\dfrac{\cos \theta + i \sin \theta}{\cos \theta - i \sin \theta} \right)^{10}$

3 (a) Find the three distinct solutions of the equation $z^3 = -8$

(b) Find the four distinct solutions of the equation $z^4 = 16i$

(c) Find the five distinct solutions of the equation $z^5 + 1 = 0$

4 Prove that:

(a) $\cos 4\theta = \cos^4\theta - 6 \cos^2\theta \sin^2\theta + \sin^4\theta$

(b) $\sin 4\theta = 4 \cos^3\theta \sin \theta - 4 \cos \theta \sin^3\theta$

(c) Deduce that $\tan 4\theta = \dfrac{4 \tan \theta - 4 \tan^3\theta}{1 - 6 \tan^2\theta + \tan^4\theta}$

(d) Also use (a) to find the values of constants a, b, c such that:

$$\cos 4\theta = a \cos^4\theta + b\cos^2\theta + c.$$

5 Use the identities $\cos\theta = \frac{1}{2}\left(e^{i\theta} + e^{-i\theta}\right)$ and $\sin\theta = \frac{1}{2i}\left(e^{i\theta} - e^{-i\theta}\right)$ to prove that $2^6\cos^3\theta\sin^4\theta = \cos 7\theta - \cos 5\theta - 3\cos 3\theta + 3\cos\theta$.

6 Determine the value of constants a, b, c and d such that:

$$2^5\cos^6\theta = a\cos 6\theta + b\cos 4\theta + c\cos 2\theta + d.$$

7 Prove that, for any complex number z_1 and z_2,

$$\left(\frac{z_1}{z_2}\right)^* = \frac{z_1{}^*}{z_2{}^*}. \quad \text{[HARD]}$$

8 If z is a complex number, describe the following loci:

(a) $|z - i| = 4$ (c) $|z - 1 - 2i| = |z - 3 - 4i|$

(b) $\arg(z) = \dfrac{\pi}{4}$ (d) $|z| = 3|z - i|$

9 Given that $1 + i$ is a root of the equation:

$$x^3 - x^2 + 2 = 0,$$

solve this equation completely.

10 If the equation $x^3 - 10x^2 + 57x - 82 = 0$ has one root equal to $(4 - 5i)$, find the real root.

11 Given that i is a root of the equation:

$$x^4 - 4x^3 + 6x^2 - 4x + 5 = 0$$

find the other three roots.

12 Solve the quadratic equation:

$$2x^2 - 2(2 + i)x + (1 + 2i) = 0$$

and state why the roots are not complex conjugates.

Write down the roots of

$$2x^2 - 2(2 - i)x + (1 - 2i) = 0$$

13 Find the locus of w under the transformation $w = \dfrac{z + 2i}{2iz - 1}$ if the locus of z is the circle $|z| = 1$.

14 Points P and Q represent complex numbers w and z respectively in an Argand diagram. If $w = u + iv$, $z = x + iy$ and $w = \dfrac{1 + zi}{z + i}$, express u and v in terms of x and y.

Prove that when P describes the portion of the imaginary axis between the points representing $-i$ and i, Q describes the whole of the positive half of the imaginary axis.

Long as it is, you will be able to remember this if you note the simple pattern followed by the subscripts. Look at the positive parts of the three terms: in term **1** we have $\alpha_2\beta_3$, in term **2** $\alpha_3\beta_1$ and in term **3** $\alpha_1\beta_2$ – i.e. **123**, **231** and **312**. In other words, the terms move around the cycle 123, repeating 1 after 3 and so on. For the negative parts of the terms, it's just a matter of switching the subscripts. For example, in the first term $\alpha_2\beta_3$ becomes $-\alpha_3\beta_2$.

Despite its messy and apparently unhelpful appearance, the vector product is a surprisingly useful idea. Once again, though, before we can develop any of its applications, we need to derive a few of its properties.

Properties

$a \times b = -b \times a$

In other words the vector product is not commutative. The proof is left as an exercise.

$a \times a$ is the zero vector

By the previous property, $a \times a = -a \times a$, and so the result must follow.

$a \times (b + c) = a \times b + a \times c$

The vector product is therefore distributive over vector addition. Again, this is left as an exercise.

$a \times b$ is orthogonal to both a and b

By definition of scalar and vector products:

$$a.(a \times b) = \alpha_1 (\alpha_2\beta_3 - \alpha_3\beta_2) + \alpha_2 (\alpha_3\beta_1 - \alpha_1\beta_3) + \alpha_3 (\alpha_1\beta_2 - \alpha_2\beta_1)$$

Removing brackets and collecting terms quickly shows that this expression is 0. We know from the properties of the scalar product that this implies a and $a \times b$ are orthogonal. In a similar way it can be proved that $b.(a \times b) = 0$, so that b too is orthogonal to $a \times b$.

$|a \times b| = |a||b| \sin \theta$

This fact is quite difficult to prove unless you know the trick – and even then it's rather messy. However, the beauty of vectors is that the mess is usually confined to establishing the properties. Making use of them is, generally speaking, much simpler and more elegant. Consider:

$$
\begin{aligned}
|a \times b|^2 + (a.b)^2 &= (a \times b).(a \times b) + (a.b)^2 \\
&= (\alpha_2\beta_3 - \alpha_3\beta_2)^2 + (\alpha_3\beta_1 - \alpha_1\beta_3)^2 \\
&\quad + (\alpha_1\beta_2 - \alpha_2\beta_1)^2 + (\alpha_1\beta_1 + \alpha_2\beta_2 + \alpha_3\beta_3)^2
\end{aligned}
$$

Removing brackets and collecting terms (a chore left to you!) will show (if you are careful) that all products of the form $\alpha_1\alpha_2\beta_1\beta_2$ cancel out and we are left with:

$$= (\alpha_1\beta_1)^2 + (\alpha_1\beta_2)^2 + (\alpha_1\beta_3)^2 + (\alpha_2\beta_1)^2 + (\alpha_2\beta_2)^2 + (\alpha_2\beta_3)^2$$
$$+ (\alpha_3\beta_1)^2 + (\alpha_3\beta_2)^2 + (\alpha_3\beta_3)^2$$
$$= (\alpha_1^2 + \alpha_2^2 + \alpha_3^2)(\beta_1^2 + \beta_2^2 + \beta_3^2) = |\,\mathbf{a}\,|^2\,|\,\mathbf{b}\,|^2$$

We have therefore proved that:

$$|\,\mathbf{a}\times\mathbf{b}\,|^2 + (\mathbf{a}.\mathbf{b})^2 = |\,\mathbf{a}\,|^2\,|\,\mathbf{b}\,|^2$$

However, we already know that $\mathbf{a}.\mathbf{b} = |\,\mathbf{a}\,|\,|\,\mathbf{b}\,|\cos\theta$ and so it follows that:

$$|\,\mathbf{a}\times\mathbf{b}\,|^2 = |\,\mathbf{a}\,|^2\,|\,\mathbf{b}\,|^2\,[1 - \cos^2\theta]$$

Using the well-known trigonometrical identity $1 - \cos^2\theta = \sin^2\theta$. This gives:

$$|\,\mathbf{a}\times\mathbf{b}\,| = |\,\mathbf{a}\,|\,|\,\mathbf{b}\,|\sin\theta$$

The last two properties form the basis of an alternative definition of the vector product, namely that:

$\mathbf{a}\times\mathbf{b} = |\,\mathbf{a}\,|\,|\,\mathbf{b}\,|\sin\theta\,\mathbf{n}$

where $\mathbf{n}$ is a unit vector normal to the plane containing $\mathbf{a}$ and $\mathbf{b}$. $\mathbf{n}$'s direction is determined by a right-hand screw rule as shown in the diagram below, and θ is measured in the direction of a screw rotation from $\mathbf{a}$ to $\mathbf{b}$.

Figure 12.2

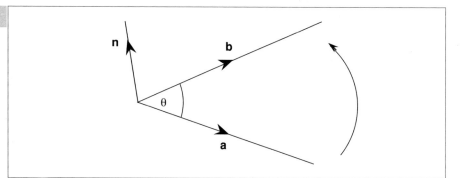

These facts are easily verified for products involving the base vectors $\mathbf{i}$, $\mathbf{j}$ and $\mathbf{k}$. For example, from both definitions:

$$\mathbf{i}\times\mathbf{j} = \mathbf{k}$$

so illustrating the effect of the right-hand screw rule. If we reverse $\mathbf{i}$ and $\mathbf{j}$, then the direction of the normal is also reversed and we produce:

$$\mathbf{j}\times\mathbf{i} = -\mathbf{k}$$

Again, of course, this is in accordance with our earlier definition.

Although there are two definitions of the vector product, you can see that they are exactly equivalent and may be used interchangeably. The trick is to use the one which is more convenient for your purposes at the time. Many of the applications of vector products are geometrical, and so the second is often preferred. You will see it in use later.

Example

Given that $\mathbf{a} = 3\mathbf{i} + 2\mathbf{j} + 2\mathbf{k}$ and $\mathbf{b} = 2\mathbf{i} + 4\mathbf{j} + 3\mathbf{k}$, find $\mathbf{a} \times \mathbf{b}$.

Confirm that $\mathbf{a} \times \mathbf{b}$ is orthogonal to $\mathbf{a}$ and $\mathbf{b}$.

Use the scalar product $\mathbf{a}.\mathbf{b}$ to determine the angle θ between $\mathbf{a}$ and $\mathbf{b}$, and use this to verify that:

$$| \mathbf{a} \times \mathbf{b} | = | \mathbf{a} | \, | \mathbf{b} | \sin \theta$$

Solution

By definition:

$$\mathbf{a} \times \mathbf{b} = [2 \times 3 - 2 \times 4]\mathbf{i} + [2 \times 2 - 3 \times 3]\mathbf{j} + [3 \times 4 - 2 \times 2]\mathbf{k}$$
$$= -2\mathbf{i} - 5\mathbf{j} + 8\mathbf{k}$$

Thus: $\quad \mathbf{a} . (\mathbf{a} \times \mathbf{b}) = 3 \times (-2) + 2 \times (-5) + 2 \times 8 = 0$

$\qquad \mathbf{b} . (\mathbf{a} \times \mathbf{b}) = 2 \times (-2) + 4 \times (-5) + 3 \times 8 = 0$

and so $\mathbf{a}$ and $\mathbf{b}$ are orthogonal to $\mathbf{a} \times \mathbf{b}$.

$$\mathbf{a}.\mathbf{b} = 3 \times 2 + 2 \times 4 + 2 \times 3 = 20$$
$$| \mathbf{a} | = \sqrt{(9 + 4 + 4)} = \sqrt{17}$$
$$| \mathbf{b} | = \sqrt{(4 + 16 + 9)} = \sqrt{29}$$

Therefore: $| \mathbf{a} | \, | \mathbf{b} | = \sqrt{(17 \times 29)} = \sqrt{493}$

Thus: $\quad \cos \theta = \dfrac{20}{\sqrt{493}}, \; \theta \approx 26°,$

and: $\quad \sin \theta = \sqrt{1 - \dfrac{400}{493}} = \dfrac{\sqrt{93}}{\sqrt{493}}$

Now $\quad | \mathbf{a} \times \mathbf{b} | = \sqrt{(4 + 25 + 64)} = \sqrt{93}$

$$= | \mathbf{a} | \, | \mathbf{b} | \sin \theta$$

You should now be able to answer Exercises 2–3 on page 248.

Applications of vector products

We now take a look at a few of the problems of two- and three-dimensional geometry in which vector products arise naturally and provide an elegant way of expressing results. As we tackle these problems, notice how we make use of the properties of scalar and vector products.

Area of a parallelogram

Figure 12.3

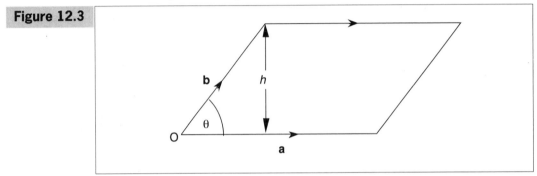

Vectors **a** and **b** form two sides of the parallelogram in the diagram above. The area we want is:

$$\text{base} \times \text{height} = |\,\mathbf{a}\,| \times h = |\,\mathbf{a}\,|\,|\,\mathbf{b}\,|\sin\theta$$

So:

> Area of a parallelogram $= |\,\mathbf{a} \times \mathbf{b}\,|$

Volume of a parallelepiped

Figure 12.4

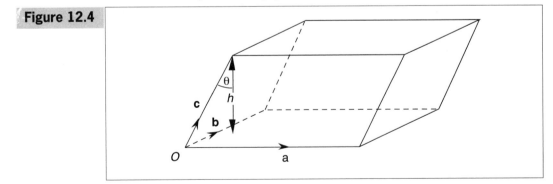

A parallelepiped – in case you have never met one before – is the figure in the diagram above, i.e. a box all of whose faces are parallelograms. Its volume is:

$$\text{base area} \times \text{height} \quad = \quad |\, \mathbf{a} \times \mathbf{b} \,| \times h$$
$$= \quad |\, \mathbf{a} \times \mathbf{b} \,|\, |\, \mathbf{c} \,| \cos \theta = \mathbf{a} \times \mathbf{b} \,.\, \mathbf{c}$$

volume of a parallelepiped $= \mathbf{a} \times \mathbf{b} \,.\, \mathbf{c}$

Distance of a point from a line

You will remember from Section 6 that the vector equation of a line can be written in the form:

$$\mathbf{r} = \mathbf{a} + \mu \mathbf{b}$$

Such a line passes through the point represented by the vector $\mathbf{a}$ and runs parallel to the vector $\mathbf{b}$. The problem here is to find an expression for the distance of this line from a point whose position vector is $\mathbf{c}$.

Figure 12.5

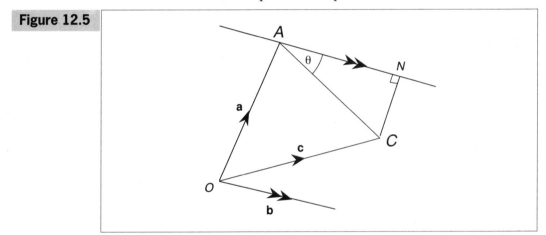

From the diagram, the required distance is:

$$CN \; = AC \sin \theta \quad = \quad |\, \mathbf{c} - \mathbf{a} \,| \sin \theta$$
$$= \quad \frac{|\, \mathbf{b} \,|\, |\, \mathbf{c} - \mathbf{a} \,| \sin \theta}{|\, \mathbf{b} \,|}$$

i.e. distance $= \quad \dfrac{|\, \mathbf{b} \times (\mathbf{c} - \mathbf{a}) \,|}{|\, \mathbf{b} \,|}$

So:

The shortest distance from a point with position vector $\mathbf{c}$ to a line with equation $\mathbf{r} = \mathbf{a} + \mu \mathbf{b}$ is given by

$$\frac{|\, \mathbf{b} \times (\mathbf{c} - \mathbf{a}) \,|}{|\, \mathbf{b} \,|}$$

Shortest distance between two lines

Unlike two-dimensional space in which pairs of non-parallel lines necessarily intersect, three-dimensional space is full of examples of non-intersecting non-parallel lines. These are said to be skew. The problem here is to find the shortest perpendicular distance between two skew lines, which we represent by:

$$r = a_1 + \mu_1 b_1 \text{ and } r = a_2 + \mu_2 b_2$$

Figure 12.6

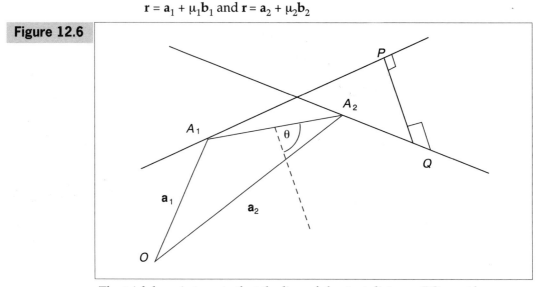

The trick here is to note that the line of shortest distance PQ must be orthogonal to both $\mathbf{b_1}$ and $\mathbf{b_2}$, and thus parallel to $\mathbf{b_1} \times \mathbf{b_2}$. A unit vector along PQ will therefore be:

$$\frac{\mathbf{b_1} \times \mathbf{b_2}}{|\,\mathbf{b_1} \times \mathbf{b_2}\,|}$$

Now A_1A_2 joins the two lines. So, if we denote by θ the angle between A_1A_2 and PQ, we have:

$$
\begin{aligned}
\text{shortest distance} &= A_1A_2 \cos \theta \\
&= |\,\mathbf{a_1} - \mathbf{a_2}\,|\cos \theta \\
&= \frac{|\,\mathbf{a_1} - \mathbf{a_2}\,|\,|\,\mathbf{b_1} \times \mathbf{b_2}\,|\cos \theta}{|\,\mathbf{b_1} \times \mathbf{b_2}\,|} \\
&= \frac{(\mathbf{a_1} - \mathbf{a_2}) \cdot \mathbf{b_1} \times \mathbf{b_2}}{|\,\mathbf{b_1} \times \mathbf{b_2}\,|}
\end{aligned}
$$

The shortest distance between the lines $\mathbf{r} = \mathbf{a}_1 + \mu_1 \mathbf{b}_1$ and $\mathbf{r} = \mathbf{a}_2 + \mu_2 \mathbf{b}_2$ is given by

$$\frac{(\mathbf{a}_1 - \mathbf{a}_2) . \mathbf{b}_1 \times \mathbf{b}_2}{|\mathbf{b}_1 \times \mathbf{b}_2|}$$

Example

Show that the area of the triangle in the diagram below is $\frac{1}{2}|\mathbf{a} \times \mathbf{b}|$

Figure 12.7

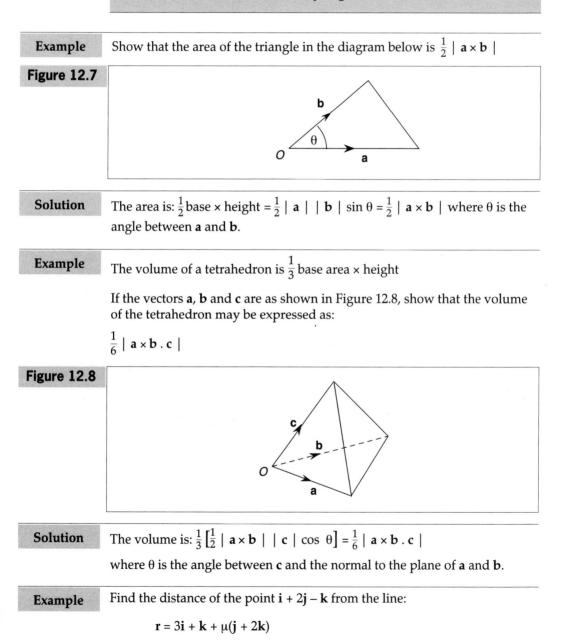

Solution

The area is: $\frac{1}{2}$ base × height $= \frac{1}{2}|\mathbf{a}||\mathbf{b}|\sin\theta = \frac{1}{2}|\mathbf{a} \times \mathbf{b}|$ where θ is the angle between $\mathbf{a}$ and $\mathbf{b}$.

Example

The volume of a tetrahedron is $\frac{1}{3}$ base area × height

If the vectors $\mathbf{a}$, $\mathbf{b}$ and $\mathbf{c}$ are as shown in Figure 12.8, show that the volume of the tetrahedron may be expressed as:

$$\frac{1}{6}|\mathbf{a} \times \mathbf{b} . \mathbf{c}|$$

Figure 12.8

Solution

The volume is: $\frac{1}{3}\left[\frac{1}{2}|\mathbf{a} \times \mathbf{b}||\mathbf{c}|\cos\theta\right] = \frac{1}{6}|\mathbf{a} \times \mathbf{b} . \mathbf{c}|$

where θ is the angle between $\mathbf{c}$ and the normal to the plane of $\mathbf{a}$ and $\mathbf{b}$.

Example

Find the distance of the point $\mathbf{i} + 2\mathbf{j} - \mathbf{k}$ from the line:

$$\mathbf{r} = 3\mathbf{i} + \mathbf{k} + \mu(\mathbf{j} + 2\mathbf{k})$$

Solution In the previous notation:

$$\mathbf{a} = 3\mathbf{i} + \mathbf{k}, \qquad \mathbf{b} = \mathbf{j} + 2\mathbf{k}, \qquad \mathbf{c} = \mathbf{i} + 2\mathbf{j} - \mathbf{k}$$

The distance is:

$$\frac{|\mathbf{b} \times (\mathbf{c} - \mathbf{a})|}{|\mathbf{b}|} = \frac{|(\mathbf{j} + 2\mathbf{k}) \times (-2\mathbf{i} + 2\mathbf{j} - 2\mathbf{k})|}{\sqrt{(1 + 4)}}$$

$$= \frac{|-6\mathbf{i} - 4\mathbf{j} + 2\mathbf{k}|}{\sqrt{5}} = \frac{\sqrt{(36 + 16 + 4)}}{\sqrt{5}} = \sqrt{\frac{56}{5}}$$

Example Find the shortest distance between the lines:

$$\mathbf{r} = -\mathbf{i} + 4\mathbf{j} + \mu_1(\mathbf{j} + \mathbf{k}) \quad \text{and} \quad \mathbf{r} = \mathbf{k} + \mu_2(3\mathbf{i} + 2\mathbf{j})$$

Solution Here $\mathbf{a}_1 = -\mathbf{i} + 4\mathbf{j}, \quad \mathbf{a}_2 = \mathbf{k}, \quad \mathbf{b}_1 = \mathbf{j} + \mathbf{k}, \quad \mathbf{b}_2 = 3\mathbf{i} + 2\mathbf{j}$

The shortest distance between the lines is therefore:

$$\frac{(\mathbf{a}_1 - \mathbf{a}_2) \cdot \mathbf{b}_1 \times \mathbf{b}_2}{|\mathbf{b}_1 \times \mathbf{b}_2|} = \frac{(-\mathbf{i} + 4\mathbf{j} - \mathbf{k}) \cdot (-2\mathbf{i} + 3\mathbf{j} - 3\mathbf{k})}{|-2\mathbf{i} + 3\mathbf{j} - 3\mathbf{k}|}$$

$$= \frac{(-1) \cdot (-2) + 4 \times 3 + (-1) \cdot (-3)}{\sqrt{(4 + 9 + 9)}} = \frac{17}{\sqrt{22}}$$

You should now be able to answer Exercise 4 on page 248.

Another look at the equation of a line

We first met the equation of a line in Section 6. It is $\mathbf{r} = \mathbf{a} + \lambda\,\mathbf{b}$, where $\mathbf{a}$ is the position vector of a point on the line and $\mathbf{b}$ gives the direction of the line.

Example Find the vector equation of the line passing through the points $A(1,7,3)$ and $P(2,10,1)$. What is the cartesian equation of this line?

Solution
$$\mathbf{a} = \begin{pmatrix} 1 \\ 7 \\ 3 \end{pmatrix} \quad \text{and} \quad \mathbf{b} = \begin{pmatrix} 2 \\ 10 \\ 1 \end{pmatrix} - \begin{pmatrix} 1 \\ 7 \\ 3 \end{pmatrix} = \begin{pmatrix} 1 \\ 3 \\ -2 \end{pmatrix}$$

$$\therefore \qquad \mathbf{r} = \begin{pmatrix} 1 \\ 7 \\ 3 \end{pmatrix} + \lambda \begin{pmatrix} 1 \\ 3 \\ -2 \end{pmatrix} \text{ is the } \textit{vector equation} \text{ of the line.}$$

If we now put $\mathbf{r} = \begin{pmatrix} x \\ y \\ z \end{pmatrix}$ we get:

$$\begin{pmatrix} x \\ y \\ z \end{pmatrix} = \begin{pmatrix} 1 \\ 7 \\ 3 \end{pmatrix} + \lambda \begin{pmatrix} 1 \\ 3 \\ -2 \end{pmatrix}$$

$\therefore$ $\quad x = 1 + \lambda, y = 7 + 3\lambda$ and $z = 3 - 2\lambda$

Eliminating λ, this reduces to:

$$\frac{x-1}{1} = \frac{y-7}{3} = \frac{z-3}{-2} = \lambda$$

which is the *cartesian equation* of the line.

You should now be able to answer Exercises 5–6 on page 248–49.

The equation of a line $(\mathbf{r} - \mathbf{a}) \times \mathbf{b} = 0$

There is another form for the vector equation of a line and this doesn't involve an unknown parameter λ. Let's see how it's derived.

We know that the equation of a line through a point with position vector $\mathbf{a}$ and direction $\mathbf{b}$ can be written $\mathbf{r} = \mathbf{a} + \lambda\,\mathbf{b}$

or $\quad \mathbf{r} - \mathbf{a} = \lambda\mathbf{b}$

Taking the vector product of both sides with $\mathbf{b}$ gives:

$$(\mathbf{r} - \mathbf{a}) \times \mathbf{b} = \lambda\mathbf{b} \times \mathbf{b}$$

But $\mathbf{b} \times \mathbf{b} = 0$ (parallel vectors always have a zero vector product).

$\therefore$ $(\mathbf{r} - \mathbf{a}) \times \mathbf{b} = 0$ is another form for the vector equation of a line.

Example	A line passes through the points A (1,7,3) and P (2,10,1). Find its vector equation in the form $(\mathbf{r} - \mathbf{a}) \times \mathbf{b} = 0$.

Solution

$$\mathbf{a} = \begin{pmatrix} 1 \\ 7 \\ 3 \end{pmatrix} \text{ and } \mathbf{b} = \begin{pmatrix} 2 \\ 10 \\ 1 \end{pmatrix} - \begin{pmatrix} 1 \\ 7 \\ 3 \end{pmatrix} = \begin{pmatrix} 1 \\ 3 \\ -2 \end{pmatrix}$$

$\therefore$ The required vector equation is: $\left[\mathbf{r} - \begin{pmatrix} 1 \\ 7 \\ 3 \end{pmatrix} \right] \times \begin{pmatrix} 1 \\ 3 \\ -2 \end{pmatrix} = 0.$

Example

The vector equation of a line is given by: $\left[\mathbf{r} - \begin{pmatrix} 1 \\ 2 \\ 3 \end{pmatrix}\right] \times \begin{pmatrix} 4 \\ 5 \\ 1 \end{pmatrix} = 0$.

What is the cartesian form for this equation?

Solution

The position vector of a point on the line is $\begin{pmatrix} 1 \\ 2 \\ 3 \end{pmatrix}$

and the direction of the line is $\begin{pmatrix} 4 \\ 5 \\ 1 \end{pmatrix}$.

∴ The required cartesian equation is: $\dfrac{x-1}{4} = \dfrac{y-2}{5} = \dfrac{z-3}{1}$

The important point to remember is therefore:

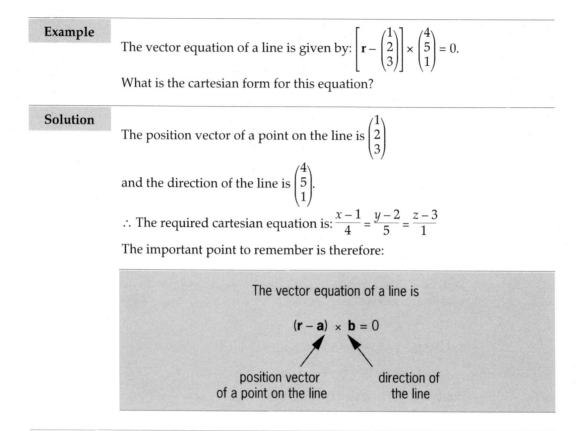

The vector equation of a line is

$$(\mathbf{r} - \mathbf{a}) \times \mathbf{b} = 0$$

position vector
of a point on the line

direction of
the line

You should now be able to answer Exercises 7–10 on page 249.

Equation of a plane

The equation of a plane is a little more complicated to derive – the consolation is that the end result is quite simple.

Let's take a plane and, although it's two dimensional, represent it as a line. We'll then mark in the origin and the perpendicular from the origin to the plane, calling the point of intersection N. Finally, we'll take a random point on the plane, calling it P, and join OP, calling the angle between OP and ON θ.

Figure 12.9

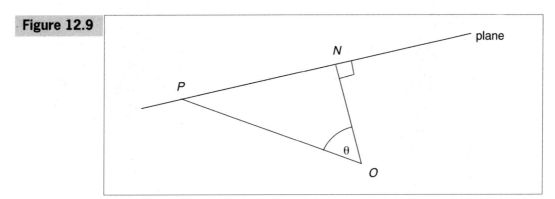

We know that we can calculate θ from:

$$\cos \theta = \frac{\overrightarrow{OP} . \overrightarrow{ON}}{|OP| \, |ON|} \quad \cdots \qquad \cdots \; ①$$

But also, from simple trigonometry, we know that

$$\cos \theta = \frac{\text{adjacent}}{\text{hypotenuse}} = \frac{|ON|}{|OP|} \qquad \cdots \; ②$$

It therefore follows that

$$\frac{\overrightarrow{OP} . \overrightarrow{ON}}{|OP| \, |ON|} = \frac{|ON|}{|OP|}$$

which rearranges to

$$\overrightarrow{OP} . \overrightarrow{ON} = |ON|^2 = d, \text{say}$$

So for planes, the normal to the plane is very important – if we call *ON* the vector **n**, the scalar product of **n** with the position vector of any point on the plane is constant, *d*.

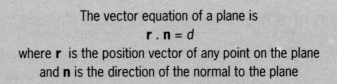

The vector equation of a plane is
r . n = d
where **r** is the position vector of any point on the plane
and **n** is the direction of the normal to the plane

If we know the direction of the normal and the co-ordinates of a point on the plane, we can calculate the constant *d* and hence find the equation of the plane.

Example

The direction of the normal to the plane Π is given by $\begin{pmatrix} 2 \\ 1 \\ 4 \end{pmatrix}$

and the point P, with co-ordinates $(1,-1,2)$, lies on Π. Find the vector equation of Π.

Solution

$\overrightarrow{OP} = \begin{pmatrix} 1 \\ -1 \\ 2 \end{pmatrix}$ and $\mathbf{n} = \begin{pmatrix} 2 \\ 1 \\ 4 \end{pmatrix}$

so $\mathbf{r} \cdot \mathbf{n} = \begin{pmatrix} 1 \\ -1 \\ 2 \end{pmatrix} \cdot \begin{pmatrix} 2 \\ 1 \\ 4 \end{pmatrix} = 9$

$\therefore$ the equation of Π is: $\mathbf{r} \cdot \begin{pmatrix} 2 \\ 1 \\ 4 \end{pmatrix} = 9$

Since $\mathbf{r}$ is the general position vector $\begin{pmatrix} x \\ y \\ z \end{pmatrix}$,

we can rewrite this last equation as: $\begin{pmatrix} x \\ y \\ z \end{pmatrix} \cdot \begin{pmatrix} 2 \\ 1 \\ 4 \end{pmatrix} = 9$

i.e. $2x + y + 4z = 9$

This is the *cartesian equation* of the plane (it's like the equation of a line in two dimensions, $2x + y = 9$, with an extra dimension added on).

You should now be able to answer Exercise 11 on page 249.

Equation of a plane passing through three given points

Suppose a plane passes through the points A, B and C. Since the vectors $\overrightarrow{AB}$ and $\overrightarrow{AC}$ must be parallel to the plane, the vector product $\overrightarrow{AB} \times \overrightarrow{AC}$ will be normal to the plane. We then proceed as before.

Example   Find the vector equation of the plane through the points A, B and C with position vectors:

$\mathbf{i} - 2\mathbf{j} + 2\mathbf{k}$, $6\mathbf{i} + 2\mathbf{j} + 4\mathbf{k}$ and $3\mathbf{i} + 4\mathbf{k}$ respectively

Give your answer in the form $\mathbf{r} \cdot \mathbf{n} = d$.

What is the cartesian equation of the plane?

Solution

$$\vec{AB} = \begin{pmatrix} 6 \\ 2 \\ 4 \end{pmatrix} - \begin{pmatrix} 1 \\ -2 \\ 2 \end{pmatrix} = \begin{pmatrix} 5 \\ 4 \\ 2 \end{pmatrix} \text{ and } \vec{AC} = \begin{pmatrix} 3 \\ 0 \\ 4 \end{pmatrix} - \begin{pmatrix} 1 \\ -2 \\ 2 \end{pmatrix} = \begin{pmatrix} 2 \\ 2 \\ 2 \end{pmatrix}$$

$$\therefore \vec{AB} \times \vec{AC} = (5\mathbf{i} + 4\mathbf{j} + 2\mathbf{k}) \times (2\mathbf{i} + 2\mathbf{j} + 2\mathbf{k})$$

$$= 4\mathbf{i} - 6\mathbf{j} + 2\mathbf{k}$$

$$\therefore \begin{pmatrix} 4 \\ -6 \\ 2 \end{pmatrix} \text{ is normal to the plane}$$

The equation of the plane is therefore given by

$$\mathbf{r} \cdot \begin{pmatrix} 4 \\ -6 \\ 2 \end{pmatrix} = \begin{pmatrix} 1 \\ -2 \\ 2 \end{pmatrix} \cdot \begin{pmatrix} 4 \\ -6 \\ 2 \end{pmatrix} = 20 \text{ (since } A \text{ lies on the plane)}$$

i.e. $$\mathbf{r} \cdot \begin{pmatrix} 2 \\ -3 \\ 1 \end{pmatrix} = 10$$

$$\therefore \text{ The equation of the plane is } \mathbf{r} \cdot \begin{pmatrix} 2 \\ -3 \\ 1 \end{pmatrix} = 10$$

This can also be written $$\begin{pmatrix} x \\ y \\ z \end{pmatrix} \cdot \begin{pmatrix} 2 \\ -3 \\ 1 \end{pmatrix} = 10 \text{ , i.e. } 2x - 3y + z = 10$$

$$\therefore \text{ The cartesian equation of the plane is } 2x - 3y + z = 10.$$

You should now be able to answer Exercises 12–15 on pages 249–250.

More about the equation of a plane

We have seen that the vector equation of a plane can be written as $\mathbf{r} \cdot \mathbf{n} = d$, when $\mathbf{r}$ is the position vector of any point on the plane and $\mathbf{n}$ is normal to the plane. However, there is also a parametric form for the equation of a plane.

The equation of a plane $\mathbf{r} = \mathbf{a} + \lambda \mathbf{l} + \mu \mathbf{m}$

The diagram below shows 4 coplanar points A, B, C and P.

Figure 12.10

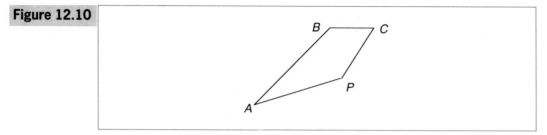

If we now add in the line *NP* parallel to *BC* we get Figure 12.11.

Figure 12.11

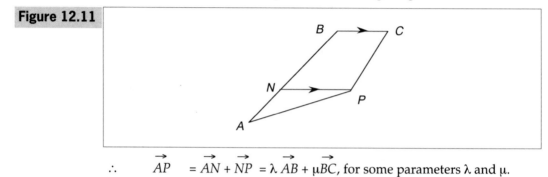

$$\therefore \quad \overrightarrow{AP} = \overrightarrow{AN} + \overrightarrow{NP} = \lambda\,\overrightarrow{AB} + \mu\overrightarrow{BC}, \text{ for some parameters } \lambda \text{ and } \mu.$$

Suppose we now add an origin to our co-ordinates and this origin *O* is outside the plane. Then if *P* is any point on the plane defined by *A*, *B* and *C*, its position vector is given by:

$$\mathbf{r} = \overrightarrow{OP} = \overrightarrow{OA} + \overrightarrow{AP} = \mathbf{a} + \lambda\overrightarrow{AB} + \mu\overrightarrow{BC}$$

$$\therefore \quad \mathbf{r} = \mathbf{a} + \lambda\overrightarrow{AB} + \mu\overrightarrow{BC}$$

> The vector equation of a plane through points *A*, *B* and *C*
> is therefore given by:
>
> $$\mathbf{r} = \mathbf{a} + \lambda\overrightarrow{AB} + \mu\overrightarrow{BC}, \text{ where } \lambda \text{ and } \mu \text{ are scalars.}$$

It is conventional to write this as $\mathbf{r} = \mathbf{a} + \lambda\mathbf{l} + \mu\mathbf{m}$, where **a** is the position vector of any point on the plane and **l** and **m** are any non-parallel vectors in the plane.

Example A plane passes through the points A $(1, -2, 2)$, B $(6, 2, 4)$ and C $(3, 0, 4)$. Find the vector equation of this plane in the form $\mathbf{r} = \mathbf{a} + \lambda\mathbf{l} + \mu\mathbf{m}$.

Solution

$$\mathbf{a} = \begin{pmatrix} 1 \\ -2 \\ 2 \end{pmatrix}, \quad \mathbf{b} = \begin{pmatrix} 6 \\ 2 \\ 4 \end{pmatrix} \text{ and } \mathbf{c} = \begin{pmatrix} 3 \\ 0 \\ 4 \end{pmatrix}$$

$\therefore \quad \overrightarrow{AB} = \mathbf{b} - \mathbf{a} = \begin{pmatrix} 5 \\ 4 \\ 2 \end{pmatrix}$ and $\overrightarrow{BC} = \mathbf{c} - \mathbf{b} = \begin{pmatrix} -3 \\ -2 \\ 0 \end{pmatrix}$

$\therefore \quad$ The vector equation of the plane ABC is:

$$\mathbf{r} = \begin{pmatrix} 1 \\ -2 \\ 2 \end{pmatrix} + \lambda \begin{pmatrix} 5 \\ 4 \\ 2 \end{pmatrix} + \mu \begin{pmatrix} -3 \\ -2 \\ 0 \end{pmatrix}, \text{ where } \lambda \text{ and } \mu \text{ are scalars.}$$

You should now be able to answer Exercise 16 on page 250.

Angle between planes

The angle between two planes can be defined as the angle between their normals.

Example Find the angle between the planes:

$$\mathbf{r} \cdot \begin{pmatrix} 1 \\ 2 \\ 3 \end{pmatrix} = 4 \text{ and } \mathbf{r} \cdot \begin{pmatrix} 3 \\ 2 \\ 4 \end{pmatrix} = 5$$

Solution

We need to find the angle between: $\begin{pmatrix} 1 \\ 2 \\ 3 \end{pmatrix}$ and $\begin{pmatrix} 3 \\ 2 \\ 4 \end{pmatrix}$

Using the scalar product we get:

$$\cos \theta = \frac{1 \times 3 + 2 \times 2 + 3 \times 4}{\sqrt{14}\sqrt{29}} \qquad \therefore \ \theta = 19.4° \text{ (1 d.p.)}$$

Angle between a line and a plane

To find the angle between a line and a plane, we find the angle between the line and the normal to the plane, and then subtract it from $90°$.

Example

Find the angle between the line $\mathbf{r} = \begin{pmatrix} 2 \\ 2 \\ 3 \end{pmatrix} + \lambda \begin{pmatrix} 4 \\ 2 \\ 3 \end{pmatrix}$ and the plane $\mathbf{r} \cdot \begin{pmatrix} 5 \\ 2 \\ 1 \end{pmatrix} = 8$.

Solution

We begin by finding the angle between $\begin{pmatrix} 4 \\ 2 \\ 3 \end{pmatrix}$ and $\begin{pmatrix} 5 \\ 2 \\ 1 \end{pmatrix}$

Using the scalar product we get:

$$\cos \theta = \frac{4 \times 5 + 2 \times 2 + 3 \times 1}{\sqrt{29} \sqrt{30}} \qquad \therefore \theta = 23.7°$$

$\therefore$ Angle between the line and the plane is $90 - 23.7 = 66.3°$ (1 d.p.)

You should now be able to answer Exercises 17–25 on pages 250–51.

EXERCISES

1. If vectors $\mathbf{i} + 6\mathbf{k}$ and $p\mathbf{i} - 3\mathbf{j} - 2\mathbf{k}$ are orthogonal, find the value of p.

2. Find $\mathbf{a} \times \mathbf{b}$ if:

   (a) $\mathbf{a} = 2\mathbf{i} + \mathbf{j} + \mathbf{k}$, $\mathbf{b} = 3\mathbf{i} + 4\mathbf{j} + 2\mathbf{k}$

   (b) $\mathbf{a} = \begin{pmatrix} 1 \\ 2 \\ 3 \end{pmatrix}$, $\mathbf{b} = \begin{pmatrix} 3 \\ 1 \\ 4 \end{pmatrix}$

3. If $\mathbf{a} = \mathbf{i} + 2\mathbf{j} + 3\mathbf{k}$ and $\mathbf{b} = 3\mathbf{i} + 4\mathbf{j} - \mathbf{k}$, find a unit vector which is perpendicular to the plane defined by $\mathbf{a}$ and $\mathbf{b}$.

4. Find the shortest distance between the lines

   $$\mathbf{r} = \begin{pmatrix} -3 \\ 6 \\ 0 \end{pmatrix} + \lambda \begin{pmatrix} -4 \\ 3 \\ 2 \end{pmatrix} \quad \text{and} \quad \mathbf{r} = \begin{pmatrix} -2 \\ 0 \\ 7 \end{pmatrix} + \mu \begin{pmatrix} -4 \\ 1 \\ 1 \end{pmatrix}$$

5. $ABCD$ is a parallelogram with $A(1, 2, 3)$, $B(3, 4, 7)$ and $D(8, 6, 10)$. Find:

   (a)   the coordinates of C

   (b)   the area of $ABCD$

   (c)   the vector equation of the line AB

   (d)   the cartesian equation of the line AB

   (e)   the distance of the point $E(10, 0, 3)$ from the line AB.

6 The position vectors of the points A and B are given by:

$$\overrightarrow{OA} = 3\mathbf{i} - 2\mathbf{j} + 1\mathbf{k}, \qquad \overrightarrow{OB} = -\mathbf{i} + \mathbf{j} + 2\mathbf{k},$$

where O is the origin. Find a vector equation of the straight line passing through A and B. Given that this line is perpendicular to the vector $\mathbf{i} + 2\mathbf{j} + p\mathbf{k}$, find the value of p.

7 The points A and B have coordinates $(2, 3, -1)$ and $(5, -2, 2)$ respectively. Calculate the acute angle between AB and the line with equation:

$$\mathbf{r} = \begin{pmatrix} 2 \\ 3 \\ -1 \end{pmatrix} + t\begin{pmatrix} 1 \\ -2 \\ -2 \end{pmatrix}$$

giving your answer correct to the nearest degree.

8 Find the acute angle (in degrees correct to one decimal place) between the lines l_1 and l_2 whose equations are:

$$\mathbf{r} = \begin{pmatrix} 2 \\ 1 \\ 3 \end{pmatrix} + \lambda\begin{pmatrix} 6 \\ -3 \\ 2 \end{pmatrix} \quad \text{and} \quad \mathbf{r} = \begin{pmatrix} -1 \\ 2 \\ 6 \end{pmatrix} + \mu\begin{pmatrix} 4 \\ 0 \\ 2 \end{pmatrix}$$

9 When do the lines $\mathbf{r} = \begin{pmatrix} 3 \\ 1 \\ 4 \end{pmatrix} + \lambda\begin{pmatrix} 1 \\ 0 \\ 4 \end{pmatrix}$ and $\mathbf{r} = \begin{pmatrix} 2 \\ 0 \\ 7 \end{pmatrix} + \mu\begin{pmatrix} 3 \\ 1 \\ 5 \end{pmatrix}$ intersect?

10 A line passes through points P and Q with position vectors $\mathbf{i} + 2\mathbf{j} + 5\mathbf{k}$ and $3\mathbf{i} + 4\mathbf{j} - \mathbf{k}$ respectively. Find the vector equation of this line in the form $(\mathbf{r} - \mathbf{a}) \times \mathbf{b} = 0$.

11 The direction of the normal to the plane Π is given by $\begin{pmatrix} 4 \\ -2 \\ 1 \end{pmatrix}$

and the point P, with coordinates $(3,1,2)$, lies on Π.

Find both the vector equation and the cartesian equation of Π.

12 A plane ABC is defined by $A(1, 2, 4)$, $B(3, 2, 6)$ and $C(3, 1, 7)$.

Find $\overrightarrow{AB} \times \overrightarrow{AC}$ and hence find the equation of the plane ABC in the form $\mathbf{r} \cdot \mathbf{n} = d$.

13 The position vectors of A, B and C are: $\begin{pmatrix} 1 \\ 1 \\ 0 \end{pmatrix}$, $\begin{pmatrix} 3 \\ 5 \\ -2 \end{pmatrix}$ and $\begin{pmatrix} 0 \\ -4 \\ 1 \end{pmatrix}$ respectively.

(a) Find $\overrightarrow{AB}, \overrightarrow{AC}$ and $\overrightarrow{AB} \times \overrightarrow{AC}$.

(b) Deduce the cartesian equation of the plane containing points A, B and C.

(c) Find the volume of the parallelepiped defined by vectors $\overrightarrow{OA}, \overrightarrow{OB}$ and $\overrightarrow{OC}$.

14 If A, B, C have, respectively, coordinates $(1, 1, 1)$, $(3, 5, -2)$ and $(2, 7, 3)$, find the cartesian equation of the plane containing A, B and C.

15 Find the vector equation of the plane through $A(1, 2, 3)$, $B(3, 5, 7)$ and $C(0, 8, 2)$ in the form $\mathbf{r} \cdot \mathbf{n} = d$.

16 The position vectors of points A, B and C are respectively $\mathbf{i} + 3\mathbf{k}$, $2\mathbf{j} + 4\mathbf{k}$ and $2\mathbf{i} + 3\mathbf{j} + 5\mathbf{k}$. Find the vector equation of the plane ABC, giving your answer in the form $\mathbf{r} = \mathbf{a} + \lambda\mathbf{l} + \mu\mathbf{m}$.

17 Find the angle between the planes: $\mathbf{r} \cdot \begin{pmatrix} 3 \\ 1 \\ 4 \end{pmatrix} = 5$ and $\mathbf{r} \cdot \begin{pmatrix} 2 \\ 4 \\ 5 \end{pmatrix} = 7$.

18 Find the angle between the line $\mathbf{r} = \begin{pmatrix} 1 \\ 0 \\ 2 \end{pmatrix} + \lambda \begin{pmatrix} 2 \\ 3 \\ 4 \end{pmatrix}$

and the plane $\mathbf{r} \cdot \begin{pmatrix} 5 \\ 1 \\ 2 \end{pmatrix} = 6$.

19 Find the angle between the line $\mathbf{r} = \begin{pmatrix} 1 \\ -1 \\ 3 \end{pmatrix} + \lambda \begin{pmatrix} 3 \\ 4 \\ 7 \end{pmatrix}$

and the plane $\mathbf{r} \cdot \begin{pmatrix} 2 \\ 1 \\ 1 \end{pmatrix} = 6$

20 Where does the line $\mathbf{r} = \begin{pmatrix} 1 \\ 2 \\ 3 \end{pmatrix} + \lambda \begin{pmatrix} 4 \\ 1 \\ 3 \end{pmatrix}$ meet the plane $\mathbf{r} \cdot \begin{pmatrix} 2 \\ 3 \\ 1 \end{pmatrix} = 39$?

21 The planes $\mathbf{r} \cdot \begin{pmatrix} 3 \\ 1 \\ -1 \end{pmatrix} = 2$ and $\mathbf{r} \cdot \begin{pmatrix} 2 \\ 4 \\ 1 \end{pmatrix} = 13$ intersect in the line l.

(a) Use a vector product to find a direction vector for l.

(b) Verify that $(1, 2, 3)$ is a point that lies on both planes

(c) Use (a) and (b) to find the equation of l in the form $\mathbf{r} = \mathbf{a} + \lambda\mathbf{b}$.

22 The points $A\,(3, 0, 0)$, $B\,(0, 2, -1)$, and $C\,(2, 0, 1)$ have position vectors $\mathbf{a}$, $\mathbf{b}$ and $\mathbf{c}$ with respect to a fixed origin O. The line L has equation $(\mathbf{r} - \mathbf{a}) \times \mathbf{b} = \mathbf{0}$. The plane Π contains L and the point C.

(a) Find $\overrightarrow{AC} \times \overrightarrow{OB}$.

(b) Hence or otherwise show that an equation of Π is $2x + y + 2z = 6$

(c) Find the perpendicular distance of Π from O

The point R is the reflection of O in Π.

(d) Find the position vector of R.

23 The position vectors of the points A, B, C and D relative to a fixed origin O, are $(-\mathbf{j} + 2\mathbf{k})$, $(\mathbf{i} - 3\mathbf{j} + 5\mathbf{k})$, $(2\mathbf{i} - 2\mathbf{j} + 7\mathbf{k})$ and $(\mathbf{j} + 2\mathbf{k})$ respectively.

(a) Find $\mathbf{p} = \overrightarrow{AB} \times \overrightarrow{CD}$

(b) Calculate $\overrightarrow{AC} \cdot \mathbf{p}$

Hence determine the shortest distance between the line containing AB and the line containing CD.

24 The lines L_1 and L_2 have equations $\mathbf{r} = \mathbf{a}_1 + s\mathbf{b}_1$ and $\mathbf{r} = \mathbf{a}_2 + t\mathbf{b}_2$ respectively, where

$$\mathbf{a}_1 = 3\mathbf{i} - 3\mathbf{j} - 2\mathbf{k}, \qquad \mathbf{b}_1 = \mathbf{j} + 2\mathbf{k},$$
$$\mathbf{a}_2 = 8\mathbf{i} + 3\mathbf{j}, \qquad \mathbf{b}_2 = 5\mathbf{i} + 4\mathbf{j} - 2\mathbf{k}$$

(a) Verify that the point P with position vector $3\mathbf{i} - \mathbf{j} + 2\mathbf{k}$ lies on both L_1 and L_2

(b) Find $\mathbf{b}_1 \times \mathbf{b}_2$

(c) Find a cartesian equation of the plane containing L_1 and L_2

The points with position vectors $\mathbf{a}_1$ and $\mathbf{a}_2$ are A_1 and A_2 respectively

(d) By expressing $\overrightarrow{A_1P}$ and $\overrightarrow{A_2P}$ as multiples of $\mathbf{b}_1$ and $\mathbf{b}_2$ respectively, or otherwise, find the area of the triangle PA_1A_2.

25 The points A $(2, 0, -1)$ and B $(4, 3, 1)$ have position vectors $\mathbf{a}$ and $\mathbf{b}$ with respect to a fixed origin O.

(a) Find $\mathbf{a} \times \mathbf{b}$

The plane Π_1 contains the points O, A and B

(b) Verify that an equation of Π_1 is $x - 2y + 2z = 0$

The plane Π_2 has equation $\mathbf{r} \cdot \mathbf{n} = d$ where $\mathbf{n} = 3\mathbf{i} + \mathbf{j} - \mathbf{k}$ and d is a constant. Given that B lies on Π_2

(c) Find the value of d

The planes Π_1 and Π_2 intersect in the line L

(d) Find an equation of L in the form $\mathbf{r} = \mathbf{p} + t\mathbf{q}$, where t is a parameter

(e) Find the position vector of the point X on L where OX is perpendicular to L.

SUMMARY   You should now know that:

- $\mathbf{a} \times \mathbf{b} = |\mathbf{a}||\mathbf{b}|\sin\theta\,\mathbf{n}$

- $$\begin{pmatrix} a_1 \\ a_2 \\ a_3 \end{pmatrix} \times \begin{pmatrix} b_1 \\ b_2 \\ b_3 \end{pmatrix} = \begin{pmatrix} a_2 b_3 - a_3 b_2 \\ a_3 b_1 - a_1 b_3 \\ a_1 b_2 - a_2 b_1 \end{pmatrix}$$

- $|\mathbf{a} \times \mathbf{b}|$ gives the area of the parallelogram specified by $\mathbf{a}$ and $\mathbf{b}$

- $|\mathbf{a} \cdot (\mathbf{b} \times \mathbf{c})|$ gives the volume of the parallelepiped specified by $\mathbf{a}$, $\mathbf{b}$ and $\mathbf{c}$.

- the formula $\dfrac{|\mathbf{b} \times (\mathbf{c} - \mathbf{a})|}{|\mathbf{b}|}$ can be used to find the distance of the point with position vector $\mathbf{c}$ from the line $\mathbf{r} = \mathbf{a} + \lambda\mathbf{b}$.

- the formula $\dfrac{(\mathbf{a}_1 - \mathbf{a}_2) \cdot \mathbf{b}_1 \times \mathbf{b}_2}{|\mathbf{b}_1 \times \mathbf{b}_2|}$ gives the shortest distance between the lines:

  $\mathbf{r} = \mathbf{a}_1 + \lambda\mathbf{b}_1$ and $\mathbf{r} = \mathbf{a}_2 + \mu\mathbf{b}_2$.

- the equation of a line can be written either as:

  $\mathbf{r} = \mathbf{a} + \lambda\mathbf{b}$ or $(\mathbf{r} - \mathbf{a}) \times \mathbf{b} = 0$

- the equation of a plane can be written either as:

  $\mathbf{r} = \mathbf{a} + \lambda\mathbf{l} + \mu\mathbf{m}$ or $\mathbf{r} \cdot \mathbf{n} = d$

- the angle between two planes is the angle between their normals

- the angle between a line and a plane is the angle between the line and the normal subtracted from 90°.

- to find where the line $\mathbf{r} = \mathbf{a} + \lambda\mathbf{b}$ meets the plane $\mathbf{r} \cdot \mathbf{n} = d$ you solve simultaneously, i.e. find λ from the equation $(\mathbf{a} + \lambda\mathbf{b}) \cdot \mathbf{n} = d$

- planes $\mathbf{r} \cdot \mathbf{n}_1 = d_1$ and $\mathbf{r} \cdot \mathbf{n}_2 = d_2$ intersect in a line which has direction vector $\mathbf{n}_1 \times \mathbf{n}_1$.

Advanced integration

In this section we are going to look at reduction formulae, which enable us to reduce a complicated integral, by successive steps, to a simple integral. Having done that, we'll then apply integration to the calculation of arc length and the area of a surface of revolution

Reduction formulae

We are now going to look at yet another method for integrating difficult functions. It is sometimes possible to find a formula that links the integral we wish to evaluate with another of related but simpler form. By repeatedly using such a formula, we may then – eventually – produce the answer we require. These **reduction formulae** are so called because they successively reduce the difficulty of the integrals involved until, at the final step, a very simple integral remains.

Enough of the general view, though. You will understand the idea more fully only when you have seen it in action, as in the following examples.

$\int_0^{\frac{\pi}{2}} \cos^n x \, dx$

For convenience we denote this integral by I_n. Now let's attempt to use integration by parts.

$$I_n = \int_0^{\frac{\pi}{2}} \cos^{(n-1)} x \cos x \, dx$$

$$= \left[\cos^{(n-1)} x \int \cos x \, dx \right]_0^{\frac{\pi}{2}} - \int_0^{\frac{\pi}{2}} \left\{ \frac{d}{dx} \left[\cos^{(n-1)}(x) \right] \int \cos x \, dx \right\} dx$$

$$= \left[\cos^{(n-1)} x \sin x \right]_0^{\frac{\pi}{2}} - \int_0^{\frac{\pi}{2}} \left[-(n-1) \sin^2 x \cos^{(n-2)} x \right] dx$$

$$= 0 + (n-1) \int_0^{\frac{\pi}{2}} \sin^2 x \cos^{(n-2)} x \, dx$$

$$= (n-1) \int_0^{\frac{\pi}{2}} [1 - \cos^2 x] \cos^{(n-2)} x \, dx$$

Therefore:

$$I_n = (n-1)\int_0^{\frac{\pi}{2}} \cos^{(n-2)} x \, dx - (n-1)\int_0^{\frac{\pi}{2}} \cos^n x \, dx$$

$$= (n-1)I_{n-2} - (n-1)I_n$$

From this we have:
$$I_n = \frac{n-1}{n} I_{n-2}$$

This is a reduction formula. As we claimed earlier, it links the integral we wish to evaluate with a related but simpler form. Of course, I_{n-2} is not much simpler than I_n, but at least we have managed to reduce the power of the integrand and so have a first foot on the ladder. To progress the rest of the way, notice that an exactly similar formula applies no matter what the value of n. In particular, we have:

$$I_{n-2} = \frac{(n-2)-1}{(n-2)} I_{n-4}$$

and similarly for I_{n-4}, I_{n-6} and so on.

Therefore

$$I_n = \frac{n-1}{n} I_{n-2} = \frac{(n-1)(n-3)}{n(n-2)} I_{n-4} = \dots$$

There are thus two cases to consider. Depending on whether n is odd or even, we have:

n odd

$$I_n = \frac{(n-1)(n-3)\dots(4)(2)}{n(n-2)\dots(5)(3)} I_1$$

But $\quad I_1 = \int_0^{\frac{\pi}{2}} \cos x \, dx = \left[\sin x\right]_0^{\frac{\pi}{2}} = 1$

and so $\quad I_n = \frac{(n-1)(n-3)\dots(4)(2)}{n(n-2)\dots(5)(3)}$

n even

$$I_n = \frac{(n-1)(n-3)\dots(3)(1)}{n(n-2)\dots(4)(2)} I_0$$

But $\quad I_0 = \int_0^{\frac{\pi}{2}} 1 \, dx = \left[x\right]_0^{\frac{\pi}{2}} = \frac{1}{2}\pi$

and so $\quad I_n = \frac{(n-1)(n-3)\dots(3)(1)}{n(n-2)\dots(4)(2)} \frac{1}{2}\pi$

This result may be used for any specific value of n. For example:

$$I_5 = \frac{(4)(2)}{(5)(3)} = \frac{8}{15}$$

and $\qquad I_6 = \dfrac{(5)\,(3)\,(1)}{(6)\,(4)\,(2)}\dfrac{1}{2}\pi = \dfrac{5\pi}{32}$

As a second example, we shall try the following integral.

$$\int_0^\infty x^n e^{-x}\, dx$$

Once again we denote the integral by I_n, and integrate by parts to get:

$$
\begin{aligned}
I_n &= \left[x^n \int e^{-x}\, dx \right]_0^\infty - \int_0^\infty \left\{ \frac{d}{dx}[x^n] \int e^{-x}\, dx \right\} dx \\
&= \left[-x^n e^{-x} \right]_0^\infty + \int_0^\infty n x^{n-1}\, e^{-x}\, dx \quad = \quad 0 + n I_{n-1}
\end{aligned}
$$

(Note: the 0 appears because, no matter how big n may be, the function $x^n e^{-x} \to 0$ as $x \to \infty$)

Therefore $\qquad I_n \;=\; n I_{n-1}$

Using this same formula with first $(n-1)$ then $(n-2)$ and so on replacing n, we eventually produce:

$$
\begin{aligned}
I_n &= n(n-1)(n-2) \ldots (2)(1)\, I_0 \\
&= n!\,\left[-e^{-x} \right]_0^\infty = n!
\end{aligned}
$$

Now let's tackle some examples, as they might be set in an examination.

Examples

1 Define $I_n = \displaystyle\int_0^{\frac{\pi}{2}} x^n \sin x\, dx$ and $J_n = \displaystyle\int_0^{\frac{\pi}{2}} x^n \cos x\, dx$

Prove that $\quad I_n = n J_{n-1}$ and $J_n = \left(\tfrac{1}{2}\pi\right)^n - n I_{n-1}$ Hence evaluate I_n

2 Define $\qquad I_{m,n} = \displaystyle\int_1^e x^m [\ln x]^n\, dx$

Prove that $\quad (m+1)I_{m,n} = e^{m+1} - n I_{m,n-1}$ and so evaluate $I_{3,2}$

Solutions

1 Using integration by parts once again:

$$
\begin{aligned}
I_n &= \left[-x^n \cos x \right]_0^{\frac{\pi}{2}} - \int_0^{\frac{\pi}{2}} \left[-n x^{n-1} \cos x \right] dx \\
&= 0 + n J_{n-1} = n J_{n-1}
\end{aligned}
$$

Similarly,

$$
\begin{aligned}
J_n &= \left[x^n \sin x \right]_0^{\frac{\pi}{2}} - \int_0^{\frac{\pi}{2}} n x^{n-1} \sin x\, dx \\
&= \left(\tfrac{1}{2}\pi\right)^n - n I_{n-1}
\end{aligned}
$$

255

Therefore $I_n = nJ_{n-1} = n\left[\left(\tfrac{1}{2}\pi\right)^{n-1} - (n-1)\,I_{n-2}\right]$

In particular,

$$I_4 = 4\left[\left(\tfrac{1}{2}\pi\right)^3 - 3I_2\right] \text{ and } I_2 = 2\left[\left(\tfrac{1}{2}\pi\right)^1 - 1I_0\right]$$

But:

$$I_0 = \int_0^{\frac{\pi}{2}} \sin x \, dx = \left[-\cos x\right]_0^{\frac{\pi}{2}} = 1, \text{ and so}$$

$$I_2 = 2\left(\tfrac{1}{2}\pi - 1\right) = \pi - 2$$

$$I_4 = 4\left(\frac{\pi^3}{8} - 3\pi + 6\right) = \tfrac{1}{2}\pi^3 - 12\pi + 24$$

2   Yet again, integration by parts gives:

$$I_{m,n} = \left[\{\ln x\}^n \int x^m \, dx\right]_1^e - \int_1^e \left[n\,\frac{1}{x}\{\ln x\}^{n-1}\int x^m \, dx\right] dx$$

$$= \left[\{\ln x\}^n \frac{x^{m+1}}{m+1}\right]_1^e - n\int_1^e \{\ln x\}^{n-1}\frac{x^m}{m+1}\, dx$$

Since $\ln e = 1$ and $\ln 1 = 0$, this produces the required reduction formula, i.e. $(m+1)\,I_{m,n} = e^{m+1} - nI_{m,n-1}$

Therefore, for $m = 3$ and $n = 2$, we have:

$$4I_{3,2} = e^4 - 2I_{3,1}$$
But $4I_{3,1} = e^4 - 1I_{3,0}$

$$= e^4 - \int_1^e x^3 \, dx$$

$$= e^4 - \left[\tfrac{1}{4}x^4\right]_1^e = \frac{3e^4}{4} + \frac{1}{4}$$

Therefore $I_{3,2} = \tfrac{1}{4}\left(e^4 - \frac{3e^4}{8} - \frac{1}{8}\right) = \frac{1}{32}(5e^4 - 1)$

You should now be able to answer Exercises 1–4 on page 262.

You have just completed a section of challenging mathematics. Though many of the methods you met here appeared difficult at first sight, you should now be feeling more confident about your ability to tackle even the most awkward-looking integration.

The ideas and techniques you have learned are a powerful combination and can be used to solve a wide range of problems. However, be warned. You will still occasionally find an integral which resists all attempts to crack it. Don't be put off by this. As we shall see later, there are some functions which really cannot be integrated – except by approximate numerical methods ... but that's another story.

Now let's move on to arc length and area of surface of revolution. You should find this much more manageable.

Arc lengths

If you have ever fiddled with pieces of string in an attempt to find the length of a curve, you have probably wondered if there was a better method. Well, there is – once again integration provides it. Consider Figure 13.1 below.

Figure 13.1

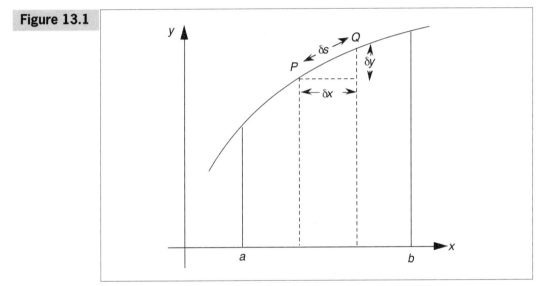

The diagram shows a general curve formed by graphing the equation $y = f(x)$. We shall suppose that we wish to find the length of the arc from $x = a$ to $x = b$.

P and Q are intermediate points on the curve, and have co-ordinates (x, y) and $(x + \delta x, y + \delta y)$ respectively. Denote the length of arc PQ by δs. Now, if P and Q are close, δx, δy and δs are small, and we may use Pythagoras's Theorem to approximate δs as follows:

$$\delta s^2 = \delta x^2 + \delta y^2$$

Therefore:

$$\delta s = \sqrt{(\delta x^2 + \delta y^2)}$$

$$= \sqrt{1 + \left(\frac{\delta y}{\delta x}\right)^2} \; \delta x$$

The arc length we require is thus:

$$\Sigma \, \delta s \; = \; \Sigma \sqrt{1 + \left(\frac{\delta y}{\delta x}\right)^2} \; \delta x$$

and, in the limit as $\delta x \to 0$, we conclude that:

$$\begin{array}{c}\text{length of arc of } y = f(x) \\ \text{between } x = a \text{ and } x = b\end{array} \;=\; \int_a^b \sqrt{1 + \left(\frac{dy}{dx}\right)^2} \; dx = s$$

The argument may be amended slightly to deal with curves whose equations are given in parametric form. If we assume, for example, that x and y are represented by functions of t, then we can write:

$$\delta s \quad = \quad \sqrt{\left(\frac{\delta x}{\delta t}\right)^2 + \left(\frac{\delta y}{\delta t}\right)^2} \; \delta t$$

so that an approximation to the arc length we require is:

$$\Sigma s \quad = \Sigma \sqrt{\left(\frac{\delta x}{\delta t}\right)^2 + \left(\frac{\delta y}{\delta t}\right)^2} \; \delta t$$

This leads, in the limit as $\delta t \to 0$, to the formula:

$$\begin{array}{c}\text{length of arc between} \\ t = \alpha \text{ and } t = \beta\end{array} \;=\; \int_\alpha^\beta \sqrt{\left(\frac{dx}{dt}\right)^2 + \left(\frac{dy}{dt}\right)^2} \; dt = s$$

Examples Find the arc lengths of the following sections of curve:

1 the parabola $y = \frac{1}{2} x^2$ between $x = 0$ and $x = 2$

2 the circle $x = a\cos t, \; y = a\sin t$.

Solutions **1** $\dfrac{dy}{dx} = x$ and so, from the formula, the required arc length is:

$$\int_0^2 \sqrt{(1 + x^2)} \; dx$$

This is a fairly familiar integral, but is difficult if you can't remember the trick – which is to substitute:

$$x = \sinh u$$

Thus $\sqrt{[1 + \sinh^2 u \,]} = \cosh u$

and $dx = \cosh u \; du$

So the integral is:

$$\int_0^{\sinh^{-1} 2} \cosh^2 u \ du = \frac{1}{2} \int_0^{\sinh^{-1} 2} [\cosh 2u + 1] \ du$$

$$= \frac{1}{2} \left[\frac{1}{2} \sinh 2u + u \right]_0^{\sinh^{-1} 2}$$

$$= \frac{1}{2} \left[\sinh u \ \cosh u + u \right]_0^{\sinh^{-1} 2}$$

$$= \frac{1}{2} [2\sqrt{(1 + 2^2)} + \sinh^{-1} 2]$$

$$= \frac{1}{2} [2\sqrt{5} + \sinh^{-1} 2]$$

2 $\dfrac{dx}{dt} = -a\sin t \qquad \dfrac{dy}{dt} = a\cos t$

and so the required arc length is:

$$\int_0^{2\pi} \sqrt{[\{-a\sin t\}^2 + \{a\cos t \ \}^2]} \ dt = \int_0^{2\pi} a\,dt = \left[at \right]_0^{2\pi} = 2\pi a$$

which confirms what you already knew about the circumference of a circle of radius *a*.

You will probably have guessed that, despite the simplicity of the second of these problems, the integrals we need to solve when calculating arc lengths often require more sophisticated methods. Problem 1 is fairly typical here – the substitution technique is frequently used.

You should now be able to answer Exercises 5–8 on page 262.

Surfaces of revolution

All the applications we have looked at so far in this section have been two-dimensional. We can take a step into the third dimension, however, by considering the solid shapes which are formed when curves are rotated around the axes. Many of the objects we meet in everyday life are of this kind, and so it is important that we can deal with them mathematically.

Here we set out to determine the surface area of the solid formed when the section of the curve $y = f(x)$ from $x = a$ and $x = b$ is rotated about the *x*-axis. Figure 13.2 illustrates the problem.

Figure 13.2

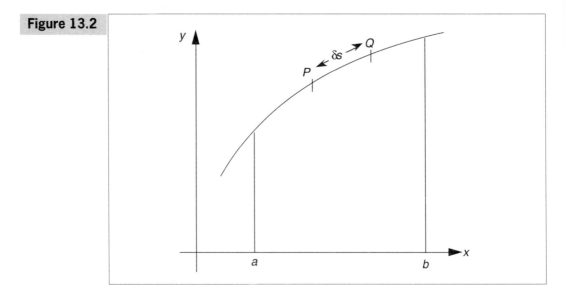

As before, if P and Q are close together, δx, δy and δs are small. Now consider the rim of the circular disc formed as the arc PQ is rotated about the x-axis. In area this will be approximately:

$$2\pi y \times \delta s$$

Summing for all such arcs gives an approximation to the surface area we require:

$$2\pi \sum y \delta s$$

But from our earlier discussion on arc length we can write this as:

$$2\pi \sum y \sqrt{1 + \left(\frac{\delta y}{\delta x}\right)^2} \ . \ \delta x$$

As $\delta x \to 0$, this leads to:

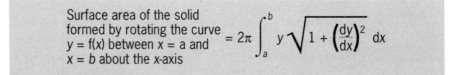

Surface area of the solid formed by rotating the curve $y = f(x)$ between $x = a$ and $x = b$ about the x-axis $= 2\pi \int_a^b y \sqrt{1 + \left(\frac{dy}{dx}\right)^2}\ dx$

When we dealt with arc lengths earlier in the section, we derived an equivalent formula for curves whose equations were given in parametric form. Exactly the same amendments may be made here to produce:

Surface area of the solid formed by rotating the curve between $t = \alpha$ and $t = \beta$ about the x-axis	$= 2\pi \displaystyle\int_{\alpha}^{\beta} y \sqrt{\left(\dfrac{dx}{dt}\right)^2 + \left(\dfrac{dy}{dt}\right)^2}\ dt$

Examples   Find the areas of the surfaces of revolution in the following cases:

1   The curve is the upper arm of the parabola $y^2 = 4x$ between $x = 0$ and $x = 3$

2   The curve is the upper half of the circle $x = a\cos t,\ y = a\sin t$

Solutions   **1**   For the upper arm of the parabola, $y = +2\sqrt{x}$

and so: $\dfrac{dy}{dx} = \dfrac{1}{\sqrt{x}}$

From the formula, the area of the surface of revolution is:

$$2\pi \int_0^3 y \sqrt{1 + \left(\frac{dy}{dx}\right)^2}\ dx\ =\ 2\pi \int_0^3 2\sqrt{x}\ \sqrt{1 + \frac{1}{x}}\ dx$$

$$= 4\pi \int_0^3 \sqrt{(x + 1)}\ dx$$

$$= 4\pi \left[\frac{2}{3}(x + 1)^{\frac{3}{2}}\right]_0^3$$

$$= \frac{8\pi}{3}(8 - 1) = \frac{56\pi}{3}$$

2 $\dfrac{dx}{dt} = -a\sin t$ and $\dfrac{dy}{dt} = a\cos t$

So the area we require is:

$$2\pi \int_0^{\pi} y \sqrt{\left(\frac{dx}{dt}\right)^2 + \left(\frac{dy}{dt}\right)^2}\ dt$$

$$= 2\pi \int_0^{\pi} a\sin t\ \sqrt{[a^2 \sin^2 t + a^2 \cos^2 t]}\ dt$$

$$= 2\pi a^2 \int_0^{\pi} \sin t\ dt$$

$$= 2\pi a^2 \big[-\cos t\big]_0^{\pi} = 4\pi a^2$$

Once again we confirm a result that you probably already knew – that the surface area of a sphere of radius a is $4\pi a^2$.

You should now be able to answer Exercises 9–15 on page 263.

EXERCISES

1   If $I_n = \int_0^{\frac{\pi}{2}} \sin^n x \, dx$, prove that $I_n = \left(\dfrac{n-1}{n}\right) I_{n-2}$.

Hence evaluate: (a) $\int_0^{\frac{\pi}{2}} \sin^7 x \, dx$ (b) $\int_0^{\frac{\pi}{2}} \sin^{10} x \, dx$

2   If $I_n = \int \dfrac{\sin nx}{\sin x} \, dx$, prove that:

$$I_n = \frac{2 \sin (n-1) x}{n-1} + I_{n-2} \cdot (n \geq 2)$$

Deduce the value of $\displaystyle\int_{\frac{\pi}{4}}^{\frac{\pi}{2}} \dfrac{\sin 4x}{\sin x} \, dx$

3   If $I_n = \int_0^{\frac{\pi}{2}} x^n \sin x \, dx$ prove that:

$$I_n = n \left(\frac{\pi}{2}\right)^{n-1} - n (n-1) I_{n-2}$$

4   If $I_{m,n} = \int_0^{\frac{\pi}{2}} \cos^m x \sin nx \, dx$, prove that:

$$(m + n) I_{m,n} = 1 + m I_{m-1, n-1}$$

Hence evaluate $\displaystyle\int_0^{\frac{\pi}{2}} \cos^5 x \, dx \sin 2x \, dx$

5   Find the length of the upper arc of $x^3 = y^2$ from $x = 0$ to $x = 2$.

6   Show that the length of the arc of the cycloid, $x = a (\theta + \sin \theta)$, $y = a (1 - \cos \theta)$, between the points $\theta = 0$ and $\theta = \pi$, is $4a$.

7   Show that the length of the arc, s, for the curve $x = e^\theta \sin \theta$, $y = e^\theta \cos \theta$ is given by:

$$s = \sqrt{2} \, e^\theta + \text{constant.}$$

8   Show that the length of the arc of the parabola $y^2 = 4ax$ cut off by the line $3y = 8x$ is $a \left(\dfrac{15}{16} + \ln 2\right)$.

9 The line $y = x \tan \alpha$, $0 \le x \le h$, is rotated through 2π radians about the x-axis, to give a cone.

Find, by integration, the curved surface area of this cone.

10 Prove that the surface area of the paraboloid obtained by the rotation of the arc of the parabola $y^2 = 4ax$ between $x = 0$ and $x = h$ about the axis of x, is:

$$\frac{8}{3}\pi \sqrt{a} \left[(h + a)^{\frac{3}{2}} - a^{\frac{3}{2}} \right]$$

11 Find the area of the surface generated when the curve $x = a \cos^3 t$, $y = a \sin^3 t$ is rotated about the x-axis.

12 The curve $x = a \ln (\sec \theta + \tan \theta) - a \sin \theta$, $y = a \cos \theta$,

between $\theta = 0$ and $\frac{\pi}{2}$ is rotated about the x axis.

Prove that the area of the curved surface is $2\pi a^2$.

13 Find the length of the arc on the curve $y = \cosh \, \theta$ between $\theta = 0$ and $\theta = 1$.

14 The curve C has equation $y = \frac{2}{3}x^{\frac{3}{2}}$. The arc of C from $(0, 0)$ to $(1, \frac{2}{3})$ is rotated through 2π about the x-axis. The surface generated has area S.

Show that $S = \dfrac{4\pi}{3} \displaystyle\int_0^1 x^{\frac{3}{2}} \sqrt{(1 + x)} \, dx$.

15 Given that

$$I_n = \int_0^{\frac{\pi}{2}} e^{\sin x} \cos x \sin^n x \, dx, \, n \ge 0 \,,$$

show that $I_n = e - nI_{n-1}, \, n \ge 1$.

Hence evaluate I_3, giving your answer in terms of e.

SUMMARY   In this section we have:

- used reduction formulae to evaluate complicated integrals
- used the formulae:

$$\int \sqrt{1 + \left(\frac{dy}{dx}\right)^2} \; dx$$

and
$$\int \sqrt{\left(\frac{dx}{dt}\right)^2 + \left(\frac{dy}{dt}\right)^2} \; dt$$

for arc length

- used the formulae:

$$2\pi \int y\sqrt{1 + \left(\frac{dy}{dx}\right)^2} \; dx$$

and
$$2\pi \int y\sqrt{\left(\frac{dx}{dt}\right)^2 + \left(\frac{dy}{dt}\right)^2} \; dt$$

for surface area of revolution about the x-axis.

Matrix algebra

INTRODUCTION In this section we shall introduce the notion of a linear transformation in two- and three-dimensional space and investigate its properties and applications. This will lead on to 2×2 and 3×3 matrices and, eventually, their eigenvalues and eigenvectors.

Linear transformations

In this section we turn our attention to certain kinds of operation that can be performed on vectors, and investigate the family of **linear transformations**. A transformation is a mapping of space into itself which transforms each vector to some other. If we denote a particular transformation by **M**, then the result of applying **M** to a vector **a** is another vector which we denote by **Ma**. Linear transformations are special in a sense we now define for three-dimensional space.

Definition

A transformation **M** of three-dimensional space is said to be linear if, for any vector **a** where $\mathbf{a} = \alpha_1\mathbf{i} + \alpha_2\mathbf{j} + \alpha_3\mathbf{k}$, the vector **Ma** has the form:

$$\mathbf{Ma} = (\mu_{11}\alpha_1 + \mu_{12}\alpha_2 + \mu_{13}\alpha_3)\mathbf{i} + (\mu_{21}\alpha_1 + \mu_{22}\alpha_2 + \mu_{23}\alpha_3)\mathbf{j}$$
$$+ (\mu_{31}\alpha_1 + \mu_{32}\alpha_2 + \mu_{33}\alpha_3)\mathbf{k}$$

where all the μ's are constants. In other words, **M** is linear if the coordinates of the resulting vector are fixed linear combinations of the coordinates of **a** – whatever **a** may be.

Linear transformations in two dimensions are defined in a similar but briefer way. Two-dimensional vectors can be represented by $\alpha_1\mathbf{i} + \alpha_2\mathbf{j}$, and two-dimensional transformations require only four numbers: μ_{11}, μ_{12}, μ_{21} and μ_{22}, but otherwise the principle is exactly the same.

It will not be obvious from the definition, but linear transformations include a great many of the operations that can be performed on space – stretches, enlargements, rotations about the origin and reflections, for example. We shall come to all of these shortly.

However, if we use a column vector i.e. $\begin{pmatrix} \alpha_1 \\ \alpha_2 \\ \alpha_3 \end{pmatrix}$ instead of $\alpha_1\,\mathbf{i} + \alpha_2\,\mathbf{j} + \alpha_3\,\mathbf{k}$,

we can write the above linear transformation more simply. We show this transformation as a **matrix**. The matrix of the transformation $\mathbf{M}$ in the definition above is:

$$\begin{pmatrix} \mu_{11} & \mu_{12} & \mu_{13} \\ \mu_{21} & \mu_{22} & \mu_{23} \\ \mu_{31} & \mu_{32} & \mu_{33} \end{pmatrix}$$

That is, $\mathbf{M}$ may be regarded simply as an array of numbers – the numbers which define the new vectors that appear when we transform the old ones. (Here we have a 3×3 matrix – so called because of its shape.) In turn, this view leads us to think of a transformation as the **multiplication** of a vector by a matrix, where this special form of multiplication is defined by:

$$\begin{pmatrix} \mu_{11} & \mu_{12} & \mu_{13} \\ \mu_{21} & \mu_{22} & \mu_{23} \\ \mu_{31} & \mu_{32} & \mu_{33} \end{pmatrix} \begin{pmatrix} \alpha_1 \\ \alpha_2 \\ \alpha_3 \end{pmatrix} = \begin{pmatrix} \mu_{11}\alpha_1 + \mu_{12}\alpha_2 + \mu_{13}\alpha_3 \\ \mu_{21}\alpha_1 + \mu_{22}\alpha_2 + \mu_{23}\alpha_3 \\ \mu_{31}\alpha_1 + \mu_{32}\alpha_2 + \mu_{33}\alpha_3 \end{pmatrix}$$

Notice that this is exactly the same statement about linear transformations that we made in the definition. Try to get used to matrix multiplication. It really isn't as complicated as it looks. You can remember the calculations by noting the pattern involved: for each entry of the result, you move simultaneously *along* the corresponding row of the matrix and *down* the column of the vector, multiplying and adding as you go. The same principle applies to two-dimensional transformations and their matrices, except that there the arrays are smaller, 2×2 instead of 3×3, and the calculations therefore shorter.

Example Find the result of multiplying the matrix $\mathbf{M}$ and vector $\mathbf{a}$ in the following cases:

(a) $\mathbf{M} = \begin{pmatrix} 1 & 0 & 2 \\ 0 & 3 & 1 \\ 4 & 1 & 0 \end{pmatrix} \qquad \mathbf{a} = \begin{pmatrix} 0 \\ -1 \\ 2 \end{pmatrix}$

(b) $\mathbf{M} = \begin{pmatrix} -1 & 3 \\ 0 & 2 \end{pmatrix} \qquad \mathbf{a} = \begin{pmatrix} 4 \\ 1 \end{pmatrix}$

Solution

(a) $\mathbf{Ma} = \begin{pmatrix} 1 \times 0 + 0 \times (-1) + 2 \times 2 \\ 0 \times 2 + 3 \times (-1) + 1 \times 2 \\ 4 \times 0 + 1 \times (-1) + 0 \times 2 \end{pmatrix} = \begin{pmatrix} 4 \\ -1 \\ -1 \end{pmatrix}$

(b) $\mathbf{Ma} = \begin{pmatrix} -1 \times 4 + 3 \times 1 \\ 0 \times 4 + 2 \times 1 \end{pmatrix} = \begin{pmatrix} -1 \\ 2 \end{pmatrix}$

You should now be able to answer Exercise 1 on page 289.

Stretches, rotations and reflections

We claimed earlier that the class of linear transformations included various familiar operations. We shall now investigate each of these in turn and see the kinds of matrices to which they correspond.

Stretches

A two-dimensional stretch is pictured in the diagram below. Notice that this is not a uniform stretch in both directions – parallel to the x-axis all measurements are doubled, but parallel to the y-axis they are multiplied by only $1\frac{1}{2}$. The result is that the unit square shown in the diagram is stretched into a rectangle with sides 2 and $1\frac{1}{2}$.

Figure 14.1

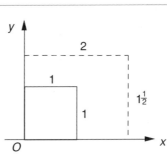

The matrix corresponding to this transformation is: $\begin{pmatrix} 2 & 0 \\ 0 & \frac{3}{2} \end{pmatrix}$

as you can easily confirm if you multiply any two-dimensional vector

$\begin{pmatrix} \alpha_1 \\ \alpha_2 \end{pmatrix}$ by it, e.g.: $\begin{pmatrix} 2 & 0 \\ 0 & \frac{3}{2} \end{pmatrix}\begin{pmatrix} \alpha_1 \\ \alpha_2 \end{pmatrix} = \begin{pmatrix} 2\alpha_1 \\ \frac{3}{2}\alpha_2 \end{pmatrix}$

As you see, the x-coordinate α_1 is doubled and the y-coordinate is increased by 50%.

Stretches in three dimensions lead to similar matrices.

For example, the matrix: $\begin{pmatrix} 3 & 0 & 0 \\ 0 & 2 & 0 \\ 0 & 0 & \frac{1}{2} \end{pmatrix}$

stretches all measurements in the directions of the x- and y-axes by factors of 3 and 2 respectively. Parallel to the z-axis measurements are halved – stretching is taken to include reduction as well. You have probably noticed the pattern which all stretching matrices reveal: they consist of numbers of any size down the main diagonal (i.e. the diagonal line running from top left to bottom right) and zeros everywhere else.

Rotations

Once again we begin with two dimensions. This time we shall assume that the points of the plane are rotated about the origin through an angle θ, and ask: How do we represent this transformation in a matrix?

The answer can be found by considering the effect of the rotation

on the vectors $\begin{pmatrix} 1 \\ 0 \end{pmatrix}$ and $\begin{pmatrix} 0 \\ 1 \end{pmatrix}$.

(i.e. the two-dimensional base vectors **i** and **j**).

Figure 14.2

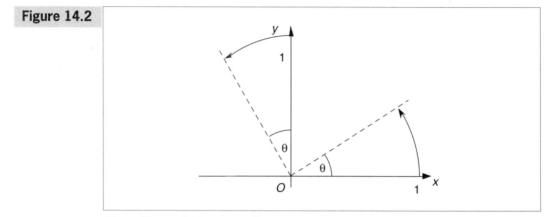

From Figure 14.2, we see that:

$$\begin{pmatrix} 1 \\ 0 \end{pmatrix} \text{ goes to } \begin{pmatrix} \cos\theta \\ \sin\theta \end{pmatrix} \quad \text{while} \quad \begin{pmatrix} 0 \\ 1 \end{pmatrix} \text{ goes to } \begin{pmatrix} -\sin\theta \\ \cos\theta \end{pmatrix}$$

These facts specify the matrix we require uniquely:

$$\begin{pmatrix} \cos\theta & -\sin\theta \\ \sin\theta & \cos\theta \end{pmatrix}$$

and we could now use it to calculate the effect of the rotation on any other vector.

This illustrates the quickest method for finding the matrix of any linear transformation. Simply find the vectors which result when **i**, **j** (and, in three dimensions, **k**) are transformed. These are the columns of the required matrix.

Exactly similar considerations apply to three dimensions. For example, the matrix:

$$\begin{pmatrix} \cos\theta & 0 & -\sin\theta \\ 0 & 1 & 0 \\ \sin\theta & 0 & \cos\theta \end{pmatrix}$$

represents a rotation about the *y*-axis through an angle θ.

Reflections

To see the sort of matrix which results from a reflection, consider the effect on **i**, **j** and **k** of a reflection in the *yz* plane. The results are:

$$\begin{pmatrix}1\\0\\0\end{pmatrix}\to\begin{pmatrix}-1\\0\\0\end{pmatrix},\ \begin{pmatrix}0\\1\\0\end{pmatrix}\to\begin{pmatrix}0\\1\\0\end{pmatrix},\ \begin{pmatrix}0\\0\\1\end{pmatrix}\to\begin{pmatrix}0\\0\\1\end{pmatrix}$$

and so the matrix is: $\begin{pmatrix}-1&0&0\\0&1&0\\0&0&1\end{pmatrix}$

Examples

1 Two-dimensional space is rotated in an anticlockwise direction about the origin through the angle $\frac{\pi}{3}$. Find the coordinates of the point to which (α,β) is transformed.

2 Find the matrix which corresponds to a reflection in the plane which contains the *z*-axis and bisects the angle between the *x*- and *y*-axes.

Solutions

1 The matrix of the transformation is:

$$\begin{pmatrix}\cos\frac{\pi}{3}&-\sin\frac{\pi}{3}\\\sin\frac{\pi}{3}&\cos\frac{\pi}{3}\end{pmatrix}=\begin{pmatrix}\frac{1}{2}&-\frac{1}{2}\sqrt{3}\\\frac{1}{2}\sqrt{3}&\frac{1}{2}\end{pmatrix}$$

and so the required coordinates are given by:

$$\begin{pmatrix}\frac{1}{2}&-\frac{1}{2}\sqrt{3}\\\frac{1}{2}\sqrt{3}&\frac{1}{2}\end{pmatrix}\begin{pmatrix}\alpha\\\beta\end{pmatrix}=\begin{pmatrix}\frac{1}{2}(\alpha-\beta\sqrt{3})\\\frac{1}{2}(\alpha\sqrt{3}+\beta)\end{pmatrix}$$

2 The base vectors are transformed as follows:

$$\begin{pmatrix}1\\0\\0\end{pmatrix}\to\begin{pmatrix}0\\1\\0\end{pmatrix},\ \begin{pmatrix}0\\1\\0\end{pmatrix}\to\begin{pmatrix}1\\0\\0\end{pmatrix},\ \begin{pmatrix}0\\0\\1\end{pmatrix}\to\begin{pmatrix}0\\0\\1\end{pmatrix}$$

The required matrix is therefore:

$$\begin{pmatrix}0&1&0\\1&0&0\\0&0&1\end{pmatrix}$$

You should now be able to answer Exercises 2–3 on pages 289–90.

Composite transformations

You may well suspect already that not all linear transformations are of the three types you have just seen. It is perfectly possible, for example, to combine an enlargement with a rotation, first stretching space and then rotating it about some axis. In general, of course, we can combine linear transformations of any sort in this way. If we denote them by **M** and **N**, the result of performing **M** first and then **N** on any vector **a** is given by:

$$N(Ma)$$

and is written **NMa**. The corresponding composite transformation is denoted by **NM**.

You may wonder at this point why we take such care to specify the order in which **M** and **N** are used. The reason is simple: the final result of the composite transformation may well be different if we use them the other way around, i.e. **NM** may not be the same as **MN**, or to put it another way, **M** and **N** may not commute.

Another word of warning: note that the order in which we write **M** and **N** in the composite **NM** is the reverse of the order in which we perform them.

These points are well illustrated by two of the transformations you saw earlier. Suppose that:

$$\mathbf{M} = \begin{pmatrix} 3 & 0 \\ 0 & \dfrac{3}{2} \end{pmatrix} \text{ and } \mathbf{N} = \begin{pmatrix} \cos\theta & -\sin\theta \\ \sin\theta & \cos\theta \end{pmatrix}$$

then:

$$\mathbf{NMi} = \begin{pmatrix} \cos\theta & -\sin\theta \\ \sin\theta & \cos\theta \end{pmatrix} \begin{pmatrix} 3 & 0 \\ 0 & \dfrac{3}{2} \end{pmatrix} \begin{pmatrix} 1 \\ 0 \end{pmatrix}$$

$$= \begin{pmatrix} \cos\theta & -\sin\theta \\ \sin\theta & \cos\theta \end{pmatrix} \begin{pmatrix} 3 \\ 0 \end{pmatrix} = \begin{pmatrix} 3\cos\theta \\ 3\sin\theta \end{pmatrix}$$

On the other hand:

$$\mathbf{MNi} = \begin{pmatrix} 3 & 0 \\ 0 & \dfrac{3}{2} \end{pmatrix} \begin{pmatrix} \cos\theta & -\sin\theta \\ \sin\theta & \cos\theta \end{pmatrix} \begin{pmatrix} 1 \\ 0 \end{pmatrix}$$

$$= \begin{pmatrix} 3 & 0 \\ 0 & \dfrac{3}{2} \end{pmatrix} \begin{pmatrix} \cos\theta \\ \sin\theta \end{pmatrix} = \begin{pmatrix} 3\cos\theta \\ \dfrac{3}{2}\sin\theta \end{pmatrix}$$

So **NMi** is not equal to **MNi**.

The question you should now be asking is: How do we find the matrix of a composite transformation?

The answer is given once again by considering its effect on the base vectors **i**, **j** and **k**. We show the process for two dimensions, then extend the pattern to three.

Let **M** and **N** be the transformations represented by:

$$\mathbf{M} = \begin{pmatrix} \alpha_{11} & \alpha_{12} \\ \alpha_{21} & \alpha_{22} \end{pmatrix} \quad \mathbf{N} = \begin{pmatrix} \beta_{11} & \beta_{12} \\ \beta_{21} & \beta_{22} \end{pmatrix}$$

then: $\mathbf{NMi} = \mathbf{N(Mi)} = \begin{pmatrix} \beta_{11} & \beta_{12} \\ \beta_{21} & \beta_{22} \end{pmatrix} \begin{pmatrix} \alpha_{11} \\ \alpha_{21} \end{pmatrix}$

$$= \begin{pmatrix} \beta_{11}\alpha_{11} + \beta_{12}\alpha_{21} \\ \beta_{21}\alpha_{11} + \beta_{22}\alpha_{21} \end{pmatrix}$$

Similarly, we can show that:

$$\mathbf{NMj} = \begin{pmatrix} \beta_{11}\alpha_{12} + \beta_{12}\alpha_{22} \\ \beta_{21}\alpha_{12} + \beta_{22}\alpha_{22} \end{pmatrix}$$

The matrix of **NM** is therefore:

$$\begin{pmatrix} \beta_{11}\alpha_{11} + \beta_{12}\alpha_{21} & \beta_{11}\alpha_{12} + \beta_{12}\alpha_{22} \\ \beta_{21}\alpha_{11} + \beta_{22}\alpha_{21} & \beta_{21}\alpha_{12} + \beta_{22}\alpha_{22} \end{pmatrix}$$

However, notice that this is exactly the answer we get if we extend our previous idea of matrix multiplication to include the multiplication of two matrices. This is accomplished simply by regarding the columns of **M** as a series of vectors, each one being multiplied by **N** to produce the corresponding column of **NM**. If you don't readily believe this, just try it out.

Now that the pattern has emerged, you will have no difficulty in seeing how it applies to three dimensions. Again, we treat the columns of the right-hand matrix as vectors, and multiply them by the left-hand matrix to form the corresponding columns of the result.

Examples

1   Find the matrix of the composite transformation **NM** in each of the cases below

(a) $\mathbf{M} = \begin{pmatrix} 0 & 3 \\ 8 & 5 \end{pmatrix} \quad \mathbf{N} = \begin{pmatrix} 2 & 1 \\ 3 & 7 \end{pmatrix}$

(b) $\mathbf{M} = \begin{pmatrix} 3 & 2 & -2 \\ -8 & -4 & 5 \\ -1 & -1 & 1 \end{pmatrix} \quad \mathbf{N} = \begin{pmatrix} 1 & 0 & 2 \\ 3 & 1 & 1 \\ 4 & 1 & 4 \end{pmatrix}$

2   For the matrix $\mathbf{L} = \begin{pmatrix} -1 & 2 \\ 0 & 4 \end{pmatrix}$ and the matrices **M** and **N** of question

1(a), show that:

  $\mathbf{N\,(ML)} = \mathbf{(NM)\,L}$

Solutions

1 (a) $\text{NM} = \begin{pmatrix} 2\times0+1\times8 & 2\times3+1\times5 \\ 3\times0+7\times8 & 3\times3+7\times5 \end{pmatrix} = \begin{pmatrix} 8 & 11 \\ 56 & 44 \end{pmatrix}$

(b) $\text{NM} = \begin{pmatrix} 1\times3+0\times-8+2\times-1 & 1\times2+0\times-4+2\times-1 & 1\times-2+0\times5+2\times1 \\ 3\times3+1\times-8+1\times-1 & 3\times2+1\times-4+1\times-1 & 3\times-2+1\times5+1\times1 \\ 4\times3+1\times-8+4\times-1 & 4\times2+1\times-4+4\times-1 & 4\times-2+1\times5+4\times1 \end{pmatrix}$

$= \begin{pmatrix} 1 & 0 & 0 \\ 0 & 1 & 0 \\ 0 & 0 & 1 \end{pmatrix}$

Note: This is a very special matrix which we shall meet again when we investigate the idea of the matrix inverse.

2 (NM) L $= \begin{pmatrix} 8 & 11 \\ 56 & 44 \end{pmatrix}\begin{pmatrix} -1 & 2 \\ 0 & 4 \end{pmatrix} = \begin{pmatrix} -8 & 60 \\ -56 & 288 \end{pmatrix}$

ML $= \begin{pmatrix} 0 & 3 \\ 8 & 5 \end{pmatrix}\begin{pmatrix} -1 & 2 \\ 0 & 4 \end{pmatrix} = \begin{pmatrix} 0 & 12 \\ -8 & 36 \end{pmatrix}$

N (ML) $= \begin{pmatrix} 2 & 1 \\ 3 & 7 \end{pmatrix}\begin{pmatrix} 0 & 12 \\ -8 & 36 \end{pmatrix} = \begin{pmatrix} -8 & 60 \\ -56 & 288 \end{pmatrix}$

The property **(NM)L = N(ML)** holds for all matrices that are capable of being multiplied together.

You should now be able to answer Exercises 4–5 on page 290.

The inverse of a matrix

Given a particular transformation **M**, it is reasonable (and, as we shall see later, productive) to ask: Is there a corresponding **N** which transforms all vectors of the form **Ma** back to the original **a**'s from which they came?

If **N** does exist, it is known as the **inverse** of **M** and is written M^{-1}.
In the case of enlargements, rotations and reflections, the existence of an inverse is clear:

● The effect of an enlargement can be reversed by a second enlargement in which the factors are the reciprocals of those of the first.

● A rotation is reversed by performing another rotation of equal size but opposite direction.

● Any reflection, if repeated, will return all vectors to their starting points.

In general, though, the problem may not be solved quite so easily.
The transformation we seek is some **N** for which:

$$\text{NMa} = \text{a} \quad \text{for any vector } \text{a}$$

This must mean that the matrix of **NM** takes a very special form. Since all vectors – including the base vectors **i**, **j** and **k** – are left unchanged by **NM**, its matrix must be:

$$\begin{pmatrix} 1 & 0 \\ 0 & 1 \end{pmatrix} \quad \text{in two dimensions, and}$$

$$\begin{pmatrix} 1 & 0 & 0 \\ 0 & 1 & 0 \\ 0 & 0 & 1 \end{pmatrix} \quad \text{in three dimensions.}$$

Matrices of this form are known as **identity** matrices (or simply as identities), since they exactly preserve the identity of any vector they multiply. The problem of finding an inverse is therefore that of finding a matrix **N** for which:

NM = I

where **I** is the appropriate identity. We shall now consider the two- and three-dimensional cases separately.

Two dimensions

If $\mathbf{M} = \begin{pmatrix} \alpha & \beta \\ \gamma & \delta \end{pmatrix}$ then $\mathbf{M}^{-1} = \dfrac{1}{\alpha\delta - \beta\gamma} \begin{pmatrix} \delta & -\beta \\ -\gamma & \alpha \end{pmatrix}$

The scalar $\alpha\delta - \beta\gamma$ is written outside the matrix for convenience but is assumed to divide every number within it. This scalar is known as the determinant of **M** and is usually written $|\mathbf{M}|$ or 'det **M**'. This determinant has a very important role to play and consequently is given a special symbol all of its own. It is usual to write $|\mathbf{M}| = \begin{vmatrix} \alpha & \beta \\ \gamma & \delta \end{vmatrix}$

$\Rightarrow \quad |\mathbf{M}| = \alpha\delta - \beta\gamma$

The proof that the form of $\mathbf{M}^{-1}$ is correct is that it works! Multiply **M** and $\mathbf{M}^{-1}$ together to give:

$$\mathbf{M}^{-1}\mathbf{M} = \frac{1}{\alpha\delta - \beta\gamma}\begin{pmatrix} \delta & -\beta \\ -\gamma & \alpha \end{pmatrix}\begin{pmatrix} \alpha & \beta \\ \gamma & \delta \end{pmatrix} = \frac{1}{\alpha\delta - \beta\gamma}\begin{pmatrix} \delta\alpha - \beta\gamma & \delta\beta - \beta\delta \\ -\gamma\alpha + \alpha\gamma & -\gamma\beta + \alpha\delta \end{pmatrix}$$

$$= \begin{pmatrix} 1 & 0 \\ 0 & 1 \end{pmatrix}$$

Don't try to remember the formula for the inverse of **M**. You will find it easier to recall the following sequence of steps:

1   Swap over the numbers on the main diagonal

2   Change the signs of the other two numbers

3   Divide by the determinant $|\mathbf{M}| = \alpha\delta - \beta\gamma$.

Three dimensions

The procedure for finding the inverse of a 3×3 matrix is more complicated, but can still be recalled with reasonable ease as a sequence of steps.

Suppose the matrix **M** is given by:
$$\begin{pmatrix} \alpha_1 & \alpha_2 & \alpha_3 \\ \beta_1 & \beta_2 & \beta_3 \\ \gamma_1 & \gamma_2 & \gamma_3 \end{pmatrix}$$

Before we can calculate $\mathbf{M}^{-1}$ we must introduce a new term. For each number in the matrix above we define a **minor**. This is the determinant of the remaining 2×2 matrix when the number's row and column are removed. For example, the minor of β_2 is the determinant of:

$$\begin{pmatrix} \alpha_1 & \alpha_3 \\ \gamma_1 & \gamma_3 \end{pmatrix}$$

We denote the minor of α_1 by A_1, the minor of β_1 by B_1 and so on.

We can now proceed with the inversion of **M**.

Step 1:   Form the matrix of minors
$$\begin{pmatrix} A_1 & A_2 & A_3 \\ B_1 & B_2 & B_3 \\ C_1 & C_2 & C_3 \end{pmatrix}$$

Step 2:   Change the signs of alternate minors
$$\begin{pmatrix} A_1 & -A_2 & A_3 \\ -B_1 & B_2 & -B_3 \\ C_1 & -C_2 & C_3 \end{pmatrix}$$

Step 3:   Transpose this matrix to form
$$\begin{pmatrix} A_1 & -B_1 & C_1 \\ -A_2 & B_2 & -C_2 \\ A_3 & -B_3 & C_3 \end{pmatrix}$$

Note: To transpose a matrix, write its rows as columns. The transpose of a matrix **N** is denoted by $\mathbf{N}^{\mathrm{T}}$.

Step 4:   Divide by the determinant $| \mathbf{M} |$ which, in the case of a three-dimensional matrix, can be calculated from:

$$| \mathbf{M} | = \alpha_1 A_1 - \alpha_2 A_2 + \alpha_3 A_3$$

The result is the required inverse $\mathbf{M}^{-1}$.

We will be able to put this procedure into practice in the next exercise. First, though, we should deal with a small problem that may have occurred to you.

In both the two- and the three-dimensional cases, finding an inverse depended on dividing by the determinant. It is quite possible that the determinant is zero, and therefore that the process cannot continue. In such cases, the inverse just does not exist and we say that the transformation and its matrix are **singular**. Clearly, wherever the determinant is non-zero the inverse does exist, and the matrix is said to be **non-singular**.

Examples

1 Find the inverses of the following matrices

(a) $\begin{pmatrix} 2 & 1 \\ -3 & 4 \end{pmatrix}$ (b) $\begin{pmatrix} 1 & 0 & 2 \\ 3 & 1 & 1 \\ 4 & 1 & 4 \end{pmatrix}$

2 Show that, if the inverses $\mathbf{M}^{-1}$ and $\mathbf{N}^{-1}$ exist, the inverse of the matrix product $\mathbf{NM}$ is $\mathbf{M}^{-1}\mathbf{N}^{-1}$.

3 Evaluate $\begin{vmatrix} 1 & 2 & 3 \\ 4 & 5 & 6 \\ 7 & 8 & 9 \end{vmatrix}$

Solutions

1 (a) The inverse is: $\dfrac{1}{2\times 4 - (-3)\times 1}\begin{pmatrix} 4 & -1 \\ 3 & 2 \end{pmatrix} = \dfrac{1}{11}\begin{pmatrix} 4 & -1 \\ 3 & 2 \end{pmatrix}$

   (b) **Step 1:** $\begin{pmatrix} 3 & 8 & -1 \\ -2 & -4 & 1 \\ -2 & -5 & 1 \end{pmatrix}$

   Step 2: $\begin{pmatrix} 3 & -8 & -1 \\ 2 & -4 & -1 \\ -2 & 5 & 1 \end{pmatrix}$

   Step 3: $\begin{pmatrix} 3 & 2 & -2 \\ -8 & -4 & 5 \\ -1 & -1 & 1 \end{pmatrix}$

   Step 4: The determinant is $1\times 3 - 0\times 8 + 2\times -1 = 1$ and so the matrix of step 3 is the inverse we require.

Notice that we have already verified this inverse in the previous set of Examples. It really does work!

2 This is remarkably easy to prove once you know how. Just notice that, provided the two inverses exist, we have:

$$(\mathbf{M}^{-1}\mathbf{N}^{-1})\mathbf{NM} \quad = \mathbf{M}^{-1}(\mathbf{N}^{-1}\mathbf{NM}) = \mathbf{M}^{-1}\mathbf{N}^{-1}\mathbf{N})\mathbf{M}$$
$$= \mathbf{M}^{-1}\mathbf{IM} \qquad = \mathbf{M}^{-1}\mathbf{M}$$
$$= \mathbf{I}$$

Notice the use we make of the associative property that we met in the previous exercise.

3 $\begin{vmatrix} 1 & 2 & 3 \\ 4 & 5 & 6 \\ 7 & 8 & 9 \end{vmatrix} = 1\times (45 - 48) - 2\times (36 - 42) + 3\times (32 - 35) = 0$

The determinant is zero $\therefore$ the matrix $\begin{pmatrix} 1 & 2 & 3 \\ 4 & 5 & 6 \\ 7 & 8 & 9 \end{pmatrix}$ is singular.

You should now be able to answer Exercise 6 on page 290.

Linear equations

One of the most important applications of inverse matrices involves the solution of simultaneous linear equations. We illustrate the method in two dimensions, but the same principles apply in three – and higher. Let us take as an example:

$$3\alpha + 2\beta = 8$$
$$4\alpha - \beta = 7$$

It would, of course, be easy to solve these by the usual methods, but here our purpose is to demonstrate the use of the matrix inverse. Notice first that the equations may be written in terms of a matrix and vectors as:

$$\begin{pmatrix} 3 & 2 \\ 4 & -1 \end{pmatrix} \begin{pmatrix} \alpha \\ \beta \end{pmatrix} = \begin{pmatrix} 8 \\ 7 \end{pmatrix}$$

If we denote by **M** the matrix: $\begin{pmatrix} 3 & 2 \\ 4 & -1 \end{pmatrix}$

and by **a** the vector: $\begin{pmatrix} \alpha \\ \beta \end{pmatrix}$

Then: $\mathbf{Ma} = \begin{pmatrix} 8 \\ 7 \end{pmatrix}$

Pre-multiplying by $\mathbf{M}^{-1}$ (i.e. multiplying on the left – remember that the order matters), we have:

$$\mathbf{M}^{-1}\mathbf{Ma} = \mathbf{M}^{-1} \begin{pmatrix} 8 \\ 7 \end{pmatrix}$$

and so, since $\mathbf{M}^{-1}\mathbf{Ma} = \mathbf{Ia} = \mathbf{a}$, it follows that:

$$\mathbf{a} = \frac{1}{3 \times -1 - 2 \times 4} \begin{pmatrix} -1 & -2 \\ -4 & 3 \end{pmatrix} \begin{pmatrix} 8 \\ 7 \end{pmatrix} = \frac{-1}{11} \begin{pmatrix} -22 \\ -11 \end{pmatrix} = \begin{pmatrix} 2 \\ 1 \end{pmatrix}$$

$$\begin{pmatrix} \alpha \\ \beta \end{pmatrix} = \begin{pmatrix} 2 \\ 1 \end{pmatrix} \quad \text{i.e. } \alpha = 2 \text{ and } \beta = 1.$$

You probably feel that this was a lot of effort for little gain. However, remember that the same basic method can be used whatever the number of unknowns. In general, any set of linear equations may be written in the form:

$$\mathbf{Ma} = \mathbf{b}$$

where **M** is a known matrix, **b** is a known vector and **a** is to be determined. Provided the inverse exists, the solution will always be:

$$\mathbf{a} = \mathbf{M}^{-1}\mathbf{b}$$

If we also have some means of finding $\mathbf{M}^{-1}$ – and even for dimensions higher than two or three, procedures for this exist – then the problem is all but solved.

Examples	Solve the following linear equations by matrix methods.

1 $2\alpha + \beta = 15$
$-4\alpha + 3\beta = 20$

2 $\alpha_1 + 2\alpha_3 = 1$
$3\alpha_1 + \alpha_2 + \alpha_3 = 1$
$4\alpha_1 + \alpha_2 + 4\alpha_3 = 1$

Solutions

1 $\begin{pmatrix} 2 & 1 \\ -4 & 3 \end{pmatrix} \begin{pmatrix} \alpha \\ \beta \end{pmatrix} = \begin{pmatrix} 15 \\ 20 \end{pmatrix}$ and so

$$\begin{pmatrix} \alpha \\ \beta \end{pmatrix} = \frac{1}{10} \begin{pmatrix} 3 & -1 \\ 4 & 2 \end{pmatrix} \begin{pmatrix} 15 \\ 20 \end{pmatrix} = \frac{1}{10} \begin{pmatrix} 25 \\ 100 \end{pmatrix}$$

Therefore $\alpha = 2\frac{1}{2}$ and $\beta = 10$.

2 $\begin{pmatrix} 1 & 0 & 2 \\ 3 & 1 & 1 \\ 4 & 1 & 4 \end{pmatrix} \begin{pmatrix} \alpha_1 \\ \alpha_2 \\ \alpha_3 \end{pmatrix} = \begin{pmatrix} 1 \\ 1 \\ 1 \end{pmatrix}$ and so

$$\begin{pmatrix} \alpha_1 \\ \alpha_2 \\ \alpha_3 \end{pmatrix} = \begin{pmatrix} 3 & 2 & -2 \\ -8 & -4 & 5 \\ -1 & -1 & 1 \end{pmatrix} \begin{pmatrix} 1 \\ 1 \\ 1 \end{pmatrix} = \begin{pmatrix} 3 \\ -7 \\ -1 \end{pmatrix}$$

Therefore $\alpha_1 = 3$, $\alpha_2 = -7$, $\alpha_3 = -1$.

Notice here that we have used the inverse that we found in the previous set of examples.

You should now be able to answer Exercises 7–9 on page 290.

The transpose of a matrix

The transpose of a matrix $\mathbf{A}$ is denoted by $\mathbf{A}^T$ and is obtained by interchanging rows and columns. For example:

$$\mathbf{A} = \begin{pmatrix} 1 & 2 \\ 3 & 4 \end{pmatrix} \Rightarrow \mathbf{A}^T = \begin{pmatrix} 1 & 3 \\ 2 & 4 \end{pmatrix}$$

Similarly $\mathbf{B} = \begin{pmatrix} 1 & 2 & 3 \\ 4 & 5 & 6 \\ 7 & 8 & 9 \end{pmatrix} \Rightarrow \mathbf{B}^T = \begin{pmatrix} 1 & 4 & 7 \\ 2 & 5 & 8 \\ 3 & 6 & 9 \end{pmatrix}$

Example	If $A = \begin{pmatrix} 3 & 4 \\ 5 & 6 \end{pmatrix}$ and $B = \begin{pmatrix} 2 & 3 \\ 7 & 1 \end{pmatrix}$ verify that $(AB)^T = B^T A^T$.

Solution	$AB = \begin{pmatrix} 3 & 4 \\ 5 & 6 \end{pmatrix}\begin{pmatrix} 2 & 3 \\ 7 & 1 \end{pmatrix} = \begin{pmatrix} 34 & 13 \\ 52 & 21 \end{pmatrix} \Rightarrow (AB)^T = \begin{pmatrix} 34 & 52 \\ 13 & 21 \end{pmatrix}$

Also $B^T A^T = \begin{pmatrix} 2 & 7 \\ 3 & 1 \end{pmatrix}\begin{pmatrix} 3 & 5 \\ 4 & 6 \end{pmatrix} = \begin{pmatrix} 34 & 52 \\ 13 & 21 \end{pmatrix}$

$\therefore$ it follows that $(AB)^T = B^T A^T$.

This is an important result and should be learnt by heart.

$$(AB)^T = B^T A^T$$
and
$$(AB)^{-1} = B^{-1} A^{-1} \quad \text{(See Examples on page 275)}$$

Symmetric matrices

A matrix A is symmetric if $A = A^T$.

For example $\begin{pmatrix} 6 & 2 \\ 2 & 8 \end{pmatrix}$ and $\begin{pmatrix} 5 & 4 & 2 \\ 4 & 8 & 7 \\ 2 & 7 & 3 \end{pmatrix}$ are symmetric matrixes.

Example	A and B are symmetric 3×3 matrices such that $AB = BA$. Prove that AB is symmetric.

Solution	$(AB)^T \quad = B^T A^T$ (see the previous example)
	$\qquad\quad = BA$ (because B and A are symmetric)
	$\qquad\quad = AB$ (a given condition)
	$\therefore (AB)^T = AB$ $\therefore AB$ is symmetric

Diagonal matrices

A diagonal matrix is one where all the entries which aren't on the main diagonal are zero. For example

$\begin{pmatrix} 3 & 0 \\ 0 & 7 \end{pmatrix}$ and $\begin{pmatrix} 1 & 0 & 0 \\ 0 & 2 & 0 \\ 0 & 0 & -3 \end{pmatrix}$ are diagonal matrices.

| Example | Is $\begin{pmatrix} 5 & 0 & 0 \\ 0 & 8 & 0 \\ 0 & 0 & 0 \end{pmatrix}$ a diagonal matrix? |

| Solution | Yes. |

| Example | If **A** and **B** are 3×3 diagonal matrices, prove that **AB** is diagonal. |

Solution

Let $\quad \mathbf{A} \quad = \begin{pmatrix} a & 0 & 0 \\ 0 & b & 0 \\ 0 & 0 & c \end{pmatrix} \quad$ and **B** $\quad = \begin{pmatrix} p & 0 & 0 \\ 0 & q & 0 \\ 0 & 0 & r \end{pmatrix}$

$\therefore \quad \mathbf{AB} = \begin{pmatrix} a & 0 & 0 \\ 0 & b & 0 \\ 0 & 0 & c \end{pmatrix}\begin{pmatrix} p & 0 & 0 \\ 0 & q & 0 \\ 0 & 0 & r \end{pmatrix} \quad = \begin{pmatrix} ap & 0 & 0 \\ 0 & bq & 0 \\ 0 & 0 & rc \end{pmatrix}$

$\therefore \quad$ **AB** is also a diagonal matrix.

Singular matrices revisited

We saw on page 275 that a matrix **M** is singular if det **M** = 0. Or, putting it another way, a matrix **M** is singular if the inverse matrix **M** does not exist.

(| **M** | and det **M** are alternative ways of saying determinant of **M**.)

| Example | Is matrix $\mathbf{A} = \begin{pmatrix} 5 & 2 \\ 10 & 4 \end{pmatrix}$ singular? |

| Solution | det $\mathbf{A} = 5 \times 4 - 2 \times 10 = 0$ |

$\therefore \quad$ matrix **A** is singular. The inverse matrix $\mathbf{A}^{-1}$ does not exist.

The equation Ax = 0

If matrix **A** is non-singular (i.e. $\mathbf{A}^{-1}$ exists) then

$$\mathbf{A}x = 0 \Rightarrow \mathbf{A}^{-1}\mathbf{A}x = \mathbf{A}^{-1}0 \Rightarrow x = 0$$

However, if $\mathbf{A}x = 0$ and $x \neq 0$ then **A** must be singular (i.e. det **A** = 0).

This is a very important result.

$$\mathbf{A}x = \mathbf{0} \text{ and } x \neq \mathbf{0} \Rightarrow \det \mathbf{A} = \mathbf{0}$$

Eigenvalues and eigenvectors

Given any matrix **B**, if you can find a non-zero vector x and a scalar λ such that $\mathbf{A}x = \lambda x$, then x is called an *eigenvector* and λ an *eigenvalue*.

For example $\begin{pmatrix} 2 & 0 & 1 \\ -1 & 2 & 3 \\ 1 & 0 & 2 \end{pmatrix}\begin{pmatrix} 1 \\ 2 \\ 1 \end{pmatrix} = \begin{pmatrix} 3 \\ 6 \\ 3 \end{pmatrix} = 3\begin{pmatrix} 1 \\ 2 \\ 1 \end{pmatrix}$

$\therefore \quad \begin{pmatrix} 1 \\ 2 \\ 1 \end{pmatrix}$ is an *eigenvector* of matrix $\begin{pmatrix} 2 & 0 & 1 \\ -1 & 2 & 3 \\ 1 & 0 & 2 \end{pmatrix}$

with corresponding *eigenvalue* $\lambda = 3$.

Finding eigenvalues

For matrix **A**, with eigenvalue λ and corresponding eigenvector x, we have $\mathbf{A}x = \lambda x$. This can be re-written as $(\mathbf{A} - \lambda \mathbf{I})x = 0$. Since $x \neq 0$ it follows that $\det(\mathbf{A} - \lambda \mathbf{I}) = 0$. This is a very important result.

> The eigenvalue λ for any given matrix **A** are found
> by solving the equation $\det(\mathbf{A} - \lambda \mathbf{I}) = 0$.

Example Find the eigenvalues of the matrix $\mathbf{A} = \begin{pmatrix} 4 & 2 \\ 1 & 3 \end{pmatrix}$

Solution

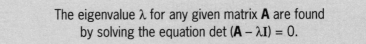

$\mathbf{A} - \lambda \mathbf{I} = \begin{pmatrix} 4 & 2 \\ 1 & 3 \end{pmatrix} - \lambda \begin{pmatrix} 1 & 0 \\ 0 & 1 \end{pmatrix} = \begin{pmatrix} 4-\lambda & 2 \\ 1 & 3-\lambda \end{pmatrix}$

$\therefore \quad \det(\mathbf{A} - \lambda \mathbf{I}) = 0 \Rightarrow \begin{vmatrix} 4-\lambda & 2 \\ 1 & 3-\lambda \end{vmatrix} = 0$

$\Rightarrow (4 - \lambda)(3 - \lambda) - 2 = 0$

$\Rightarrow \lambda^2 - 7\lambda + 10 = 0 \Rightarrow \lambda = 2 \text{ or } 5$

Example Find the eigenvectors of the matrix $\mathbf{A} = \begin{pmatrix} 4 & 2 \\ 1 & 3 \end{pmatrix}$

Solution We saw in the previous example that $\lambda = 2$ was one of the eigenvalues. Corresponding to this we have eigenvector x, where $\mathbf{A}x = 2x$.

$\therefore \quad \begin{pmatrix} 4 & 2 \\ 1 & 3 \end{pmatrix}\begin{pmatrix} x \\ y \end{pmatrix} = 2\begin{pmatrix} x \\ y \end{pmatrix} \Rightarrow \begin{array}{l} 4x + 2y = 2x. \\ x + 3y = 2y \end{array} \Rightarrow y = -x$

$\therefore \quad$ the corresponding eigenvector $\begin{pmatrix} x \\ y \end{pmatrix}$ is such that $y = -x$.

∴ the corresponding eigenvector is $\begin{pmatrix} x \\ -x \end{pmatrix} = x \begin{pmatrix} 1 \\ -1 \end{pmatrix}$

∴ the corresponding eigenvector is a scalar multiple of $\begin{pmatrix} 1 \\ -1 \end{pmatrix}$

∴ the eigenvector corresponding to the eigenvalue $\lambda = 2$ is a scalar multiple of $\begin{pmatrix} 1 \\ -1 \end{pmatrix}$.

We also saw in the previous example that $\lambda = 5$ was the other eigenvalue.

∴ $\mathbf{A}x = 5x \Rightarrow \begin{pmatrix} 4 & 2 \\ 1 & 3 \end{pmatrix}\begin{pmatrix} x \\ y \end{pmatrix} = 5\begin{pmatrix} x \\ y \end{pmatrix} \Rightarrow \begin{array}{c} 4x + 2y = 5x \\ x + 3y = 5y \end{array} \Rightarrow 2y = x$

∴ the corresponding eigenvector $\begin{pmatrix} x \\ y \end{pmatrix}$ is such that $2y = x$

∴ the corresponding eigenvector is $\begin{pmatrix} 2y \\ y \end{pmatrix} = y \begin{pmatrix} 2 \\ 1 \end{pmatrix}$

∴ the corresponding eigenvector is a scalar multiple of $\begin{pmatrix} 2 \\ 1 \end{pmatrix}$

∴ the eigenvector corresponding to the eigenvalue of $\lambda = 5$ is a scalar multiple of $\begin{pmatrix} 2 \\ 1 \end{pmatrix}$.

You must try to master this as it will almost certainly be the basis of an 'A' level question. As far as the examination is concerned, you are likely to be given a 3×3 matrix and asked to find its eigenvalues and eigenvectors. The *process* is exactly the same as for a 2×2 matrix but the evaluation of the 3×3 determinant and the solutions of the corresponding simultaneous equations is just a little more tricky.

Let's work through a 3×3 example now.

Example

Find the eigenvalues of the matrix $\mathbf{A} = \begin{pmatrix} 1 & 4 & -1 \\ -1 & 6 & -1 \\ 2 & -2 & 4 \end{pmatrix}$

Solution

$\mathbf{A} - \lambda\mathbf{I} = \begin{pmatrix} 1 & 4 & -1 \\ -1 & 6 & -1 \\ 2 & -2 & 4 \end{pmatrix} - \lambda \begin{pmatrix} 1 & 0 & 0 \\ 0 & 1 & 0 \\ 0 & 0 & 1 \end{pmatrix} = \begin{pmatrix} 1-\lambda & 4 & -1 \\ -1 & 6-\lambda & -1 \\ 2 & -2 & 4-\lambda \end{pmatrix}$

$$\therefore \quad \det(\mathbf{A} - \lambda\mathbf{I}) = 0 \Rightarrow \begin{vmatrix} 1-\lambda & 4 & -1 \\ -1 & 6-\lambda & -1 \\ 2 & -2 & 4-\lambda \end{vmatrix} = 0$$

$$\Rightarrow \quad (1-\lambda)\left[(6-\lambda)(4-\lambda)-2\right] - 4\left[-(4-\lambda)+2\right] - 1\left[2-2(6-\lambda)\right] = 0$$

$$\Rightarrow \quad (1-\lambda)(\lambda^2 - 10\lambda + 22) - 4(\lambda - 2) - 1(2\lambda - 10) = 0$$

$$\Rightarrow \quad (\text{eventually!}) - \lambda^3 + 11\lambda^2 - 38\lambda + 40 = 0$$

Changing all the signs, we now have to solve the equation

$$\lambda^3 - 11\lambda^2 + 38\lambda - 40 = 0$$

By inspection $\lambda = 2$ works $\therefore \quad (\lambda - 2)$ is a factor.

Long division gives $(\lambda - 2)(\lambda^2 - 9\lambda + 20) = 0$

$$\therefore \quad (\lambda - 2)(\lambda - 4)(\lambda - 5) = 0$$

$\therefore \quad$ A has eigenvalues 2, 4 and 5.

Example

Find the eigenvectors of the matrix $A = \begin{pmatrix} 1 & 4 & -1 \\ -1 & 6 & -1 \\ 2 & -2 & 4 \end{pmatrix}$

Solution

The eigenvalues have been found in the previous example.

Corresponding to $\lambda = 2$ we have

$$\begin{pmatrix} 1 & 4 & -1 \\ -1 & 6 & -1 \\ 2 & -2 & 4 \end{pmatrix}\begin{pmatrix} x \\ y \\ z \end{pmatrix} = 2\begin{pmatrix} x \\ y \\ z \end{pmatrix} \Rightarrow \begin{array}{l} x + 4y - z = 2x \\ -x + 6y - z = 2y \\ 2x - 2y + 4z = 2z \end{array}$$

$$\Rightarrow \quad \begin{array}{l} -x + 4y - z = 0 \\ -x + 4y - z = 0 \\ 2x - 2y + 2z = 0 \end{array} \Rightarrow y = 0 \text{ and } x = -z$$

$\therefore \quad$ the corresponding eigenvector is $\begin{pmatrix} -z \\ 0 \\ z \end{pmatrix} = z\begin{pmatrix} -1 \\ 0 \\ 1 \end{pmatrix}$

Corresponding to $\lambda = 4$ we have:

$$\begin{pmatrix} 1 & 4 & -1 \\ -1 & 6 & -1 \\ 2 & -2 & 4 \end{pmatrix}\begin{pmatrix} x \\ y \\ z \end{pmatrix} = 4\begin{pmatrix} x \\ y \\ z \end{pmatrix} \Rightarrow \begin{array}{l} x + 4y - z = 4x \\ -x + 6y - z = 4y \\ 2x - 2y + 4z = 4z \end{array}$$

$$\begin{array}{l} -3x + 4y - z = 0 \\ \Rightarrow -x + 2y - z = 0 \\ 2x - 2y = 0 \end{array} \Rightarrow x = y = z$$

$\therefore \quad$ the corresponding eigenvector is $\begin{pmatrix} x \\ x \\ x \end{pmatrix} = x\begin{pmatrix} 1 \\ 1 \\ 1 \end{pmatrix}$

Corresponding to $\lambda = 5$ we have

$$\begin{pmatrix} 1 & 4 & -1 \\ -1 & 6 & -1 \\ 2 & -2 & 4 \end{pmatrix}\begin{pmatrix} x \\ y \\ z \end{pmatrix} = 5\begin{pmatrix} x \\ y \\ z \end{pmatrix} \Rightarrow \begin{array}{l} x + 4y - z = 5x \\ -x + 6y - z = 5y \\ 2x - 2y + 4z = 5z \end{array}$$

$$\begin{array}{l} 4x + 4y - z = 0 \\ -x + y - z = 0 \\ 2x - 2y - z = 0 \end{array} \Rightarrow x = y \text{ and } z = 0$$

∴ the corresponding eigenvector is $\begin{pmatrix} y \\ y \\ 0 \end{pmatrix} = y\begin{pmatrix} 1 \\ 1 \\ 0 \end{pmatrix}$

∴ Matrix **A** has eigenvalues 2, 4 and 5 with corresponding eigenvector

scalar multiples of $\begin{pmatrix} -1 \\ 0 \\ 1 \end{pmatrix}, \begin{pmatrix} 1 \\ 1 \\ 1 \end{pmatrix}$ and $\begin{pmatrix} 1 \\ 1 \\ 0 \end{pmatrix}$ respectively.

You should now be able to answer Exercises 10–11 on page 291.

Diagonalising a matrix A

The interesting thing about eigenvectors is that, if you put them in columns to make up a matrix **P** (say), then $\mathbf{P}^{-1}\mathbf{AP}$ always works out as something rather special. Let's see what happens.

In the earlier examples we saw that the matrix $\mathbf{A} = \begin{pmatrix} 4 & 2 \\ 1 & 3 \end{pmatrix}$ had

eigenvectors which were scalar multiples of $\begin{pmatrix} 1 \\ -1 \end{pmatrix}$ and $\begin{pmatrix} 2 \\ 1 \end{pmatrix}$

∴ Let $\mathbf{P} = \begin{pmatrix} 1 & 2 \\ -1 & 1 \end{pmatrix}$ (no need to include the multiple bit)

∴ $\mathbf{P}^{-1} = \frac{1}{3}\begin{pmatrix} 1 & -2 \\ 1 & 1 \end{pmatrix}$

∴ $\mathbf{P}^{-1}\mathbf{AP} = \frac{1}{3}\begin{pmatrix} 1 & -2 \\ 1 & 1 \end{pmatrix}\begin{pmatrix} 4 & 2 \\ 1 & 3 \end{pmatrix}\begin{pmatrix} 1 & 2 \\ -1 & 1 \end{pmatrix}$

$$= \frac{1}{3}\begin{pmatrix} 2 & -4 \\ 5 & 5 \end{pmatrix}\begin{pmatrix} 1 & 2 \\ -1 & 1 \end{pmatrix} = \frac{1}{3}\begin{pmatrix} 6 & 0 \\ 0 & 15 \end{pmatrix}$$

∴ $\mathbf{P}^{-1}\mathbf{AP} = \begin{pmatrix} 2 & 0 \\ 0 & 5 \end{pmatrix}$

But we saw earlier that **A** had eigenvalues of 2 and 5!

And *that* is the special result:

If matrix **A** has eigenvalues λ_1 and λ_2 and corresponding eigenvectors $\mathbf{x}_1$ and $\mathbf{x}_2$, then if matrix **P** has columns $\mathbf{x}_1$ and $\mathbf{x}_2$,

$$\mathbf{P}^{-1}\mathbf{A}\mathbf{P} = \begin{pmatrix} \lambda_1 & 0 \\ 0 & \lambda_2 \end{pmatrix}$$

This result generalises to 3×3 matrices :

If the 3×3 matrix **A** has eigenvalues λ_1, λ_2 and λ_3 with corresponding eigenvectors $\mathbf{x}_1$, $\mathbf{x}_2$ and $\mathbf{x}_3$, then, if matrix **P** has columns $\mathbf{x}_1$, $\mathbf{x}_2$ and $\mathbf{x}_3$,

$$\mathbf{P}^{-1}\mathbf{A}\mathbf{P} = \begin{pmatrix} \lambda_1 & 0 & 0 \\ 0 & \lambda_2 & 0 \\ 0 & 0 & \lambda_3 \end{pmatrix}$$

You need to learn the above result by heart, for your examination. You will either be expected to quote it from memory or to verify that it is true.

You should now be able to answer Exercises 12–16 on page 291.

A closer look at the matrix P

Two things will have occurred to you by now concerning the matrix **P**.

The first is that **P** is not unique. For example, we saw above that the matrix

$\mathbf{P} = \begin{pmatrix} 1 & 2 \\ -1 & 1 \end{pmatrix}$ diagonalises matrix $\mathbf{A} = \begin{pmatrix} 4 & 2 \\ 1 & 3 \end{pmatrix}$ because it gave us $\mathbf{P}^{-1}\mathbf{A}\mathbf{P} = \begin{pmatrix} 2 & 0 \\ 0 & 5 \end{pmatrix}$

But we could just as well have taken different scalar multiples of the

eigenvectors $\begin{pmatrix} 1 \\ -1 \end{pmatrix}$ and $\begin{pmatrix} 2 \\ 1 \end{pmatrix}$. For instance we might have taken $\mathbf{P} = \begin{pmatrix} 3 & 4 \\ -3 & 2 \end{pmatrix}$

In that case we would have had $\mathbf{P}^{-1} = \dfrac{1}{18} \begin{pmatrix} 2 & -4 \\ 3 & 3 \end{pmatrix}$ giving us:

$$\begin{aligned} \mathbf{P}^{-1}\mathbf{A}\mathbf{P} &= \frac{1}{18} \begin{pmatrix} 2 & -4 \\ 3 & 3 \end{pmatrix}\begin{pmatrix} 4 & 2 \\ 1 & 3 \end{pmatrix}\begin{pmatrix} 3 & 4 \\ -3 & 2 \end{pmatrix} \\[2mm] &= \frac{1}{18} \begin{pmatrix} 4 & -8 \\ 15 & 15 \end{pmatrix}\begin{pmatrix} 3 & 4 \\ -3 & 2 \end{pmatrix} \\[2mm] &= \frac{1}{18} \begin{pmatrix} 36 & 0 \\ 0 & 90 \end{pmatrix} = \begin{pmatrix} 2 & 0 \\ 0 & 5 \end{pmatrix} \end{aligned}$$

Once again we have ended up with $\mathbf{P}^{-1}\mathbf{AP} = \begin{pmatrix} 2 & 0 \\ 0 & 5 \end{pmatrix}$

but this time with a different matrix $\mathbf{P}$.

And so the first thing to notice about matrix $\mathbf{P}$ is that we've got plenty of choices!

The second thing that will have occurred to you by now is how tedious it is having to find the inverse matrix $\mathbf{P}^{-1}$ all of the time. If only there was an easier way!

Well, in many cases there is. *If we can find a matrix $\mathbf{P}$ such that its column vectors are mutually perpendicular and of unit length, then $\mathbf{P}^{-1}$ is always equal to $\mathbf{P}^T$.* And $\mathbf{P}^T$ is easy to write down.

Example

Verify that the column vectors of matrix $\mathbf{P}$, where

$$\mathbf{P} = \begin{pmatrix} \frac{1}{3} & \frac{2}{3} & \frac{2}{3} \\ \frac{2}{3} & \frac{1}{3} & \frac{-2}{3} \\ \frac{-2}{3} & \frac{2}{3} & \frac{-1}{3} \end{pmatrix}$$

are (a) mutually perpendicular and (b) of unit length.

Verify further that $\mathbf{P}^T = \mathbf{P}^{-1}$.

Solution

(a)   Vectors are perpendicular if their scalar product is zero.

Now $\begin{pmatrix} \frac{1}{3} \\ \frac{2}{3} \\ \frac{-2}{3} \end{pmatrix} \cdot \begin{pmatrix} \frac{2}{3} \\ \frac{1}{3} \\ \frac{2}{3} \end{pmatrix} = \frac{2}{9} + \frac{2}{9} - \frac{4}{9} = 0$

$\therefore$ Vectors $\begin{pmatrix} \frac{1}{3} \\ \frac{2}{3} \\ \frac{-2}{3} \end{pmatrix}$ and $\begin{pmatrix} \frac{2}{3} \\ \frac{1}{3} \\ \frac{2}{3} \end{pmatrix}$ are perpendicular.

Similarly $\begin{pmatrix} \frac{1}{3} \\ \frac{2}{3} \\ \frac{-2}{3} \end{pmatrix} \cdot \begin{pmatrix} \frac{2}{3} \\ \frac{-2}{3} \\ \frac{-1}{3} \end{pmatrix} = 0$ and $\begin{pmatrix} \frac{2}{3} \\ \frac{1}{3} \\ \frac{2}{3} \end{pmatrix} \cdot \begin{pmatrix} \frac{2}{3} \\ \frac{-2}{3} \\ \frac{-1}{3} \end{pmatrix} = 0$

$\therefore$ All 3 column vectors are mutually perpendicular.

(b)   The length of any vector $\mathbf{v} = \begin{pmatrix} a \\ b \\ c \end{pmatrix}$ is given by :

$$| \mathbf{v} | = \sqrt{a^2 + b^2 + c^2} .$$

$\therefore$ the length of $\begin{pmatrix} \frac{1}{3} \\ \frac{2}{3} \\ \frac{-2}{3} \end{pmatrix}$ is $\sqrt{\left(\tfrac{1}{3}\right)^2 + \left(\tfrac{2}{3}\right)^2 + \left(-\tfrac{2}{3}\right)^2} = \sqrt{\tfrac{9}{9}} = 1$

$\therefore$ The vector $\begin{pmatrix} \frac{1}{3} \\ \frac{2}{3} \\ \frac{-2}{3} \end{pmatrix}$ has unit length.

Similarly the vectors $\begin{pmatrix} \frac{2}{3} \\ \frac{1}{3} \\ \frac{2}{3} \end{pmatrix}$ and $\begin{pmatrix} \frac{2}{3} \\ \frac{-2}{3} \\ \frac{-1}{3} \end{pmatrix}$ have unit length

$\therefore$ all 3 column vectors have unit length.

Finally $\mathbf{P}^{\mathrm{T}} = \begin{pmatrix} \frac{1}{3} & \frac{2}{3} & \frac{-2}{3} \\ \frac{2}{3} & \frac{1}{3} & \frac{2}{3} \\ \frac{2}{3} & \frac{-2}{3} & \frac{-1}{3} \end{pmatrix}$

and $\mathbf{P}^{\mathrm{T}} = \begin{pmatrix} \frac{1}{3} & \frac{2}{3} & \frac{-2}{3} \\ \frac{2}{3} & \frac{1}{3} & \frac{2}{3} \\ \frac{2}{3} & \frac{-2}{3} & \frac{-1}{3} \end{pmatrix} \begin{pmatrix} \frac{1}{3} & \frac{2}{3} & \frac{2}{3} \\ \frac{2}{3} & \frac{1}{3} & \frac{-2}{3} \\ \frac{-2}{3} & \frac{2}{3} & \frac{-1}{3} \end{pmatrix} = \begin{pmatrix} 1 & 0 & 0 \\ 0 & 1 & 0 \\ 0 & 0 & 1 \end{pmatrix}$

$\therefore$ $\mathbf{P}^{\mathrm{T}}\mathbf{P} = \mathbf{I}$ $\therefore$ $\mathbf{P}^{\mathrm{T}} = \mathbf{P}^{-1}$.

A quick method when the matrix A is symmetric

If the matrix A is symmetric then it is always possible to find eigenvectors which are mutually perpendicular and of unit length. It follows that $\mathbf{P}^{-1} = \mathbf{P}^{\mathrm{T}}$.

This gives us a very important result which you need to learn by heart (as well as it being time-saving).

Given a *symmetric* matrix **A**, choose eigenvectors
which are mutually perpendicular and of unit length.
If Matrix **P** then has these vectors as columns,
and if the eigenvalues of **A** are λ_1, λ_2 and λ_3, then

$$\mathbf{P}^T \mathbf{AP} = \begin{pmatrix} \lambda_1 & 0 & 0 \\ 0 & \lambda_2 & 0 \\ 0 & 0 & \lambda_3 \end{pmatrix}$$

For symmetric matrices, therefore, there is no need to calculate the inverse
matrix $\mathbf{P}^{-1}$. It is sufficient to use $\mathbf{P}^T$ instead.

Example

Calculate the eigenvalues of the matrix $\mathbf{A} = \begin{pmatrix} 0 & 1 & 0 \\ 1 & 0 & 1 \\ 0 & 1 & 0 \end{pmatrix}$ and find three

eigenvectors $\mathbf{v}_1$, $\mathbf{v}_2$, $\mathbf{v}_3$ of *unit* length, one for each eigenvalue.

If **P** denotes the matrix whose columns are $\mathbf{v}_1$, $\mathbf{v}_2$, $\mathbf{v}_3$ verify that:

(a) $\mathbf{P}^T\mathbf{P} = \mathbf{I}$ (b) $\mathbf{P}^T\mathbf{AP}$ is a diagonal matrix.

What is the inverse of **P**?

Solution

$$\det (\mathbf{A} - \lambda\mathbf{I}) = 0 \implies \begin{vmatrix} -\lambda & 1 & 0 \\ 1 & -\lambda & 1 \\ 0 & 1 & -\lambda \end{vmatrix} = 0$$

$$\implies -\lambda (\lambda^2 - 1) - 1 (-\lambda) = 0$$

$$\implies -\lambda^3 + 2\lambda = 0$$

$$\implies -\lambda (\lambda - \sqrt{2}) (\lambda + \sqrt{2}) = 0$$

$$\implies \lambda = 0, \sqrt{2} \text{ and } -\sqrt{2} \text{ are the eigenvalues}$$

(i) $\lambda = 0 \implies \begin{pmatrix} 0 & 1 & 0 \\ 1 & 0 & 1 \\ 0 & 1 & 0 \end{pmatrix}\begin{pmatrix} x \\ y \\ z \end{pmatrix} = 0 \begin{pmatrix} x \\ y \\ z \end{pmatrix} \implies \begin{matrix} y = 0 \\ x + z = 0 \\ y = 0 \end{matrix} \implies x = -z \text{ and } y = 0$

$\therefore$ the corresponding eigenvector has the form $x \begin{pmatrix} 1 \\ 0 \\ -1 \end{pmatrix}$

In order to have *unit* length, take x as $\dfrac{1}{\sqrt{2}}$.

$\therefore$ $\mathbf{v}_1 = \dfrac{1}{\sqrt{2}} \begin{pmatrix} 1 \\ 0 \\ -1 \end{pmatrix}$.

(ii) $\lambda = \sqrt{2} \Rightarrow \begin{pmatrix} 0 & 1 & 0 \\ 1 & 0 & 1 \\ 0 & 1 & 0 \end{pmatrix} \begin{pmatrix} x \\ y \\ z \end{pmatrix} = \sqrt{2} \begin{pmatrix} x \\ y \\ z \end{pmatrix} \Rightarrow \begin{array}{l} y = \sqrt{2}x \\ x + z = \sqrt{2}y \\ y = \sqrt{2}z \end{array} \Rightarrow \begin{array}{l} x = z \\ \text{and} \\ y = \sqrt{2}x \end{array}$

$\therefore$ the corresponding eigenvector has the form $x \begin{pmatrix} 1 \\ \sqrt{2} \\ 1 \end{pmatrix}$

In order to have *unit* length, take x as $\frac{1}{2}$.

$\therefore$ $\mathbf{v}_2 = \frac{1}{2} \begin{pmatrix} 1 \\ \sqrt{2} \\ 1 \end{pmatrix}$

(iii) $\lambda = -\sqrt{2} \Rightarrow \begin{pmatrix} 0 & 1 & 0 \\ 1 & 0 & 1 \\ 0 & 1 & 0 \end{pmatrix} \begin{pmatrix} x \\ y \\ z \end{pmatrix} = \sqrt{2} \begin{pmatrix} x \\ y \\ z \end{pmatrix} \Rightarrow x = z \text{ and } y = -\sqrt{2}\,x$

$\therefore$ the corresponding eigenvector has the form $x \begin{pmatrix} 1 \\ -\sqrt{2} \\ 1 \end{pmatrix}$

In order to have *unit* length, take x as $\frac{1}{2}$.

$\therefore$ $\mathbf{v}_3 = \frac{1}{2} \begin{pmatrix} 1 \\ -\sqrt{2} \\ 1 \end{pmatrix}$

$\therefore$ $\mathbf{P} = \begin{pmatrix} \frac{1}{\sqrt{2}} & \frac{1}{2} & \frac{1}{2} \\ 0 & \frac{\sqrt{2}}{2} & \frac{-\sqrt{2}}{2} \\ \frac{-1}{\sqrt{2}} & \frac{1}{2} & \frac{1}{2} \end{pmatrix} \Rightarrow \mathbf{P}^{\mathrm{T}} = \begin{pmatrix} \frac{1}{\sqrt{2}} & 0 & \frac{-1}{\sqrt{2}} \\ \frac{1}{2} & \frac{\sqrt{2}}{2} & \frac{1}{2} \\ \frac{1}{2} & \frac{-\sqrt{2}}{2} & \frac{1}{2} \end{pmatrix}$

(a) $\therefore$ $\mathbf{P}^{\mathrm{T}}\mathbf{P} = \begin{pmatrix} \frac{1}{\sqrt{2}} & 0 & \frac{-1}{\sqrt{2}} \\ \frac{1}{2} & \frac{\sqrt{2}}{2} & \frac{1}{2} \\ \frac{1}{2} & \frac{-\sqrt{2}}{2} & \frac{1}{2} \end{pmatrix} \begin{pmatrix} \frac{1}{\sqrt{2}} & \frac{1}{2} & \frac{1}{2} \\ 0 & \frac{\sqrt{2}}{2} & \frac{-\sqrt{2}}{2} \\ \frac{-1}{\sqrt{2}} & \frac{1}{2} & \frac{1}{2} \end{pmatrix} = \begin{pmatrix} 1 & 0 & 0 \\ 0 & 1 & 0 \\ 0 & 0 & 1 \end{pmatrix}$

as required (and expected, since $\mathbf{A}$ is symmetric).

(b) $\mathbf{P}^{\mathrm{T}}\mathbf{A}\mathbf{P} = \begin{pmatrix} \frac{1}{\sqrt{2}} & 0 & \frac{-1}{\sqrt{2}} \\ \frac{1}{2} & \frac{\sqrt{2}}{2} & \frac{1}{2} \\ \frac{1}{2} & \frac{-\sqrt{2}}{2} & \frac{1}{2} \end{pmatrix} \begin{pmatrix} 0 & 1 & 0 \\ 1 & 0 & 1 \\ 0 & 1 & 0 \end{pmatrix} \begin{pmatrix} \frac{1}{\sqrt{2}} & \frac{1}{2} & \frac{1}{2} \\ 0 & \frac{\sqrt{2}}{2} & \frac{-\sqrt{2}}{2} \\ \frac{-1}{\sqrt{2}} & \frac{1}{2} & \frac{1}{2} \end{pmatrix}$

$$= \begin{pmatrix} 0 & 0 & 0 \\ \dfrac{\sqrt{2}}{2} & 1 & \dfrac{\sqrt{2}}{2} \\ \dfrac{-\sqrt{2}}{2} & 1 & \dfrac{-\sqrt{2}}{2} \end{pmatrix} \begin{pmatrix} \dfrac{1}{\sqrt{2}} & \dfrac{1}{2} & \dfrac{1}{2} \\ 0 & \dfrac{\sqrt{2}}{2} & \dfrac{-\sqrt{2}}{2} \\ \dfrac{-1}{\sqrt{2}} & \dfrac{1}{2} & \dfrac{1}{2} \end{pmatrix}$$

$$= \begin{pmatrix} 0 & 0 & 0 \\ 0 & \sqrt{2} & 0 \\ 0 & 0 & -\sqrt{2} \end{pmatrix}$$

as required (and expected, since **A** is symmetric).

Finally, since **A** is symmetric, the inverse of **P** must equal $\mathbf{P}^{T.}$

$$\therefore \quad \mathbf{P}^{-1} = \mathbf{P}^{T} = \begin{pmatrix} \dfrac{1}{\sqrt{2}} & 0 & \dfrac{-1}{\sqrt{2}} \\ \dfrac{1}{2} & \dfrac{\sqrt{2}}{2} & \dfrac{1}{2} \\ \dfrac{1}{2} & \dfrac{-\sqrt{2}}{2} & \dfrac{1}{2} \end{pmatrix}$$

You should now be able to answer Exercises 17–24 on pages 291–92.

EXERCISES

1 Simplify the following:

(a) $\begin{pmatrix} 4 & 5 \\ 6 & 2 \end{pmatrix} \begin{pmatrix} 3 \\ 7 \end{pmatrix}$

(b) $\begin{pmatrix} 5 & 2 \\ 7 & 3 \end{pmatrix} \begin{pmatrix} 3 \\ 1 \end{pmatrix}$

(c) $\begin{pmatrix} 2 & 3 & 4 \\ 5 & 6 & 7 \\ 8 & 9 & 10 \end{pmatrix} \begin{pmatrix} 11 \\ 12 \\ 13 \end{pmatrix}$

(d) $\begin{pmatrix} 1 & 2 & 3 \\ 3 & 1 & 2 \\ 2 & 3 & 1 \end{pmatrix} \begin{pmatrix} 1 \\ 2 \\ 3 \end{pmatrix}$

2 Write down the 2-dimensional matrices that correspond to the following transformations:

(a) An anti-clockwise rotation about the origin through 90°.

(b) A rotation of π radians about the origin

(c) A reflection in the line $y = x$

(d) A reflection in the line $y = -x$

(e) A reflection in the x-axis

(f) A reflection in the y-axis

3 Write down the 3-dimensional matrices that correspond to the following transformations:

(a) A rotation about the z-axis through angle θ anti-clockwise.

(b) A reflection in the x-y plane.

4 Simplify the following:

(a) $\begin{pmatrix} 1 & 2 \\ 3 & 4 \end{pmatrix}\begin{pmatrix} 5 & 6 \\ 7 & 8 \end{pmatrix}$

(b) $\begin{pmatrix} 5 & 6 \\ 7 & 8 \end{pmatrix}\begin{pmatrix} 1 & 2 \\ 3 & 4 \end{pmatrix}$

(c) $\begin{pmatrix} 1 & 2 & 3 \\ 4 & 5 & 6 \\ 7 & 8 & 9 \end{pmatrix}\begin{pmatrix} 3 & 2 & 1 \\ 1 & 3 & 2 \\ 2 & 1 & 3 \end{pmatrix}$

(d) $\begin{pmatrix} 1 & 0 & 1 \\ 0 & 1 & 0 \\ 1 & 1 & 1 \end{pmatrix}\begin{pmatrix} 3 & 4 & 5 \\ 6 & 7 & 8 \\ 9 & 10 & 11 \end{pmatrix}$

5 Find the 2 × 2 matrix which represents an anti-clockwise rotation through $\frac{\pi}{2}$ radians about the origin, followed by a reflection in the line $y = x$, followed by reflection in the y-axis. Can you give a simple description of the set of composite transformations?

6 Find the inverses of the following matrices:

(a) $\begin{pmatrix} 4 & 2 \\ 3 & 5 \end{pmatrix}$

(b) $\begin{pmatrix} 3 & 4 \\ 5 & -2 \end{pmatrix}$

(c) $\begin{pmatrix} 3 & 4 & 5 \\ 4 & 3 & 11 \\ 1 & 0 & 3 \end{pmatrix}$

(d) $\begin{pmatrix} 4 & 8 & 3 \\ 3 & 5 & 1 \\ 1 & 4 & 3 \end{pmatrix}$

7 Use a matrix method to solve these simultaneous equations:

$3x + 4y = 9$

$2x + 5y = 11$.

8 If $\mathbf{A} = \begin{pmatrix} 1 & 2 & 3 \\ 2 & 3 & 4 \\ 1 & 1 & 2 \end{pmatrix}$ and $\mathbf{B} = \begin{pmatrix} -2 & 1 & 1 \\ 0 & 1 & -2 \\ 1 & -1 & 1 \end{pmatrix}$.

find **AB** and **BA**. Hence write down $\mathbf{A}^{-1}$.

Use a matrix method to solve the simultaneous equations

$\alpha + 2\beta + 3\gamma = 6$

$2\alpha + 3\beta + 4\gamma = 9$

$\alpha + \beta + 2\gamma = 4$.

9 If $\mathbf{W} = \begin{pmatrix} 1 & 0 & 1 \\ 0 & 1 & 0 \\ 1 & 2 & 3 \end{pmatrix}$ and $\mathbf{V} = \begin{pmatrix} 3 & 2 & -1 \\ 0 & 2 & 0 \\ -1 & -2 & 1 \end{pmatrix}$

find **WV** and **VW**. Hence find $\mathbf{W}^{-1}$. Also find matrix **F** where $\mathbf{W}^2\mathbf{F} = \mathbf{I}$.

10 Find the eigenvalues of the matrix $A = \begin{pmatrix} 2 & 4 \\ 3 & 6 \end{pmatrix}$ and determine the corresponding eigenvectors.

11 Find the eigenvalues of the matrix $A = \begin{pmatrix} 2 & -2 & 3 \\ 1 & 1 & 1 \\ 1 & 3 & -1 \end{pmatrix}$ and determine the corresponding eigenvectors.

12 Given the matrix $A = \begin{pmatrix} 2 & 4 \\ 3 & 6 \end{pmatrix}$, find a matrix **P** such that $P^{-1} AP$ is a diagonal matrix. Verify the validity of your answer.

(Hint: see Exercise 10.)

13 Given the matrix $A = \begin{pmatrix} 2 & -2 & 3 \\ 1 & 1 & 1 \\ 1 & 3 & -1 \end{pmatrix}$, find a matrix **P** such that $P^{-1}AP$ is a diagonal matrix. Verify the validity of your answer.

(Hint: see Exercise 11)

14 Given the matrix $A = \begin{pmatrix} 1 & 4 & -1 \\ -1 & 6 & -1 \\ 3 & -2 & 4 \end{pmatrix}$, find a matrix **P** such that $P^{-1}AP$ is a diagonal matrix. Verify the validity of your answer.

15 If $P^{-1}AP = \begin{pmatrix} \lambda_1 & 0 \\ 0 & \lambda_2 \end{pmatrix}$ simplify $P^{-1}A^nP$.

16 Matrices **A**, **D** are defined by:

$$A = \begin{pmatrix} 1 & -3 & -3 \\ -8 & 6 & -3 \\ 8 & -2 & 7 \end{pmatrix}, \quad D = \begin{pmatrix} 1 & 0 & 0 \\ 0 & 4 & 0 \\ 0 & 0 & 9 \end{pmatrix}$$

For each of the eigenvalues 1, 4 and 9 of **A** find a corresponding eigenvector. Write down a matrix **P** such that $P^{-1}AP = D$, and calculate P^{-1}. Write down a matrix **C** such that $C^2 = D$. Hence find a matrix **B** such that $B^2 = A$.

17 Prove that the eigenvalues of the matrix **A**, where:

$$A = \begin{pmatrix} 1 & 0 & 2 \\ 0 & 2 & 0 \\ 2 & 0 & 1 \end{pmatrix}$$

are -1, 2 and 3. Find the corresponding unit eigenvectors. Hence find a matrix **P** such that $P^{-1}AP$ is a diagonal matrix. Obtain P^{-1} and calculate the elements of the diagonal matrix.

18 Find the eigenvalues of the matrix **A**, where:

$$\mathbf{A} = \begin{pmatrix} 3 & -6 & -4 \\ -6 & 4 & 2 \\ -4 & 2 & -1 \end{pmatrix}$$

and obtain the corresponding normalised eigenvectors. Verify that these vectors are mutually perpendicular. If **B** is the matrix whose columns are these unit vectors, verify that **AB** = **BL**, where **L** is a 3×3 diagonal matrix to be determined.

19 Find the complex eigenvalues and eigenvectors for the matrix

$$\mathbf{A} = \begin{pmatrix} 0 & 1 \\ -1 & 0 \end{pmatrix}$$ and hence find a complex matrix **P** which diagonalises **A**.

20 Given that $\mathbf{p} = \begin{pmatrix} 1 \\ -2 \\ -2 \end{pmatrix}$ and $\mathbf{q} = \begin{pmatrix} -2 \\ -2 \\ 1 \end{pmatrix}$ are eigenvectors of the matrix **M**,

where $\mathbf{M} = \begin{pmatrix} -1 & -2 & 0 \\ -2 & 0 & 2 \\ 0 & 2 & 1 \end{pmatrix}$

find the three eigenvalues and a third eigenvector.

21 Evaluate the determinant of matrix **A** where:

$$\mathbf{A} = \begin{pmatrix} 7 & 13 & 9 \\ 1 & 3 & 1 \\ 2 & 1 & 4 \end{pmatrix}$$

Does **A** have an inverse?

22 Factorise $\det \begin{pmatrix} 1 & a & a^2 \\ a^2 & 1 & a \\ a & a^2 & 1 \end{pmatrix}$

23 Prove that $\begin{vmatrix} 3-\lambda & -6 & -4 \\ -6 & 4-\lambda & 2 \\ -4 & 2 & -1-\lambda \end{vmatrix} = 44 + 51\lambda + 6\lambda^2 - \lambda^3$

Hence solve $\begin{vmatrix} 3-\lambda & -6 & -4 \\ -6 & 4-\lambda & 2 \\ -4 & 2 & -1-\lambda \end{vmatrix} = 0$

24 [Revision]

$$\mathbf{M} = \begin{pmatrix} 1 & 0 & 0 \\ x & 2 & 0 \\ 3 & 1 & 1 \end{pmatrix}$$

Find $\mathbf{M}^{-1}$ in terms of x.

SUMMARY   You should now be able to:

- write down matrices that represent stretches, rotations and reflections
- combine a set of successive transformations
- find the determinant of a 2×2 or 3×3 matrix
- find the inverse of 2×2 and 3×3 non-singular matrices
- solve equations involving 2×2 and 3×3 matrices.
- write down the transpose $\mathbf{A}^\mathsf{T}$ of a matrix $\mathbf{A}$

  e.g. $\mathbf{A} = \begin{pmatrix} 1 & 2 & 3 \\ 4 & 5 & 6 \\ 7 & 8 & 9 \end{pmatrix} \Rightarrow \mathbf{A}^\mathsf{T} = \begin{pmatrix} 1 & 4 & 7 \\ 2 & 5 & 8 \\ 3 & 6 & 9 \end{pmatrix}$

- recognise a symmetric matrix

  e.g. $\mathbf{B} = \begin{pmatrix} 1 & 4 & 5 \\ 4 & 2 & 6 \\ 5 & 6 & 3 \end{pmatrix}$, because $\mathbf{B}^\mathsf{T} = \mathbf{B}$

- recognise and manipulate diagonal matrices

  e.g. $\mathbf{C} = \begin{pmatrix} 2 & 0 & 0 \\ 0 & 3 & 0 \\ 0 & 0 & 4 \end{pmatrix} \Rightarrow \mathbf{C}^2 = \begin{pmatrix} 4 & 0 & 0 \\ 0 & 9 & 0 \\ 0 & 0 & 16 \end{pmatrix}$

- use the equation $\det(\mathbf{A} - \lambda\mathbf{I}) = 0$ to find the eigenvalues of matrix $\mathbf{A}$
- use the equation $\mathbf{A}x = \lambda x$ to find the corresponding eigenvectors
- quote from memory (and be able to verify) the following important results:

  If a 3×3 matrix $\mathbf{A}$ has eigenvalues λ_1, λ_2 and λ_3 with corresponding eigenvectors x_1, x_2 and x_3 then, if matrix $\mathbf{P}$ has columns x_1, x_2 and x_3,

  $$\mathbf{P}^{-1}\mathbf{AP} = \begin{pmatrix} \lambda_1 & 0 & 0 \\ 0 & \lambda_1 & 0 \\ 0 & 0 & \lambda_3 \end{pmatrix}$$

- quote from memory (and be able to verify) the following special case:

  If a *symmetric* 3×3 matrix $\mathbf{A}$ has eigenvalues λ_1, λ_2 and λ_3, then it is possible to choose corresponding eigenvectors x_1, x_2 and x_3 which are mutually perpendicular and of unit length.

  Furthermore if matrix $\mathbf{P}$ has columns x_1, x_2 and x_3, then:

  $$\mathbf{P}^\mathsf{T}\mathbf{AP} = \begin{pmatrix} \lambda_1 & 0 & 0 \\ 0 & \lambda_2 & 0 \\ 0 & 0 & \lambda_3 \end{pmatrix}$$

  In this special case $\mathbf{P}^\mathsf{T} = \mathbf{P}^{-1}$.

Numerical methods

INTRODUCTION In this section we will look at two ways of estimating the value of a definite integral. The methods are known as the trapezium rule and Simpson's rule. We'll then look at three ways of obtaining approximate numerical solutions to differential equations and then finish off by finding series solutions to these equations.

The Trapezium Rule for estimating a definite integral

Let's take the curve of a hard-to-integrate function and see what approximation we could use for the area underneath. And since the area underneath is given by $\int_a^b f(x)\,dx$, we are really trying to approximate the integral.

Figure 15.1

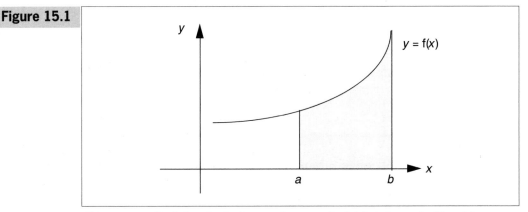

We want to find the shaded area, the top of which is bounded by this function, $f(x)$. As a first approximation, we could say that the upper boundary is a straight line, in which case the area is a trapezium whose value is quite easily calculated.

Figure 15.2

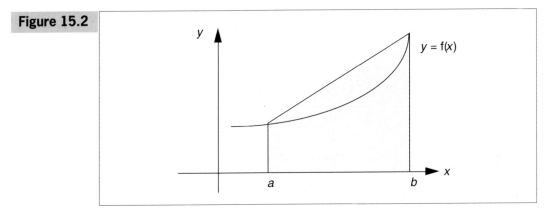

From this example, we can see that with just one trapezium the approximation might not be particularly good. If we divide the area into two strips and make each of these a trapezium as shown below, the approximation is already greatly improved:

Figure 15.3

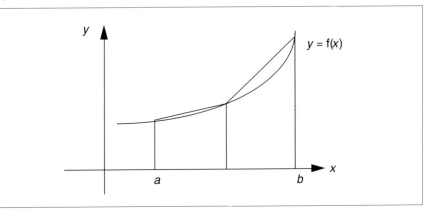

and with a larger number of strips we can expect a better result. If we needed a very accurate value we would probably use a computer or programmable calculator, where it's very easy to increase the number of strips indefinitely. Most questions, however, only call for a value correct to two or three significant figures and state how many strips are necessary for this, usually quite a small number.

Deriving the formula

So that's the idea behind this particular method – divide the area to be calculated into a series of strips and suppose each of these to be a trapezium. The area is then approximated by the sum of all these trapezia. Let's see how this works for our original area which we shall divide into three strips of equal width, calling the two new x-coordinates m_1 and m_2:

Figure 15.4

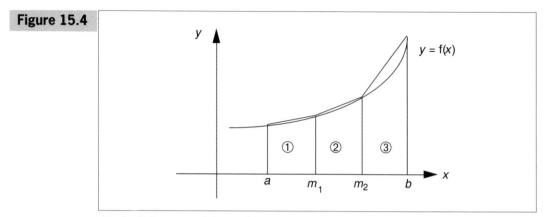

To find the area of these three trapezia we need the height of the parallel sides at a, m_1, m_2, and b, which is the value of the function at these points. Then, calling the width of each strip h,

Figure 15.5

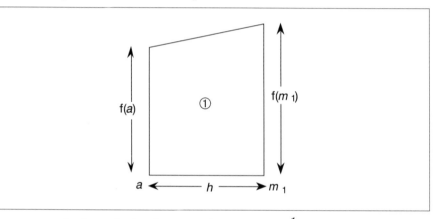

we can use the formula for the area of a trapezium ($\frac{1}{2}$ width × sum of parallel sides) to find that:

$$\text{Area } \textcircled{1} \quad = \quad \tfrac{1}{2}h\left(f(a) + f(m_1)\right)$$

and similarly

$$\text{Area } \textcircled{2} \quad = \quad \tfrac{1}{2}h\left(f(m_1) + f(m_2)\right)$$

and $$\text{Area } \textcircled{3} \quad = \quad \tfrac{1}{2}h\left(f(m_2) + f(b)\right)$$

Adding these up, and noting that apart from $f(a)$ and $f(b)$ the other sides are counted in two areas each, the total area is:

$$\text{Area } \textcircled{1} + \textcircled{2} + \textcircled{3} = \tfrac{1}{2}h\left[f(a) + f(b) + 2\left\{ f(m_1) + f(m_2)\right\}\right]$$

No matter how many strips we take, we always count the first and last sides once, and the rest twice, so we can say generally that:

> The approximate area is:
> half width × (first + last + twice the rest)

Remember that the first, last and rest refer to the heights – a common mistake is to use the x-values for these instead of the y-values.

An example with the error calculated

As an example, let's find an approximate value for the integral

$$\int_0^1 \frac{1}{1+x^2}\,dx$$

using four strips. Then let's integrate it exactly and so work out the error in the approximation.

Since we use the first and last values of the function once only, whereas the rest are doubled, we write these separately to simplify the working. To see more clearly what's happening we'll make a sketch of the area, although normally we would not trouble to do this:

Figure 15.6

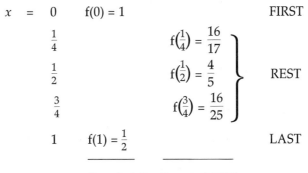

You can see that the equally spaced x-coordinates are at $0, \frac{1}{4}, \frac{1}{2}, \frac{3}{4}$ and 1. The corresponding values of the function are:

$$
\begin{array}{lll}
x = 0 & f(0) = 1 & \text{FIRST} \\
\frac{1}{4} & f\left(\frac{1}{4}\right) = \frac{16}{17} & \\
\frac{1}{2} & f\left(\frac{1}{2}\right) = \frac{4}{5} & \text{REST} \\
\frac{3}{4} & f\left(\frac{3}{4}\right) = \frac{16}{25} & \\
1 & f(1) = \frac{1}{2} & \text{LAST}
\end{array}
$$

Sum is 1.5   Sum is 2.3812

297

The distance between each successive pair of x points is $\frac{1}{4}$ so $h = \frac{1}{4}$.

$$\text{Area} \approx \frac{1}{2}h \left[f(0) + f(1) + 2\{\text{Rest}\} \right]$$

$$= \frac{1}{8}\left(1.5 + 2(2.3812)\right) = \frac{1}{8}(6.2624) = 0.7828$$

As you may have seen, in this case the integral can be evaluated exactly so that we can compare results:

$$\int_0^1 \frac{1}{1 + x^2}\,dx = \left[\tan^{-1}x\right]_0^1 \quad \text{(See Section 5.)}$$

$$= \frac{\pi}{4} = 0.7854$$

You can see that the approximation differs from this only in the third decimal place, which is a very reasonable degree of accuracy for such a simple method. We will now look at another example – this time we'll take a trigonometric function, in which case we must remember to use radians.

Example   Find an approximate value for the integral:

$$\int_0^{\frac{\pi}{2}} \frac{1}{\sqrt{1 + \cos\theta}}\,d\theta$$

by using the trapezium rule with three strips.

Solution   The subdivisions are at $0, \frac{\pi}{6}, \frac{\pi}{3}, \frac{\pi}{2}$:

$$x = 0 \qquad f(0) = \frac{1}{\sqrt{2}}$$

$$\frac{\pi}{6} \qquad\qquad f\!\left(\frac{\pi}{6}\right) = \frac{1}{\sqrt{1 + \frac{\sqrt{3}}{2}}} = \frac{\sqrt{2}}{\sqrt{2 + \sqrt{3}}}$$

$$\frac{\pi}{3} \qquad\qquad f\!\left(\frac{\pi}{3}\right) = \frac{1}{\sqrt{1 + \frac{1}{2}}} = \frac{\sqrt{2}}{\sqrt{3}}$$

$$\frac{\pi}{2} \qquad f\!\left(\frac{\pi}{2}\right) = 1$$

$$\text{Sum is } 1.707 \qquad\qquad \text{Sum is } 1.549$$

Then approximate area is:

$$\frac{1}{2} \times \frac{\pi}{6}\{1.707 + 2(1.549)\}$$

$$= \frac{\pi}{12}(4.805) = 1.258$$

Again, in fact we can integrate precisely, although it's difficult.

$$\int_0^{\frac{\pi}{2}} \frac{1}{\sqrt{1 + \cos\theta}}\, d\theta = \int_0^{\frac{\pi}{2}} \frac{1}{\sqrt{1 + \cos 2\left(\frac{\theta}{2}\right)}}\, d\theta$$

$$= \int_0^{\frac{\pi}{2}} \frac{1}{\sqrt{2\cos^2\frac{\theta}{2}}}\, d\theta$$

(Using $1 + \cos 2A = 2\cos^2 A$.)

$$= \frac{1}{\sqrt{2}} \int_0^{\frac{\pi}{2}} \frac{1}{\cos\frac{\theta}{2}}\, d\theta = \frac{1}{\sqrt{2}} \int_0^{\frac{\pi}{2}} \sec\frac{\theta}{2}\, d\theta$$

$$= \left[\sqrt{2}\ln\left(\sec\frac{\theta}{2} + \tan\frac{\theta}{2}\right) \right]_0^{\frac{\pi}{2}} *$$

$$= \sqrt{2}\ln(\sqrt{2} + 1)$$

$$= 1.246$$

Not quite so good an approximation this time – but still only about 1% in error and we could always use more strips if we wanted the answer more precisely.

[* Your 'A' level formula booklet gives:

$$\int \sec x\, dx = \ln(\sec x + \tan x).$$

This generalises to give:

$$\int \sec ax\, dx = \frac{1}{a}\ln(\sec ax + \tan ax)$$

You should be able to verify this formula by differentiation.]

You should now be able to answer Exercises 1–4 on page 312.

Simpson's Rule

We've now seen how the trapezium rule can be used to estimate an integral. However, there is a more accurate method of estimation and that is known as Simpson's Rule.

When we used the trapezium rule to estimate an integral we had the formula:

half width × (first + last + twice the rest)

This could also be written as:

$$\frac{h}{2}\left[(y_0 + y_n) + 2\,(y_1 + y_2 + \ldots + y_{n-1})\right]$$

Simpson came up with a more refined method for estimating an integral. It is:

$$\frac{h}{3}\left[(y_0 + y_n) + 4\,(y_1 + y_3 + \ldots + y_{n-1}) + 2\,(y_2 + y_4 + \ldots + y_{n-2})\right]$$

where h is the length of one of the equal intervals.

Using Simpson's Rule

Luckily you don't have to learn the formula (it is given in your formula booklet) but, unfortunately, the *rule only works for an even number of intervals*. As far as your examination is concerned, then, the chances are that you'll be given either 2 or 4 intervals (any more than that and it would probably take too long).

With 2 intervals, Simpson's rule becomes:

$$\frac{h}{3}\left[y_0 + y_2 + 4y_1\right]$$

With 4 intervals, Simpson's rule becomes:

$$\frac{h}{3}\left[y_0 + y_4 + 4(y_1 + y_3) + 2y_2\right]$$

You may decide that these two special cases are worth learning by heart.

Example   Use Simpson's rule with 2 intervals to estimate the integral:

$$\int_0^1 e^{-x^2}\,dx$$

Solution   First set up a table with 2 equal intervals.

x:	0	0.5	1
$y = e^{-x^2}$:	1	$e^{-0.25}$	e^{-1}

Since the intervals are of length 0.5, $h = 0.5$.

$$\therefore \quad \int_0^1 e^{-x^2}\,dx \quad \approx \quad \frac{h}{3}\left[y_0 + y_2 + 4y_1\right\}$$

$$= \quad \frac{0.5}{3}\left[1 + e^{-1} + 4e^{2-0.25}\right]$$

$$= \quad 0.7472$$

Example

Use Simpson's rule with 4 intervals to estimate the integral:

$$\int_0^1 e^{-x^2}\, dx$$

Solution

x:	0	0.25	0.5	0.75	1
$y = e^{-x^2}$:	1	$e^{-0.0625}$	$e^{-0.25}$	$e^{-0.5625}$	e^{-1}

$$\therefore \quad \int_0^1 e^{-x^2}\, dx \approx \frac{0.25}{3}\left[1 + e^{-1} + 4\left(e^{0.0625} + e^{-0.5625}\right) + 2e^{-0.25}\right]$$

$$= 0.7469$$

Comparing with the previous example, we see that we have already estimated the integral to 3 d.p. accuracy (i.e. 0.747). Simpson's rule is a very powerful method of estimation.

Example

Use Simpson's rule, with 2 equal intervals, to estimate:

$$\int_1^2 x^3\, dx.$$

How accurate is this estimate?

Solution

x:	1	1.5	2
$y = x^3$:	1	1.5^3	2^3

$$\therefore \quad \int_1^2 x^3\, dx \approx \frac{0.5}{3}\left[1 + 2^3 + 4 \times 1.5^3\right] = 3.75.$$

However $\quad \int_1^2 x^3\, dx \approx \left[\frac{x^4}{4}\right] = 3.75$

In this case, Simpson's rule is 100% accurate and with just 2 intervals! In fact, Simpson's rule is always 100% accurate for any quadratic or cubic function. It is indeed a most powerful rule.

You should now be able to answer Exercises 5–8 on page 312.

Solving differential equations

In Module P3 we saw how some differential equations could be solved by integration. For example, a useful technique was separation of the variables. But what happens if the variables aren't separable and none of the other techniques work either? In that case we would have to use numerical methods to solve the differential equation. So that is what we'll do now.

Maclaurin's theorem revisited

In Module P3, Section 2 we saw that Maclaurin's theorem gave us:

$$f(x) = f(0) + \frac{f'(0)}{1!} x + \frac{f''(0)}{2!} x^2 + \frac{f'''(0)}{3!} x^3 + \ldots$$

If we use the notation $y = f(x)$, then $f(0)$ can be written $y(0)$. (The zero in the bracket indicates that y is to be evaluated with $x = 0$.) If we also write y' instead of $f'(x)$ then $f'(0)$ becomes $y'(0)$. Similarly we can write

$y'' = f''(x)$ so that $y''(0) = f''(0)$.

Maclaurin's theorem can therefore be rewritten as:

$$y = y(0) + \frac{y'(0)}{1!} x + \frac{y''(0)}{2!} x^2 + \frac{y'''(0)}{3!} x^3 + \ldots$$

Obtaining series solutions of differential equations

The method simply involves finding the values of $y(0)$, $y'(0)$, $y''(0)$, $y'''(0)$, and so on. These can be obtained either directly from the given differential equation or by differentiation. Let's look at some examples.

Example

Given the differential equation $\dfrac{dy}{dx} = 1 + y$ and $y = 1$ at $x = 0$, find y as a series in ascending powers of x up to and including the term in x^4. Use your series to obtain y at $x = 0.1$, giving your answer to 3 decimal places.

Solution

The given information can be rewrittten as:

$y' = 1 + y$ with $y(0) = 1$

Replacing x by zero in the differential equation gives:

$y'(0) = 1 + y(0) \Rightarrow y'(0) = 1 + 1 = 2$

Now differentiate the differential equation to get:

$y'' = y'$ $\Rightarrow$ $y''(0) = y'(0) = 2$

Further differentiation gives:

$y''' = y'' \Rightarrow y'''(0) = y''(0) = 2$

Similarly $y'''' = y''' \Rightarrow \quad y''''(0) = y'''(0) = 2$

And so we've now got that:

$$y(0) = 1, \; y'(0) = 2, \; y''(0) = 2, \; y'''(0) = 2 \text{ and } y''''(0) = 2$$

∴   Maclaurin's theorem gives us:

$$y = 1 + \frac{2}{1!}x + \frac{2}{2!}x^2 + \frac{2}{3!}x^3 + \frac{2}{4!}x^4 + \dots$$

i.e. $y = 1 + 2x + x^2 + \frac{1}{3}x^3 + \frac{1}{12}x^4 + \dots$

Finally, $x = 0.1 \Rightarrow y(0.1) \quad = 1 + 2 \times 10^{-1} + 10^{-2} + \frac{1}{3} \times 10^{-3} + \frac{1}{12} \times 10^{-4} + \dots$

$$= 1.2103417 = 1.210 \text{ to 3 d.p.}$$

Example

Given the differential equation $\dfrac{dy}{dx} = x + y^2$ and $y = 1$ at $x = 0$, find y as a series in ascending powers of x up to and including the term in x^4.

Solution

The given information can be rewritten as:

$$y' \;= x + y^2 \quad \text{with} \quad y(0) = 1.$$

∴ $y'(0) = 0 + y(0)^2 \; = 0 + 1^2 = 1 \quad \Rightarrow \; y'(0) = 1.$

Now differentate the differential equation to get:

$$y'' \;= 1 + 2yy'$$

(If this caused trouble, look back at implicit differentiation in Section 5 of Module P2.)

∴ $y''(0) = 1 + 2y(0)y'(0) \; = 1 + 2 \times 1 \times 1 = 3 \Rightarrow y''(0) = 3.$

Differentiating again we get:

$$y''' = 0 + 2y\,y'' + 2y'y' \Rightarrow y''' = 2yy'' + 2(y')^2$$

(Once again you may need to refer back to implicit differentiation.)

∴ $y'''(0) = 2y(0)y''(0) + 2y'(0)^2 \; = \; 2 \times 1 \times 3 + 2\,(1)^2 \; = 8$

$$\Rightarrow y'''(0) = 8$$

Differentiating again we get:

$$y'''' = 2yy''' + 2y'y'' + 4\,(y')\,y'' = 2yy''' + 6y'y''$$

(Always simplify whenever you can.)

∴ $y''''(0) = 2y(0)y'''(0) + 6y'(0)y''(0) \quad = \; 2 \times 1 \times 8 + 6 \times 1 \times 3 = 34$

$$\Rightarrow y''''(0) = 34$$

And so we've now got that:

$$y(0) = 1, \; y'(0) = 1, \; y''(0) = 3, \; y'''(0) = 8, \; y''''(0) = 34.$$

∴ Maclaurin's theorem gives us:

$$y = 1 + \frac{1}{1!}x + \frac{3}{2!}x^2 + \frac{8}{3!}x^3 + \frac{34}{4!}x^4 + \dots$$

i.e. $$y = 1 + x + \frac{3x^2}{2} + \frac{4x^3}{3} + \frac{17x^4}{12} + \dots$$

You should now be able to answer Exercises 9–13 on page 313.

Step-by-step methods for solving differential equations

Your syllabus mentions three step-by-step methods that can be used to solve differential equations. You need to be able both to prove these formulae and use them efficiently. Let's look at them one by one.

The approximation $\left(\dfrac{dy}{dx}\right)_0 \approx \dfrac{(y_1 - y_0)}{h}$

The sketch below shows a curve which passes through the points $P(x_0, y_0)$ and $Q(x_1, y_1)$. The tangent at P has also been drawn.

Figure 15.7

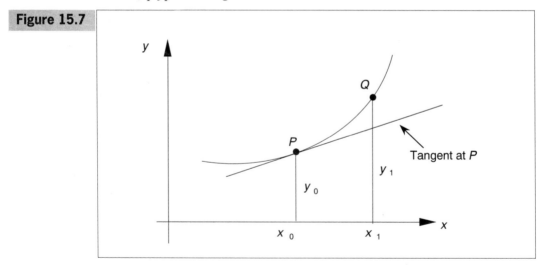

The gradient of the tangent at $P = \left(\dfrac{dy}{dx}\right)_0$ i.e. y'_0.

But, from the sketch above, this *approximately* equals $\dfrac{y_1 - y_0}{x_1 - x_0}$.

∴ $\left(\dfrac{dy}{dx}\right)_0 \approx \dfrac{y_1 - y_0}{x_1 - x_0}$ or $y'_0 \approx \dfrac{y_1 - y_0}{h}$, where $h = x_1 - x_0$.

This can be rewritten to give $y_1 \approx y_0 + hy'_0$

It is this latter formula that Euler used to solve differential equations numerically.

You are given the coordinates of P and the gradient at P so, using the formula, you can *estimate* the co-ordinates at Q.

i.e. $\qquad y_1 \qquad \approx \qquad y_0 \qquad + \qquad hy'_0$

y-value wanted $\qquad$ y-value given $\qquad$ step from one x-value to the next $\qquad$ gradient at given point

Let's look at some examples.

Example

Given the differential equation $\dfrac{dy}{dx} = xy$ and $y = 4$ when $x = 0.1$, estimate y when $x = 0.2$.

Solution

The given information can be rewritten as $y' = xy$ and $y(0.1) = 4$.

Now use Euler's equation to estimate y at $x = 0.2$

$\therefore \quad y(0.2) \approx y(0.1) + 0.1\, y'(0.1) \Rightarrow y(0.2) \approx 4 + 0.1 \times 0.4 = 4.04$

$\therefore \quad y(0.2) \approx 4.04$

$\therefore \quad y$ is approximately 4.04 when $x = 0.2$.

Example

Given the differential equation $\dfrac{dy}{dx} = x^2 + y$ and $y = 1$ when $x = 0$, use Euler's formula to estimate y when $x = 0.1, 0.2$ and 0.3.

Solution

The given information can be rewritten as $y' = x^2 + y$ and $y(0) = 1$.

Replacing x by 0 in the differential equation gives $y'(0) = 0^2 + 1 = 1$.

Euler's formula therefore gives $y(0.1) \approx y(0) + 0.1 \times y'(0) = 1 + 0.1 \times 1 = 1.1$

$\therefore \quad$ So far we have $y(0.1) \approx 1.1$.

Replacing x by 0.1 in the differential equation gives:

$\quad y'(0.1) = 0.1^2 + y(0.1) \approx 0.1^2 + 1.1 = 1.11$

Euler's formula therefore gives:

$\quad y(0.2) \approx y(0.1) + 0.1 \times y'(0.1) \approx 1.1 + 0.1 \times 1.11 = 1.211$

$\therefore \quad$ we now have $y(0.2) \approx 1.211$

Replacing x by 0.2 in the differential equation gives:

$\quad y'(0.2) = 0.2^2 + y(0.2) \approx 0.2^2 + 1.211 = 1.251$

305

Euler's formula therefore gives:

$$y(0.3) \approx y(0.2) + 0.1 \times y'(0.2) \approx 1.211 + 0.1 \times 1.251 = 1.3361$$

So finally we have $y(0.3) \approx 1.3361$.

This is summarised in the table below:

$x:$	0	0.1	0.2	0.3
$y:$	1	1.1	1.211	1.3361

The procedure is therefore

- find the value of $\dfrac{dy}{dx}$ from the given differential equation

- estimate the value of y by using Euler's formula $y_1 \approx y_0 + hy'_0$

- keep repeating this process as necessary.

You should now be able to answer Exercises 14–17 on page 313.

The approximation $\left(\dfrac{dy}{dx}\right)_0 \approx \dfrac{(y_1 - y_{-1})}{2h}$

The sketch below shows a curve which passes through points $P(x_{-1}, y_{-1})$, $Q(x_0, y_0)$ and $R(x_1, y_1)$. The tangent at Q has also been drawn.

Figure 15.8

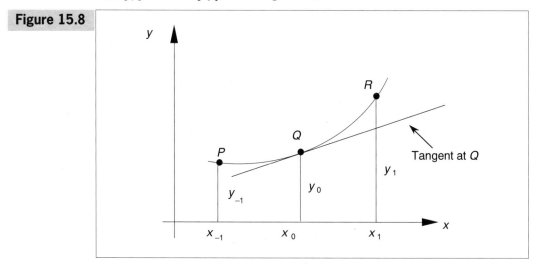

The gradient of the tangent at $Q = \left(\dfrac{dy}{dx}\right)_0$ i.e. y'_0.

But, from the sketch above, this *approximately* equals $\dfrac{y_1 - y_{-1}}{x_1 - x_{-1}}$.

$$\therefore \quad \left(\frac{dy}{dx}\right)_0 \approx \frac{y_1 - y_{-1}}{x_1 - x_{-1}} \quad \text{or} \quad y'_0 \approx \frac{y_1 - y_{-1}}{2h} \text{, where } h = x_0 - x_{-1} \text{ or } x_1 - x_0.$$

This can be rewritten to give $y_1 \approx y_{-1} + 2hy'_0$

This is a refinement of Euler's formula and is therefore more accurate. You are given the co-ordinates of P and the gradient at Q so, using this formula, you can *estimate* the co-ordinates of R.

i.e.

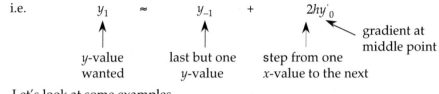

$$\begin{array}{ccccc} y_1 & \approx & y_{-1} & + & 2hy'_0 \end{array}$$

y-value wanted   last but one y-value   step from one x-value to the next   gradient at middle point

Let's look at some examples.

Example

Given the differential equation $\dfrac{dy}{dx} = xy$ with $y = 4$ when $x = 0$ and $y = 4.02$ when $x = 0.1$, estimate y when $x = 0.2$.

Solution

The given information can be rewritten as

$y' = xy$ and $y(0) = 4$ and $y(0.1) = 4.02$.

Replacing x by 0.1 in the differential equation gives

$y'(0.1) = 0.1 \times 4.02 \Rightarrow y'(0.1) = 0.402$.

Now use Euler's 'improved' formula to give:

$$y(0.2) \approx y(0) + 2 \times 0.1 \times y'(0.1) \quad = \quad 4 + 2 \times 0.1 \times 0.402 \quad = \quad 4.0804$$

$\therefore \qquad y(0.2) \approx 4.0804$

$\therefore \qquad y$ is approximately 4.0804 when $x = 0.2$.

Example

A function $f(x)$ is such that $f'(x) = x + f(x)$ with $f(0) = 2$ and $f(0.1) = 2.216$. Use Euler's 'improved' formula to estimate $f(0.2)$, $f(0.3)$ and $f(0.4)$.

Solution

The given information can be rewritten as $y' = x + y$ with $y(0) = 2$ and

$y(0.1) = 2.216$.

The differential equation now gives us:

$y'(0.1) = 0.1 + 2.216 \Rightarrow y'(0.1) = 2.316$.

Euler's 'improved' formula now gives us:

$$y(0.2) \approx y(0) + 2 \times 0.1 \times y'(0.1) = 2 + 2 \times 0.1 \times 2.316 = 2.4632$$

The differential equation now gives us:

$y'(0.2) = 0.2 + 2.4632 \Rightarrow y'(0.2) = 2.6632$.

Euler's 'improved' formula now gives us:

$$y(0.3) \approx y(0.1) + 2 \times 0.1 \times y'(0.2) \approx 2.216 + 2 \times 0.1 \times 2.6632 = 2.74864$$

The differential equation now gives us:

$$y'(0.3) = 0.3 + 2.74864 \Rightarrow y'(0.3) = 3.04864$$

Euler's 'improved' formula now gives us:

$$y(0.4) \approx y(0.2) + 2 \times 0.1 \times y'(0.3) \approx 2.4632 + 2 \times 0.1 \times 3.04864 = 3.072928$$

$\therefore$ (correct to 4 d.p.) $f(0.2) = 2.4632$, $f(0.3) = 2.7486$ and $f(0.4) = 3.0729$

You should now be able to answer Exercises 18–19 on pages 313–14.

The approximation $\left(\dfrac{d^2y}{dx^2}\right)_0 \approx \dfrac{(y_1 - 2y_0 + y_{-1})}{h^2}$

Suppose that y has a sketch as illustrated below:

Figure 15.9

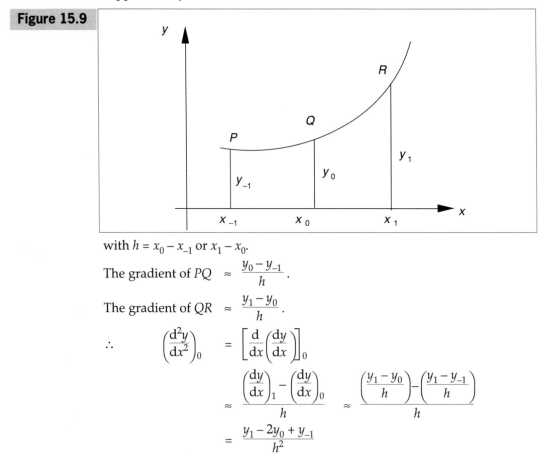

with $h = x_0 - x_{-1}$ or $x_1 - x_0$.

The gradient of PQ $\approx \dfrac{y_0 - y_{-1}}{h}$.

The gradient of QR $\approx \dfrac{y_1 - y_0}{h}$.

$\therefore$

$$\left(\frac{d^2y}{dx^2}\right)_0 = \left[\frac{d}{dx}\left(\frac{dy}{dx}\right)\right]_0$$

$$\approx \frac{\left(\dfrac{dy}{dx}\right)_1 - \left(\dfrac{dy}{dx}\right)_0}{h} \approx \frac{\left(\dfrac{y_1 - y_0}{h}\right) - \left(\dfrac{y_1 - y_{-1}}{h}\right)}{h}$$

$$= \frac{y_1 - 2y_0 + y_{-1}}{h^2}$$

(A rather tricky proof but probably not too difficult to learn.)

This can be rewritten as:

$$y''_0 \approx \frac{y_1 - 2y_0 + y_{-1}}{h^2} \qquad \text{or} \qquad y_1 \approx 2y_0 - y_{-1} + h^2 y''_0$$

In an examination you would be given the first formula but it's probably easier to use the second version.

Let's look at an example.

Example

Use the formula $\left(\dfrac{d^2y}{dx^2}\right)_0 \approx \dfrac{(y_1 - 2y_0 + y_{-1})}{h^2}$

to find a step-by-step solution to $\dfrac{d^2y}{dx^2} = 4y$ starting with $x = 0$ when $y = 0$ and $x = 0.1$ when $y = 0.403$ and taking intervals of 0.1 up to $x = 0.4$.

Solution

The given information can be rewritten as

$$y'' = 4y \text{ and } y(0) = 0 \text{ and } y(0.1) = 0.403.$$

The differential equation now gives us:

$$y''(0.1) = 4 \times 0.403 \Rightarrow y''(0.1) = 1.612$$

The second version of the approximation formula now gives us:

$$y(0.2) \approx 2y(0.1) - y(0) + 0.1^2 \times y''(0.1)$$
$$= 2 \times 0.403 - 0 + 0.1^2 \times 1.612 = 0.82212$$

The differential equation now gives us:

$$y''(0.2) = 4 \times 0.82212 \Rightarrow y''(0.2) = 3.28848$$

The second version of the approximation formula now gives us:

$$y(0.3) \approx 2y(0.2) - y(0.1) + 0.1^2 \times y''(0.2)$$
$$= 2 \times 0.82212 - 0.403 + 0.1^2 \times 3.28848 = 1.2741 \text{ (correct to 4 d.p.)}$$

The differential equation now gives us:

$$y''(0.3) = 4 \times 1.2741 \Rightarrow y''(0.3) = 5.0965$$

The second version of the approximation formula now gives us:

$$y(0.4) \approx 2y(0.3) - y(0.2) + 0.1^2 \times y''(0.3)$$
$$= 2 \times 1.2741 - 0.82212 + 0.1^2 \times 5.0965 = 1.7770 \text{ (correct to 4 d.p.)}$$

This summarises to give (correct to 4 d.p.):

x:	0	0.1	0.2	0.3	0.4
y:	0	0.403	0.8221	1.2741	1.7770

Example

$$\frac{d^2y}{dx^2} = 3x - 7y^2 + 5, \quad y = 1 \text{ and } \frac{dy}{dx} = \frac{1}{2} \text{ at } x = 0$$

(a) Use the Taylor series method to obtain y as a series in ascending powers of x up to and including the term in x^3, and hence obtain an approximate value for y when $x = 0.1$.

(b) Use the result

$$\left(\frac{d^2y}{dx^2}\right)_0 \approx \left(\frac{y_1 - 2y_0 + y_{-1}}{h^2}\right)$$

with $h = 0.1$, and your value of $y(0.1)$ obtained in (a), to find an approximate value for y when $x = 0.2$, giving your answer to 3 decimal places.

Solution

(a) We are given that $y(0) = 1$, $y'(0) = \frac{1}{2}$ and $y'' = 3x - 7y^2 + 5$

The differential equation now gives us:

$y''(0) = 3 \times 0 - 7y(0)^2 + 5 = -2 \implies y''(0) = -2$

Differentiate the differential equation to get:

$y''' = 3 - 14yy'$

$\therefore\ y'''(0) = 3 - 14y(0)y'(0) = 3 - 14 \times 1 \times \frac{1}{2} = -4 \implies y'''(0) = -4$

And so now we have:

$y(0) = 1,\ y'(0) = \frac{1}{2},\ y''(0) = -2 \text{ and } y'''(0) = -4$

$\therefore$ Maclaurin's theorem gives us the following (Taylor) series:

$$y = 1 + \frac{\frac{1}{2}x}{1!} + \frac{-2x^2}{2!} + \frac{-4x^3}{3!} \cdots$$

$\therefore\ y \approx 1 + \frac{1}{2}x - x^2 - \frac{2}{3}x^3$

$\therefore\ y(0.1) \approx 1 + \frac{1}{2}(0.1) - (0.1)^2 - \frac{2}{3}(0.1)^3 = 1.039$

$\therefore\ y(0.1) \approx 1.039$

(b) The differential equation now gives us:

$y''(0.1) = 3 \times (0.1) - 7y(0.1)^2 + 5$

$= 0.3 - 7 \times 1.039^2 + 5 = -2.26 \implies y''(0.1) \approx -2.26$

The given result can be rewritten as

$y_1 \approx 2y_0 - y_{-1} + h^2 y''_0$

$\therefore\ y(0.2) \approx 2y(0.1) - y(0) + 0.1^2 y''(0.1)$

$\approx 2 \times 1.039 - 1 + 0.1^2 \times (-2.26) = 1.055$

$\therefore\ y(0.2) \approx 1.055$

Example	$\dfrac{d^2y}{dx^2} + \dfrac{3dy}{dx} - \sin y = 8x^2$, $y = 0.3$ and $\dfrac{dy}{dx} = 0$ at $x = 0$

(a) Find the Maclaurin series for y up to and including the term in x^3.

Hence obtain approximate values for y and $\dfrac{dy}{dx}$ at $x = 0.1$

(b) Use the result $\left(\dfrac{d^2y}{dx^2}\right)_0 \approx \dfrac{y_1 - 2y_0 + y_{-1}}{h2}$ together with your results from

(a) to deduce an approximate value for y when $x = 0.2$.

Solution	(a) We are given that $y(0) = 0.3$, $y'(0) = 0$ and $y'' + 3y' - \sin y = 8x^2$

The differential equation now gives us:

$y''(0) = 0 - 3 \times 0 + \sin 0.3 = 0.2955$ (using radians)

Differentiate the differential equation to get

$y''' = 16x - 3y'' + \cos y \times y'$

$\therefore\ y'''(0)\quad = 16 \times 0 - 3y''(0) + \cos y(0) \times y'(0)$

$\qquad\qquad = 0 - 3 \times 0.2955 + \cos 0.5 \times 0 = -0.8866$

And so we've now got:

$y(0) = 0.3$, $y'(0) = 0$, $y''(0) = 0.2955$ and $y'''(0) = -0.8866$

$\therefore\ $ Maclaurin's theorem gives us the following series:

$y \approx 0.3 + \dfrac{0x}{1!} + \dfrac{0.2955x^2}{2!} - \dfrac{0.8866x^3}{3!}$

$\therefore\ y \approx 0.3 + 0.1478x^2 - 0.1478x^3$

$\therefore\ y(0.1) \approx 0.3 + 0.1478(0.1)^2 - 0.1478(0.1)^3 = 0.30133$

Differentiation of the Maclaurin series gives us:

$\qquad y' \quad \approx 0.2956x - 0.4434x^2$

$\therefore\ y'(0.1)\ \approx 0.2956(0.1) - 0.4434(0.1)^2 = 0.02513$

(b) The differential equation now gives us:

$y''(0.1)\quad = 8(0.1)^2 - 3y'(0.1) + \sin(0.1)$

$\qquad\qquad = 8(0.1)^2 - 3(0.02513) + \sin(0.1) = 0.1044$

The given result finally gives us

$\qquad y(0.2)\quad \approx 2y(0.1) - y(0) + 0.1^2\,y''(0.1)$

$\qquad\qquad\qquad \approx 2(0.30133) - 0.3 + 0.1^2(0.1044) = 0.304$

$\therefore\ y(0.2)\quad \approx 0.304$ (3 d.p.)

You should now be able to answer Exercises 20–22 on page 314.

EXERCISES

1 Use the trapezium rule with five strips of equal width to estimate, to three significant figures, the value of $\int_0^1 10^x \, dx$.

2 Use the trapezium rule, with ordinates at $x = 1$, $x = 2$ and $x = 3$, to estimate the value of:

$$\int_1^3 \sqrt{(40 - x^3)} \, dx \ .$$

3 Use the trapezium rule with three ordinates to estimate the value of the integral:

$$\int_1^2 e^{-x^2} dx$$

giving your answer to three decimal places.

4 Estimate the value of the integral:

$$\int_{0\cdot01}^{0\cdot49} \frac{1}{1 + 2\sqrt{x}} \, dx$$

by using the trapezium rule with three ordinates, giving your answer to two decimal places.

Using the substitution $u^2 = x$, or otherwise, obtain the exact value of the integral.

5 Use Simpson's rule with 2 intervals of equal size to estimate:

$$\int_1^2 \frac{dx}{1 + \sqrt{x}} \ , \text{ correct to 3 d.p.}$$

6 Use Simpson's rule with 4 intervals of equal size to estimate:

$$\int_1^3 \sqrt{1 + \frac{1}{x}} \, dx, \text{ correct to 3 d.p.}$$

7 Use Simpson's rule with 3 equally spaced ordinates to estimate:

$$\int_0^{\frac{\pi}{2}} \sqrt{\cos x} \ dx, \text{ correct to 3 d.p.}$$

[Hint: remember to use the radian mode on your calculator.]

8 Use Simpson's rule with 9 equally spaced ordinates to estimate:

$$\int_0^4 \frac{1}{1 + x^2} \, dx, \text{ correct to 3 d.p.}$$

What is the exact value of $\int_0^4 \frac{1}{1 + x^2} \, dx$?

9 If $\dfrac{dy}{dx} = 4x + 5y^2$ find an expression for $\dfrac{d^2y}{dx^2}$.

10 If $\dfrac{dy}{dx} = x^2 + y^2$ find an expression for $\dfrac{d^2y}{dx^2}$ and $\dfrac{d^3y}{dx^3}$.

11 Given the differential equation $\dfrac{dy}{dx} = 2x^2 + 3y$ and $y = 1$ when $x = 0$,

find y as a series in ascending powers of x up to and including the term in x^4.

12 Given the differential equation $\dfrac{dy}{dx} = x^2 + 3y^2$ and $y = 2$ when $x = 0$, find

y as a series in ascending powers of x up to and including the term in x^4.

13 Given the differential equation $\dfrac{d^2y}{dx^2} + x\,\dfrac{dy}{dx} + y = 0$ and $y = 1$, $\dfrac{dy}{dx} = 0$

at $x = 0$, find y as a series in ascending powers of x up to and including the term in x^4.

14 Given the differential equation $\dfrac{dy}{dx} = x^2 - y^2$ and $y = 1$ when $x = 2$,

use Euler's formula and a step of 0.2 to estimate y when $x = 2.2$.

15 Given the differential equation $\dfrac{dy}{dx} = 2x + y$ and $y = 2$ when $x = 0$, use

Euler's formula and steps of 0.2 to estimate y when $x = 0.2$, 0.4 and 0.6.

16 If $\dfrac{dy}{dx} = \dfrac{4}{x^2}$ and $y = 0$ when $x = 2$, use Euler's formula to estimate y when

$x = 2.2$.

Now use separation of the variables to find y as a function of x.
Hence show that Euler's formula overestimates y by exactly 10%.

17 If $\dfrac{dy}{dx} = xe^{-x^2}$, use Euler's formula to complete this table:

x:	0.1	0.2	0.3	0.4
y:	−0.495			

(Round all answers to 3 decimal places.)

18 Given the differential equation $\dfrac{dy}{dx} = x^2 + y$ with $y = 1$ when $x = 0$ and

$y = 1.106$ when $x = 0.1$, use Euler's 'improved' formula to estimate y when $x = 0.2$, 0.3 and 0.4. (Give your answers correct to 4 d.p.)

19 A function $y = f(x)$ is such that $\dfrac{dy}{dx} = x^2 - y^2$ with $f(0) = 1$ and $f(0.1) = 0.9094$. Use the formula $f(x + h) - f(x - h) \approx 2hf'(x)$ to estimate $f(0.2)$, $f(0.3)$ and $f(0.4)$. (Give your answers correct to 4 d.p.)

20 Use the formula $\left(\dfrac{d^2y}{dx^2}\right)_0 \approx \dfrac{(y_1 - 2y_0 + y_{-1})}{h^2}$ to find a step by step

solution to $\dfrac{d^2y}{dx^2} = x + y$ starting with $x = 0$ when $y = 2$ and $x = 0.1$ when $y = 1.91$ and taking intervals of 0.1 up to $x = 0.4$.

(Give answers correct to 4 d.p.)

21 Use the formula $\left(\dfrac{d^2y}{dx^2}\right)_0 \approx \dfrac{(y_1 - 2y_0 + y_{-1})}{h^2}$ to find a step by step

solution to $\dfrac{d^2y}{dx^2} = 1 - y$ starting with $x = 0$ when $y = 2$ and $x = 0.1$ when $y = 2.095$ and taking intervals of 0.1 up to $x = 0.4$.

22 $\dfrac{d^2y}{dx^2} = y + y^2$, $y = 1$ and $\dfrac{dy}{dx} = 0.2$ at $x = 0$

(a) Find the Maclaurin series for y up to and including the x^3 term. Hence obtain an approximate value for y when $x = 0.1$.

(b) Use the result $\left(\dfrac{d^2y}{dx^2}\right)_0 \approx \dfrac{y_1 - 2y_0 + y_{-1}}{h^2}$ and your value of $y(0.1)$

from (a) to find an approximate value for y when $x = 0.2$, giving your answer to 3 d.p.

You should now be able to:

● use the trapezium rule:

$$\frac{h}{2} [\text{1st} + \text{last} + 2 \times \text{rest}]$$

to estimate a definite integral

● use Simpson's rule:

$$\frac{h}{3} [\text{1st} + \text{last} + 4 (y_1 + y_3 + \dots) + 2 (y_2 + y_4 + \dots)]$$

to estimate a definite integral (providing there are an even number of intervals).

● use the Maclaurin expansion:

$$y = y(0) + \frac{y'(0)}{1!} x + \frac{y''(0)}{2!} x^2 + \frac{y'''(0)}{3!} x^3 + \dots$$

to find series solutions of differential equations.

● prove (and use) Euler's approximation formula:

$$\left(\frac{dy}{dx}\right)_0 \approx \frac{(y_1 - y_0)}{h} \Rightarrow y_1 \approx y_0 + hy'_0$$

to obtain a step-by-step solution of a given differential equation.

● prove (and use) Euler's improved approximation formula:

$$\left(\frac{dy}{dx}\right)_0 \approx \frac{(y_1 - y_{-1})}{2h} \Rightarrow y_1 \approx y_{-1} + 2hy'_0$$

to obtain step-by-step solution of a given differential equation.

● prove (and use) the approximation formula:

$$\left(\frac{d^2y}{dx^2}\right)_0 \approx \frac{(y_1 - 2y_0 + y_{-1})}{h^2} \Rightarrow y_1 \approx 2y_0 - y_{-1} + h^2y''_0$$

to obtain a step-by-step solution of a given differential equation.

Methods of proof

In this final section we are going to look at three methods of proof. The first is induction which gives us a method of proving that a suggested result is true. For example, we could use induction to prove that $\sum_{r=1}^{r=n} r = \dfrac{n(n+1)}{2}$.

The second method involves counter-examples, i.e. the presentation of a specific example to demonstrate that a suggested result is false. The third and final method involves proof by contradiction, i.e. we assume the *opposite* of what is suggested and get a contradiction.

How an induction works

Suppose that we wanted to prove that $\sum_{r=1}^{r=n} r = \dfrac{n(n+1)}{2}$

i.e. we wanted to show that

$n = 1$: 1 $= \dfrac{1 \times 2}{2} = 1$

$n = 2$: $1 + 2$ $= \dfrac{2 \times 3}{2} = 3$

$n = 3$: $1 + 2 + 3$ $= \dfrac{3 \times 4}{2} = 6$

$n = 4$: $1 + 2 + 3 + 4$ $= \dfrac{4 \times 5}{2} = 10$ and so on.

If we pick one of these lines at random, the whole line will read:

$$n = k \ : \ 1 + 2 + 3 + \ldots + k \ = \ \frac{k(k+1)}{2}$$

Then we say – 'Suppose this line is true',

[This gives us something definite to work from and we try to use this to deduce that the next line would also be true, i.e. we want to show that:

$$n = k + 1 \ : \ 1 + 2 + 3 + 4 + \ldots k + (k+1) \ = \ \frac{(k+1)(k+2)}{2}$$

is true if the line for $n = k$ is true.]

To get to the left-hand side of this next line, where $n = k + 1$, is quite easy – all we have to do is add the next term of the series, which is $(k + 1)$. Of course, in order to keep the sides in balance we have to add this to both sides. This gives:

$$1 + 2 + 3 + 4 + \ldots + k + \underline{(k + 1)} = \frac{k(k + 1)}{2} + \underline{(k + 1)}$$

Having made the left-hand side of the next line, we turn our attention to the right-hand side. We can simplify this by taking out a common factor …

$$\frac{k(k + 1)}{2} + (k + 1) = (k + 1) \left[\frac{k}{2} + 1\right]$$

$$= (k + 1) \left(\frac{k + 2}{2}\right)$$

$$= \frac{(k + 1)(k + 2)}{2}$$

which is the right-hand side of the next line, as we wanted. So we've succeeded in showing that if the sum is correct for the first k terms, it's also correct for the first $k + 1$ terms.

Note that although we selected one particular value and proved it to be true, in fact it was a random choice. This means we've shown that, if any one of the lines is true, then the next line will also be true.

The next step is usually very easy – we have to show that one particular line is true. In practice, we almost always take the case when $n = 1$. For the series we're looking at now, the line when $n = 1$ says simply:

$$n = 1 : 1 = \tfrac{1}{2}(1)(2) = 1$$

which is obviously true.

Now the two steps are combined. The first step has shown that, if any line is true, the next is also true. The second step has shown that the first line is true. But from the first step, this means that the second line is true. And this in turn means that the third line is true and so on and so on, for all the positive integers. This completes the proof by induction.

Let's summarise the method and then use it for a slightly different kind of result.

PROOF BY INDUCTION

STEP 1: Assume that the result is true for some value of n, say $n = k$. Using this result as the base, build on it to show that the next result would also be true, i.e. when $n = k + 1$

STEP 2: Show that the result is true for some particular value of n, usually $n = 1$.

Divisibility

The example we're going to look at now involves an expression being divisible by a certain number. In order to write this properly in the form of an equation, let's see what it means to say that, for example, 51 is divisible by 3. This is another way of saying that there is some whole number, p say, such that

$$51 = 3p$$

p being in this case 17. Similarly, if we want to express the fact that $n^3 - n$ is always divisible by 6 (which it is), we could write

$$n^3 - n = 6q, \text{ for some integer } q$$

Example Show that $5^n + 3$ is divisible by 4 for all positive integers n.

Solution Proof by induction.

Step 1: Assume that the result is true for some n, say $n = k$. We can write this as:

$$5^k + 3 = 4s, \text{ for some integer } s \qquad \qquad \text{... [1]}$$

[Now it's a good idea to work out what the next result along would be, so that we've got something to aim for. In this case, we want to use the assumed result above to show that $5^{k+1} + 3$ is also divisible by 4.]

Consider, then, $5^{k+1} + 3$

This can be re-written as $5 \times 5^k + 3$

$$\therefore \; 5^{k+1} + 3 \quad = 5 \times 5^k + 3$$

$$= 5 \times (4s - 3) + 3 \text{ (using assumption [1])}$$

$$= 20s - 15 + 3$$

$$= 20s - 12$$

$$= 4(5s - 3)$$

$\therefore \; 5^{k+1} + 3$ is also divisible by 4

So that completes the first step.

Step 2: Putting $n = 1$, $5^n + 3 = 8$, so that result is true for $n = 1$.

From the first step, this means that the next step, at $n = 2$, is also true, etc, so the result is true for all positive integers by induction.

Factorials

Let's have a look at another example, this time involving factorials. These can be awkward to combine at first, until you're familiar with a particular technique. This is that:

$$(n + 1) \times n! = (n + 1) \times n \times (n - 1) \times (n - 2) \times \ldots \times 2 \times 1$$
$$= (n + 1)!$$

– knowing this makes the factorial type of problem quite straightforward.

Example

Prove by induction that:

$$(1^2 + 1)\, 1! + (2^2 + 1)\, 2! + (3^2 + 1)\, 3! + \ldots + (n^2 + 1)\, n! = n\,(n + 1)!$$

Solution

Assume the result is true for some value of n, say at $n = k$. Then:

$$(1^2 + 1)\, 1! + (2^2 + 1)\, 2! + (3^2 + 1)\, 3! + \ldots + (k^2 + 1)\, k! = k\,(k + 1)!$$

[At this point remember where we're heading – we're trying to show that if this is true, the next result along, at $n = k + 1$, will also be true. So we put this value of n into the right-hand side which would give $(k + 1)\,(k + 2)!$ and now we know what we're aiming for.]

Add the next term of the series, $\left[(k + 1)^2 + 1\right](k + 1)!$ to both sides:

$$(1^2 + 1)\, 1! + (2^2 + 1)\, 2! + \ldots + (k^2 + 1)\, k! + \left[(k + 1)^2 + 1\right](k + 1)!$$

$$= k\,(k + 1)! + \left[(k + 1)^2 + 1\right](k + 1)!$$

The left-hand side is just the $(k + 1)$ terms of the series. Now we turn to the right-hand side and try and combine the two terms. The common factor is $(k + 1)!$ in this case

$$k(k + 1)! + \left[(k + 1)^2 + 1\right](k + 1)! = (k + 1)!\left[\,k + \left\{(k + 1)^2 + 1\right\}\right]$$
$$= (k + 1)!\left[\,k + k^2 + 2k + 1 + 1\,\right]$$
$$= (k + 1)!\left[\,k^2 + 3k + 2\,\right]$$
$$= (k + 1)!\,(k + 1)\,(k + 2)$$

[Since $(k + 1)! \times (k + 2) = (k + 2)!$] $= (k + 1)\,(k + 2)!$

which is the sum of the $(k + 1)$ terms, as we had already worked out.

We've now shown the first step.

Step 2: When $n = 1$, $\quad (1^2 + 1)\, 1! = 1(2)!$

i.e. $\qquad\qquad\qquad\qquad 2 = 2$

which is true.

Hence we can say that the result is true for all positive integers by induction.

Powers

It's not obvious at first sight that

$$3k \times 3^k = k3^{k+1}$$

but remember that you can move the 3 in the product anywhere since all the terms are multiplied together, i.e.

$$3k \times 3^k = k \times 3 \times 3^k = k \times 3^{k+1} \quad \text{as required.}$$

This type of working occurs in the following example.

Example	Prove, by induction or otherwise, that:

$$\sum_{r=1}^{n} 2^{r-1}(r+1) = 2^n n$$

Solution	This is the most usual form for the question, so let's work it through entirely in this notation.

Assume the result is true for some integer, say when $n = k$.

Then: $\quad \displaystyle\sum_{r=1}^{k} 2^{r-1}(r+1) = 2^k k$

The next term of the series is $2^k(k+2)$. Add this to both sides.

$$\sum_{r=1}^{k} 2^{r-1}(r+1) + 2^k(k+2) = 2^k k + 2^k(k+2)$$

i.e. $\displaystyle\sum_{r=1}^{k+1} 2^{r-1}(r+1) = 2^k \left[k + k + 2\right]$

$$= 2^k \left[2k + 2\right]$$
$$= 2^k \, 2(k+1)$$
$$= 2^{k+1}(k+1)$$

but this is the result with $n = k + 1$. Hence if the result is true for $n = k$, it's also true for $n = k + 1$.

When $n = 1$, the result gives $2^0(2) = 2.1$ which is true.

Hence, by induction, the result is true for all positive integers.

Inequalities

Let's see how induction might be applied to a problem involving inequalities.

Example

Prove by induction that $\displaystyle\sum_{r=1}^{n} \frac{2r-1}{2r} < n-\frac{1}{2}$ for all positive integers $n \geq 2$.

Solution

We have to show that

$$\frac{1}{2} + \frac{3}{4} + \frac{5}{6} + \ldots + \frac{2n-1}{2n} < n - \frac{1}{2}$$

Assume that the result is true for $n = k$

$$\therefore \quad \frac{1}{2} + \frac{3}{4} + \frac{5}{6} + \ldots + \frac{2k-1}{2k} < k - \frac{1}{2} \qquad \ldots \text{①}$$

We now consider

$$\frac{1}{2} + \frac{3}{4} + \frac{5}{6} + \ldots + \frac{2k-1}{2k} + \frac{2k+1}{2k+2}$$

and have to deduce that this is less than $(k+1) - \dfrac{1}{2}$ i.e. less than $k + \dfrac{1}{2}$.

And so here we go!

$$\frac{1}{2} + \frac{3}{4} + \frac{5}{6} + \ldots + \frac{2k-1}{2k} + \frac{2k+1}{2k+2} < k - \frac{1}{2} + \frac{2k+1}{2k+2}$$

(using the assumption①)

$$= k - \frac{1}{2} + 1 - \frac{1}{2k+2}$$

(having done some long division)

$$= k + \frac{1}{2} - \frac{1}{2k+2}$$

But this is clearly less than $k + \dfrac{1}{2}$, since $k \geq 2$

$\therefore$ The result is true for $n = k + 1$.

Also, when $n = 2$ we get $\frac{1}{2} + \frac{3}{4} = 1\frac{1}{4}$ which is clearly less than $2 - \frac{1}{2} = 1\frac{1}{2}$

$\therefore$ the result is true for $n = 2$

$\therefore$ By induction the result is true for all n.

A final selection

Since induction is often found to be rather tricky, I have gathered together another four examples. These should help to clarify all the preceding work.

Example

Prove by induction that $\displaystyle\sum_{r=1}^{n} \frac{1}{r(r+1)} = \frac{n}{n+1}$

Solution

Assume the result is true for $n = k$.

$$\therefore \quad \frac{1}{1 \times 2} + \frac{1}{2 \times 3} + \frac{1}{3 \times 4} + \dots + \frac{1}{k(k+1)} = \frac{k}{k+1} \quad (*)$$

[Now we want to use this to show that the next result along, with $n = k + 1$ is also true, i.e.

$$\frac{1}{1 \times 2} + \frac{1}{2 \times 3} + \dots + \frac{1}{k(k+1)} + \frac{1}{(k+1)(k+2)} = \frac{k+1}{k+2}]$$

Add the next terms of the series to both sides of (*)

$$\therefore \quad \frac{1}{1 \times 2} + \frac{1}{2 \times 3} + \frac{1}{3 \times 4} + \dots + \frac{1}{(k+1)} + \frac{1}{(k+1)(k+2)}$$

$$= \frac{k}{k+1} + \frac{1}{(k+1)(k+2)} = \frac{1}{k+1} \left[k + \frac{1}{k+2} \right]$$

$$= \frac{1}{k+1} \left[\frac{k^2 + 2k + 1}{k+2} \right] = \frac{1}{k+1} \times \frac{(k+1)^2}{(k+2)} = \frac{k+1}{k+2}$$

which is the result with $n = k + 1$.

Putting $n = 1$ gives $\dfrac{1}{1 \times 2} = \dfrac{1}{1+1}$ which is true.

$\therefore$ By induction the result is true for all n.

Example

Prove by induction that $7^n + 4^n + 1$ is divisible by 6, for all positive integers n.

Solution

Assume $7^k + 4^k + 1 = 6\lambda \quad \dots (*)$

Consider $7^{k+1} + 4^{k+1} + 1 \quad = 7 \times 7^k + 4 \times 4^k + 1$

$$= 7(6\lambda - 4^k - 1) + 4 \times 4^k + 1 \quad \text{(from *)}$$

$$= 42\lambda - 7 \times 4^k - 7 + 4 \times 4^k + 1 = 42\lambda - 6 - 3 \times 4^k$$

Clearly 42λ and -6 are both divisible by 6 and, since 4^k must be even, 3×4^k is also divisible by 6.

$\therefore$ Result true for $n = k + 1$.

Putting $n = 1$ gives $7 + 4 + 1 = 12$, which is divisible by 6.

$\therefore$ By induction the result is true for all n.

Example

Prove by induction that if $\mathbf{M} = \begin{pmatrix} 1 & 0 \\ 3 & 1 \end{pmatrix}$ then:

$$\mathbf{M}^n = \begin{pmatrix} 1 & 0 \\ 3n & 1 \end{pmatrix}, \text{ for positive integers } n.$$

Solution

Assume $\mathbf{M}^k = \begin{pmatrix} 1 & 0 \\ 3k & 1 \end{pmatrix}$

Consider $\mathbf{M}^{k+1} = \mathbf{M}^k \cdot \mathbf{M}$

$$= \begin{pmatrix} 1 & 0 \\ 3k+3 & 1 \end{pmatrix} \begin{pmatrix} 1 & 0 \\ 3 & 1 \end{pmatrix}$$

$$= \begin{pmatrix} 1 & 0 \\ 3k+3 & 1 \end{pmatrix} = \begin{pmatrix} 1 & 0 \\ 3(k+1) & 1 \end{pmatrix}$$

$\therefore$ Result true for $n = k + 1$.

Putting $n = 1$ gives $\mathbf{M}^1 = \begin{pmatrix} 1 & 0 \\ 3 \times 1 & 1 \end{pmatrix} = \begin{pmatrix} 1 & 0 \\ 3 & 1 \end{pmatrix}$ which is true.

$\therefore$ By induction the result is true or all n.

Example

By considering the first few values of n, suggest a formula for the following sum:

$$1.1! + 2.2! + 3.3! + \ldots + n.n!$$

Then prove it by induction.

Solution

$1.1!$	$= 1 =$	$2 - 1 =$	$2! - 1$
$1.1! + 2.2!$	$= 5 =$	$6 - 1 =$	$3! - 1$
$1.1! + 2.2! + 3.3!$	$= 23 =$	$24 - 1 =$	$4! - 1$

$\therefore$ it appears likely that:

$$1.1! + 2.2! + 3.3! + \ldots + n.n! = (n + 1)! - 1$$

Assume true for $n = k$, i.e.

$$1.1! + 2.2! + \ldots + k.k! = (k + 1)! - 1$$

Add the next term of the series to both sides:

$$\therefore \; 1.1! + 2.2! + \ldots + k.k! + (k + 1).(k + 1)! = (k + 1)! - 1 + (k + 1).(k + 1)!$$
$$= (k + 1)! \, [1 + (k + 1)] - 1$$
$$= (k + 1)! \, (k + 2) - 1$$
$$= (k + 2)! - 1$$

∴ Result true for $n = k + 1$

But we already know the result is true for $n = 1$

∴ By induction the result is true for all n.

You should now be able to answer Exercises 1–4 on pages 326–27.

Counter examples

Sometimes we come across a formula and can't be sure whether or not is is true. For example if we've got two points on the circumference of a circle, then that circle is divided into two regions.

2 points A and B ⇒   ⇒ 2 regions ① and ②

Similarly, three points give us 4 regions

3 points A , B and C ⇒ ⇒ 4 regions ① , ② , ③ , and ④

And four points give us 8 regions

4 points A, B, C and D ⇒ ⇒ 8 regions

It is then hardly surprising that five points give us 16 regions.

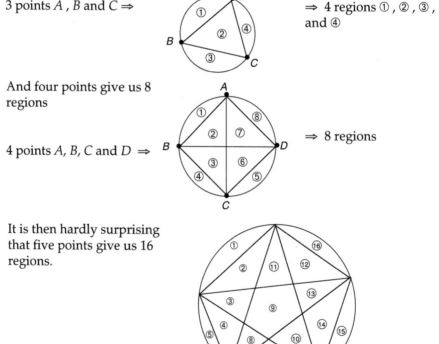

So far then we have:

points	2	3	4	5
regions	2	4	8	16

It looks obvious then (doesn't it?) that six points will give us 32 regions and that, in general, n points will give 2^{n-1} regions.

If we now set about trying to prove this result by induction we would get into a real muddle – because *the suggested general formula above is false.*

We can demonstrate that it is false by providing a *counter-example* i.e. a specific example showing that the rule is false. I'll leave this part to you but, however hard you try, you'll only be able to find **31** regions with six points. Give it a try if you don't believe me!

Example   Prove that the following statement is false:

$$\frac{1}{2} + \frac{2}{2^2} + \frac{3}{2^3} + \dots + \frac{n}{2^n} = 2 - \frac{n+2}{2^n} + (n-1)(n-2)(n-3)$$

Solution   Let's try a few values for n.

Putting $n = 1$ gives $\dfrac{1}{2} = 2 - \dfrac{3}{2} + 0$, which is true.

Putting $n = 2$ gives $\dfrac{1}{2} + \dfrac{2}{2^2} = 2 - \dfrac{4}{2^2} + 0$, which is also true.

Putting $n = 3$ gives $\dfrac{1}{2} + \dfrac{2}{2^2} + \dfrac{3}{2^3} = 2 - \dfrac{5}{2^3} + 0$, which is also true.

Surely then it must always be true? Not a bit of it!

Putting $n = 4$ gives $\dfrac{1}{2} + \dfrac{2}{2^2} + \dfrac{3}{2^3} + \dfrac{4}{2^4} = 2 - \dfrac{6}{2^4} + 6$

which is *not* true.

This, then, gives us our counter-example. The formula is incorrect so, thank goodness, we didn't start trying to prove it by induction!

You should now be able to answer Exercise 5 on page 327.

Proof by contradiction

This method involves assuming the opposite of what is stated and then getting a contradiction.

Example	Prove by contradiction that $\log_{10}5$ is irrational.

Solution	Let us assume that $\log_{10}5$ is rational.

$\therefore \log_{10}5 = \dfrac{p}{q}$ where p and q are integers in their lowest terms

$\therefore 5 = 10^{\frac{p}{q}}$

$\therefore 5^q = 10^p$

$\therefore 5^q = 5^p \times 2^p$

But this is clearly impossible because it would make 5^q an even number.

$\therefore$ our assumption must be false

$\therefore \log_{10}5$ must be irrational.

You should now be able to answer Exercises 6–7 on page 327.

EXERCISES

1 Prove the following by induction. In all cases $n = 1, 2, 3 \ldots$

(a) $1^2 + 2^2 + 3^3 + \ldots + n^2 = \dfrac{n(n+1)(2n+1)}{6}$

(b) $1.2 + 2.3 + 3.4 + \ldots + n(n+1) = \dfrac{n(n+1)(n+2)}{3}$

(c) $2 + 3.2 + 4.2^2 + 5.2^3 + \ldots + (n+1).2^{n-1} = n.2^n$

(d) $\displaystyle\sum_{r=1}^{n} \dfrac{1}{r(r+2)} = \dfrac{n(3n+5)}{4(n+1)(n+2)}$

(e) $3^{2n} - 1$ is always divisible by 8

(f) $2^{n+2} + 3^{2n+1}$ is always divisible by 7

(g) If $A = \begin{pmatrix} 3 & -1 \\ 4 & -1 \end{pmatrix}$ then $A^n = \begin{pmatrix} 2n+1 & -n \\ 4n & 1-2n \end{pmatrix}$.

Section 2

1 (a) $1 + \left(\frac{1}{3}\right)x + \dfrac{\left(\frac{1}{3}\right)\left(-\frac{2}{3}\right)x^2}{2!}$

$+ \dfrac{\left(\frac{1}{3}\right)\left(-\frac{2}{3}\right)\left(-\frac{5}{3}\right)x^3}{3!} + \dots$

$= 1 + \dfrac{x}{3} - \dfrac{x^2}{9} + \dfrac{5x^3}{81}$

(b) $1 - \left(\frac{1}{2}\right)x + \dfrac{\left(\frac{1}{2}\right)\left(-\frac{1}{2}\right)(-x)^2}{2!}$

$+ \dfrac{\left(\frac{1}{2}\right)\left(-\frac{1}{2}\right)\left(-\frac{3}{2}\right)(-x)^3}{3!}$

$= 1 - \dfrac{x}{2} - \dfrac{x^2}{8} - \dfrac{x^3}{16}$

(c) $1 + \dfrac{(-1)(2x)}{1} + \dfrac{(-1)(-2)(2x)^2}{2!}$

$+ \dfrac{(-1)(-2)(-3)(2x)^3}{3!}$

$= 1 - 2x + 4x^2 - 8x^3$

(d) $1 + \left(\frac{2}{3}\right)(-3x) + \dfrac{\left(\frac{2}{3}\right)\left(-\frac{1}{3}\right)(-3x)^2}{2!} +$

$\dfrac{\left(\frac{2}{3}\right)\left(-\frac{1}{3}\right)\left(-\frac{4}{3}\right)(-3x)^3}{3!}$

$= 1 - 2x - x^2 - \dfrac{4}{3}x^3$

(e) $1 + \left(-\frac{1}{2}\right)(-2x) + \dfrac{\left(-\frac{1}{2}\right)\left(-\frac{3}{2}\right)(-2x)^2}{2!}$

$+ \dfrac{\left(-\frac{1}{2}\right)\left(-\frac{3}{2}\right)\left(-\frac{5}{2}\right)(-2x)^3}{3!}$

$= 1 + x + \dfrac{3x^2}{2} + \dfrac{5x^3}{2}$

(f) $1 + (-2)\left(\frac{x}{2}\right) + \dfrac{(-2)(-3)\left(\frac{x}{2}\right)^2}{2!} +$

$\dfrac{(-2)(-3)(-4)\left(\frac{x}{2}\right)^3}{3!}$

$= 1 - x + \dfrac{3x^2}{4} - \dfrac{x^3}{2}$

2 (a) $(1 - 2x)^{-1} = 1 + 2x + \dfrac{(-1)(-2)(-2x)^2}{2!}$

$+ \dfrac{(-1)(-2)(-3)(-2x)^3}{3!}$

$= 1 + 2x + 4x^2 + 8x^3$

$\therefore (1 + 2x)(1 - 2x)^{-1}$

$= 1 + 2x + 4x^2 + 8x^3 + 2x + 4x^2 + 8x^3$

$= 1 + 4x + 8x^2 + 16x^3$ up to terms in x^2

(b) $(1 + x)^{-1/2} = 1 - \dfrac{x}{2} + \dfrac{\left(-\frac{1}{2}\right)\left(-\frac{3}{2}\right)x^2}{2!}$

$+ \dfrac{\left(-\frac{1}{2}\right)\left(-\frac{3}{2}\right)\left(-\frac{5}{2}\right)x^3}{3!}$

$= 1 - \dfrac{x}{2} + \dfrac{3x^2}{8} - \dfrac{5x^3}{16}$

$(1 - x)(1 + x)^{-1/2}$

$= 1 - \dfrac{1x}{2} + \dfrac{3x^2}{8} - \dfrac{5x^3}{16} - x + \dfrac{x^2}{2} - \dfrac{3x^3}{8}$

$= 1 - \dfrac{3x}{2} + \dfrac{7x^2}{8} - \dfrac{11x^3}{16}$

3 (a) $(8 + x)^{1/3} = \left[8\left(1 + \dfrac{x}{8}\right)\right]^{1/3}$

$= 8^{1/3}\left(1 + \dfrac{x}{8}\right)^{1/3} = 2\left(1 + \dfrac{x}{8}\right)^{1/3}$

(b) $\dfrac{1}{x + 2} = (2 + x)^{-1} = \left[2\left(1 + \dfrac{x}{2}\right)\right]^{-1}$

$= 2^{-1}\left(1 + \dfrac{x}{2}\right)^{-1} = \dfrac{1}{2}\left(1 + \dfrac{x}{2}\right)^{-1}$

(c) $\dfrac{1}{\sqrt{9 - x}} = (9 - x)^{-1/2} = \left[9\left(1 - \dfrac{x}{9}\right)\right]^{-1/2}$

$= 9^{-1/2}\left(1 - \dfrac{x}{9}\right)^{-1/2} = \dfrac{1}{3}\left(1 - \dfrac{x}{9}\right)^{-1/2}$

4 (a) $(1 + 2x - x^2)^{-1} = 1 + (-1)(2x - x^2)$

$+ \dfrac{(-1)(-2)(2x - x^2)^2}{2!} + \dfrac{(-1)(-2)(-3)(2x - x^2)^3}{3!}$

$= 1 - 2x + x^2 + 4x^2 - 4x^3 - 8x^3$

$= 1 - 2x + 5x^2 - 12x^3$

(b) $\left(1 - \dfrac{4}{x}\right)^{1/2} = 1 + \left(\dfrac{1}{2}\right)\left(-\dfrac{4}{x}\right) + \dfrac{\left(\frac{1}{2}\right)\left(-\frac{1}{2}\right)\left(-\frac{4}{x}\right)^2}{2}$

$= 1 - \dfrac{2}{x} - \dfrac{2}{x^2}$

5 From Exercise 1
(a) $|x| < 1$
(b) $|x| < 1$
(c) $|x| < 0.5$
(d) $|x| < \frac{1}{3}$
(e) $|x| < 0.5$
(f) $|x| < 2$
From Exercise 2
(a) $|x| < 0.5$
(b) $|x| < 1$
From Exercise 3
(a) $|x| < 8$
(b) $|x| < 2$
(c) $|x| < 9$
From Exercise 4
(a) $|2x - x^2| < 1 \Rightarrow -1 < 2x - x^2 < 1$
$\Rightarrow x^2 - 2x + 1 > 0$ and $x^2 - 2x - 1 < 0$
$\Rightarrow (x-1)^2 > 0$ and $(x-1)^2 < 2$
$\Rightarrow x \neq 1$ and $-\sqrt{2} < x - 1 < \sqrt{2}$
$\Rightarrow x \neq 1$ and $1 - \sqrt{2} < x < 1 + \sqrt{2}$
$\therefore \quad 1 - \sqrt{2} < x < 1$ or $1 < x < 1 + \sqrt{2}$

(b) $\left|\frac{4}{x}\right| < 1 \Rightarrow |x| > 4$

6 $f(x) = \dfrac{2 + 11x}{(2 + x)(1 - 2x)} \equiv \dfrac{A}{2 + x} + \dfrac{B}{1 - 2x}$

$= \dfrac{A(1 - 2x) + B(2 + x)}{(2 + x)(1 - 2x)}$

i.e. $2 + 11x \quad \equiv A(1 - 2x) + B(2 + x)$

$x = \dfrac{1}{2} \qquad \dfrac{15}{2} \equiv B\left(\dfrac{5}{2}\right) \Rightarrow B = 3$

$x = -2 \qquad -20 \equiv 5A \Rightarrow A = -4$

i.e. $f(x) = \dfrac{-4}{2 + x} + \dfrac{3}{1 - 2x}$

$= -4(2 + x)^{-1} + 3(1 - 2x)^{-1}$

$= -4 \times 2^{-1}\left(1 + \dfrac{x}{2}\right)^{-1} + 3(1 - 2x)^{-1}\left(1 + \dfrac{x}{2}\right)^{-1}$

$= 1 - \dfrac{x}{2} + \dfrac{(-1)(-2)}{2!}\left(\dfrac{x}{2}\right)^2 + \dfrac{(-1)(-2)(-3)}{3!}\left(\dfrac{x}{2}\right)^3$

$= (1 - 2x)^{-1} = 1 + 2x + 4x^2 + 8x^3$

so the coefficient if x^3 is

$\left[-4 \times 2^{-1} \times -\left(\dfrac{1}{2}\right)^3\right] + 3 \times 8$

$= \dfrac{1}{4} + 24 = 24\dfrac{1}{4}$

Expansion is valid when both $\left|\dfrac{x}{2}\right| < 1$
and $|2x| < 1$

i.e. $|x| < 2$ and $|x| < \dfrac{1}{2}$, so $|x| < \dfrac{1}{2}$

7 $\displaystyle\sum_{r=1}^{r=n}(n + 2r + 1) = \sum_{r=1}^{r=n} n + 2\sum_{r=1}^{r=n} r + \sum_{r=1}^{r=n} 1$

$= n^2 + \dfrac{2 \times n(n + 1)}{2} + n$

$= 2n^2 + 2n$

8 (a) $\dfrac{20 \times 21 \times 41}{6} = 2870$

(b) $\displaystyle\sum_{r=10}^{r=20} r^2 = \sum_{r=1}^{r=20} r^2 - \sum_{r=1}^{r=9} r^2$

$= 2870 - \dfrac{9 \times 10 \times 19}{6}$

$= 2870 - 285 = 2585$

9 $\displaystyle\sum_{r=1}^{r=n} r^2 + \sum_{r=1}^{r=n} r = \dfrac{n(n + 1)(2n + 1)}{6} + \dfrac{n(n + 1)}{2}$

$= \dfrac{n(n + 1)}{6}\left[(2n + 1) + 3\right]$

$= \dfrac{n(n + 1)(2n + 4)}{6}$

$= \dfrac{n(n + 1)(n + 2)}{3}$

10 $\dfrac{1}{r(r + 2)} = \dfrac{A}{r} + \dfrac{B}{r + 2} \quad \therefore \quad 1 = A(r + 2) + Br$
Setting $r = 0$ and $r = -2$ gives $A = 0.5$ and
$B = -0.5$

$\therefore \quad \dfrac{1}{r(r + 2)} = \dfrac{0.5}{r} - \dfrac{0.5}{r + 2}$

$\therefore \text{ Sum} = 0.5\left[\displaystyle\sum_{r=1}^{r=n}\dfrac{1}{r} - \sum_{r=1}^{r=n}\dfrac{1}{r + 2}\right]$

$= 0.5\left[\left(\dfrac{1}{1} + \dfrac{1}{2} + \dfrac{1}{3} + \ldots + \dfrac{1}{n}\right) - \right.$

$\left. \left(\dfrac{1}{3} + \dfrac{1}{4} + \dfrac{1}{5} + \ldots + \dfrac{1}{n} + \dfrac{1}{n + 1} + \dfrac{1}{n + 2}\right)\right]$

$= 0.5\left[1 + \dfrac{1}{2} - \dfrac{1}{n + 1} - \dfrac{1}{n + 2}\right]$

$= \dfrac{1}{2}\left[\dfrac{3}{2} - \dfrac{1}{n + 1} - \dfrac{1}{n + 2}\right]$

$= \dfrac{n(3n + 5)}{4(n + 1)(n + 2)}$

11 $\dfrac{2}{4x^2-1} = \dfrac{2}{(2x-1)(2x+1)} = \dfrac{A}{2x-1} + \dfrac{B}{2x+1}$

$\therefore\ 2 = A(2x+1) + B(2x-1)$

Setting $x = -\dfrac{1}{2}$ and $x = +\dfrac{1}{2}$

gives $B = -1$ and $A = 1$

$\therefore\ \dfrac{2}{4x^2-1} = \dfrac{1}{2x-1} - \dfrac{1}{2x+1}$

$\therefore\ \displaystyle\sum_{r=1}^{r=n} \dfrac{2}{4r^2-1} = \sum_{r=1}^{r=n}\left(\dfrac{1}{2r-1} - \dfrac{1}{2r+1}\right)$

$= \left[\left(\dfrac{1}{1}+\dfrac{1}{3}+\dfrac{1}{5}+\dots+\dfrac{1}{2n-1}\right)\right.$

$\left.-\left(\dfrac{1}{3}+\dfrac{1}{5}+\dots+\dfrac{1}{2n-1}+\dfrac{1}{2n+1}\right)\right]$

$= \left[1 - \dfrac{1}{2n+1}\right] = \dfrac{2n}{2n+1}$

12 (a) $f(x) = \cos x$ $\therefore\ f(0) = 1$

$f'(x) = -\sin x$ $\therefore\ f'(x) = 0$

$f''(x) = -\cos x$ $\therefore\ f''(0) = -1$

$f'''(x) = \sin x$ $\therefore\ f'''(0) = 0$

$f^{IV}(x) = \cos x$ $\therefore\ f^{IV}(0) = 1$

$f^{V}(x) = -\sin x$ $\therefore\ f^{V}(0) = 0$

$f^{VI}(x) = -\cos x$ $\therefore\ f^{VI}(0) = -1$

$\therefore\ \cos x = f(x)$

$= 1 + \dfrac{0x}{1!} - \dfrac{1x^2}{2!} + \dfrac{0x^3}{3!} + \dfrac{1x^4}{4!} + \dfrac{0x^5}{5!} - \dfrac{1x^6}{6!}$

$\therefore\ \cos x = 1 - \dfrac{x^2}{2} + \dfrac{x^4}{24} - \dfrac{x^6}{720}$

(b)   Replace x by $2x$ in (a)

$\therefore\ \cos 2x = 1 - \dfrac{(2x)^2}{2} + \dfrac{(2x)^4}{24} - \dfrac{(2x)^6}{720}$

$= 1 - 2x^2 + \dfrac{2x^4}{3} - \dfrac{4x^6}{45}$

(c) Multiply the expansion in (a) by x.

$\therefore\ x\cos x = x - \dfrac{x^3}{2} + \dfrac{x^5}{24} - \dfrac{x^7}{720}\dots$

(d) We know that $e^x = 1 + x + \dfrac{x^2}{2} + \dfrac{x^3}{6}\dots$

Replacing x by $2x$ this gives

$e^{2x} = 1 + (2x) + \dfrac{(2x)^2}{2} + \dfrac{(2x)^3}{6}$

$= 1 + 2x + 2x^2 + \dfrac{4x^3}{3}$

(e) $f(x) = \ln(2+x)$ $\therefore\ f(1) = \ln 2$

$\therefore\ f'(x) = \dfrac{1}{2+x}$ $\therefore\ f'(0) = \dfrac{1}{2}$

$\therefore\ f''(x) = \dfrac{-1}{(2+x)^2}$ $\therefore\ f''(0) = -\dfrac{1}{4}$

$\therefore\ f'''(x) = \dfrac{2}{(2+x)^3}$ $\therefore\ f'''(0) = \dfrac{1}{4}$

$\therefore\ \ln(2+x) = f(x)$

$= \ln 2 + \dfrac{\frac{1}{2}x}{1!} - \dfrac{\frac{1}{4}x^2}{2!} + \dfrac{\frac{1}{4}x^3}{3!}$

$\therefore\ \ln(2+x) = \ln 2 + \dfrac{1}{2}x - \dfrac{1}{8}x^2 + \dfrac{1}{24}x^3$

13 $e^x = 1 + x + \dfrac{x^2}{2} + \dfrac{x^3}{6}$ and $\cos x = 1 - \dfrac{x^2}{2}$

$\therefore\ \cos 3x = 1 - \dfrac{(3x)^2}{2}$ or $1 - \dfrac{9x^2}{2}$

$\therefore\ e^x\cos 3x = \left(1 + x + \dfrac{x^2}{2} + \dfrac{x^3}{6}\right)\left(1 - \dfrac{9x^2}{2}\right)$

$= 1 + x + \dfrac{1}{2}x^2 - \dfrac{9}{2}x^2 + \dfrac{1}{6}x^3 - \dfrac{9}{2}x^3$

(ignoring powers higher than 3)

$= 1 + x - 4x^2 - 4\dfrac{1}{3}x^3$

14 $\cos x = 1 - \dfrac{x^2}{2} + \dfrac{x^4}{24}\dots$ and $\ln(1+x) = x - \dfrac{x^2}{2}\dots$

$\therefore\ \ln(\cos x) = \ln\left(1 - \dfrac{x^2}{2} + \dfrac{x^4}{24}\right)$

$= \ln\left(1 + \left[-\dfrac{x^2}{2} + \dfrac{x^4}{24}\right]\right)$

$= \left[-\dfrac{x^2}{2} + \dfrac{x^4}{24}\right] - \dfrac{1}{2}\left[-\dfrac{x^2}{2} + \dfrac{x^4}{24}\right]^2$

$= -\dfrac{x^2}{2} + \dfrac{x^4}{24} - \dfrac{x^4}{8}$

(ignoring powers higher than 4)

$\therefore\ \ln(\cos x) = -\dfrac{x^2}{2} - \dfrac{x^4}{12}$

Finally $\ln(\sec x) = \ln\left(\dfrac{1}{\cos x}\right)$

$= -\ln(\cos x) = \dfrac{x^2}{2} + \dfrac{x^4}{12}.$

333

Section 3

1 (a) $\operatorname{Sin} x = \dfrac{\sqrt{3}}{2}$ and the calculator gives $60°$

$\therefore$ the general solution is:

$$x = n180° + (-1)^n\, 60°$$

or $\quad x = n\pi + (-1)^n\, \dfrac{\pi}{3}$ in radians.

(b) $\operatorname{Cos} x = -\dfrac{1}{\sqrt{2}}$, and the calculator gives $135°$.

This gives a general solution of:

$$x = n360° \pm 135°$$

or $\quad x = 2n\pi \pm \dfrac{3\pi}{4}$

(c) $\operatorname{Tan} x = -1$, and the calculator gives $-45°$

The general solution is:

$$x = n180° - 45°$$

or $\quad x = n\pi - \dfrac{\pi}{4}$

(d) $\operatorname{Sin} x = -1$, and the calculator gives $-90°$

The general solution is:

$$x = n180° - (-1)^n\, 90°$$

or $\quad x = n\pi - (-1)^n\, \dfrac{\pi}{2}$

(e) $\cos x = 0$, and the calculator gives $90°$

The general solution is:

$$x = n \times 360° \pm 90°$$

or $\quad x = 2n\pi \pm \dfrac{\pi}{2}$

(f) $\operatorname{Tan} x = 0$, and the calculator gives $0°$

The general solution is:

$$x = n180°$$

or $\quad x = n\pi$

(g) $2x = n\,180° + (-1)^n\, 30°$

$\therefore x = n \times 90° + (-1)^n\, 15°$

or $\quad 2x = n\pi + (-1)^n\, \dfrac{\pi}{6} \quad \therefore \quad x = \dfrac{n\pi}{2} + (-1)^n\, \dfrac{\pi}{12}$

(h) $2x = n \times 360° \pm 30° \quad \therefore \quad x = n \times 180° \pm 15°$

or $\quad 2x = 2n\pi \pm \dfrac{\pi}{6} \quad \therefore \quad x = n\pi \pm \dfrac{\pi}{12}$

(i) $\quad x - \dfrac{\pi}{3} = n\pi + \dfrac{\pi}{4} \quad \therefore x = n\pi + \dfrac{7\pi}{12}$

or $\quad x - 60° = n \times 180° + 45°$

$\therefore \quad x = n \times 180° + 105°$

2 We can rewrite this equation as:

$$2 \cos \dfrac{4\theta + 2\theta}{2}\ \cos \dfrac{4\theta - 2\theta}{2} = 0$$

i.e. $2 \cos 3\theta \cos \theta = 0$

So either (a) $\cos 3\theta = 0$ or (b) $\cos \theta = 0$.

(a) $3\theta = n360° \pm 90°$

$\therefore \theta = n120° \pm 30°$

$\therefore \theta = 30°, 90°$ or $150°$

(b) $\theta = 90°$

$\therefore \theta = 30°, 90°$ or $150°$

3 Rewritten, it becomes

$$2 \cos \dfrac{\theta + 5\theta}{2}\ \cos \dfrac{\theta - 5\theta}{2} = 2 \cos 2\theta$$

i.e. $\cos 3\theta \cos (-2\theta) = \cos 2\theta$

But $\cos (-\theta) = \cos \theta$

so $\quad \cos 3\theta \cos 2\theta = \cos 2\theta$

$\quad \cos 2\theta\, (\cos 3\theta - 1) = 0$

So either (a) $\cos 2\theta = 0$ or (b) $\cos 3\theta = 1$.

(a) $2\theta = n360° \pm 90°$

$\therefore \theta = n180° \pm 45°$

$\therefore \theta = 45°, 135°, 225°, 315°$

(b) $3\theta = n360° \pm 0$

$\therefore \theta = n120°$

$\therefore \theta = 0°, 120°, 240°, 360°$

So $\quad \theta = 0°, 45°, 120°, 135°, 225°, 240°, 315°$

or $360°$

4 Write it as $\sin 8\theta - \sin 2\theta = 0$

i.e. $2 \cos 5\theta \sin 3\theta = 0$

So either (a) $\cos 5\theta = 0$ or (b) $\sin 3\theta = 0$.

(a) $5\theta = 2n\pi \pm \dfrac{\pi}{2}$

$\therefore \theta = \dfrac{2n\pi}{5} \pm \dfrac{\pi}{10} \quad \therefore \theta = \dfrac{\pi}{10}, \dfrac{3\pi}{10}, \dfrac{5\pi}{10}$

(b) $3\theta = n\pi + (-1)^n\, 0$

$\therefore \theta = \dfrac{n\pi}{3} \quad \therefore \theta = 0, \dfrac{\pi}{3}$

$\therefore \theta = 0, \dfrac{\pi}{10}, \dfrac{3\pi}{10}, \dfrac{\pi}{3}, \dfrac{\pi}{2}$

5 Rewritten, it becomes

$$2 \sin \left(\dfrac{2\theta + 6\theta}{2}\right) \cos \left(\dfrac{2\theta - 6\theta}{2}\right) = 2 \sin 4\theta$$

i.e. $\sin 4\theta \cos (-2\theta) = \sin 4\theta$

So either (a) $\sin 4\theta = 0$ or (b) $\cos 2\theta = 0$

(a) $4\theta = n\pi$ $\therefore$ $\theta = \dfrac{n\pi}{4}$ $\therefore$ $\theta = 0, \dfrac{\pi}{4}, \dfrac{\pi}{2}, \dfrac{3\pi}{4}, \pi$

(b) $2\theta = 2n\pi \pm \dfrac{\pi}{2}$ $\therefore$ $\theta = n\pi \pm \dfrac{\pi}{4}$ $\therefore$ $\theta = \dfrac{\pi}{4}, \dfrac{3\pi}{4}$

$\theta = 0, \dfrac{\pi}{4}, \dfrac{\pi}{2}, \dfrac{3\pi}{4}, \pi$

6 (a) Expanding the RHS gives:

$\sqrt{3}\cos\theta - \sin\theta = R\cos\theta\cos\alpha - R\sin\theta\sin\alpha$

Then we want

$\qquad R\cos\alpha = \sqrt{3}$ ...① (putting $\theta = 0$)

and $R\sin\alpha = 1$ ... ② (putting $\theta = 90°$)

Squaring and adding these, we get:

$\qquad R^2\cos^2\alpha + R^2\sin^2 x = 3 + 1$

i.e. $R^2 = 4$

$\qquad R = 2$ (taking the positive value)

Then dividing ② by ① gives:

$\qquad \tan\alpha = \dfrac{1}{\sqrt{3}} \Rightarrow \alpha = 30°$

i.e. $\sqrt{3}\cos\theta - \sin\theta = 2\cos(\theta + 30°)$

(b) $\cos\theta + \sin\theta \equiv R\cos\theta\cos\alpha + R\sin\theta\sin\alpha$

$R\cos\alpha = 1$, $R\sin\alpha = 1 \Rightarrow R^2 = 2$ and $R = \sqrt{2}$

$\tan\alpha = 1 \Rightarrow \alpha = 45°$

$\cos\theta + \sin\theta = \sqrt{2}\cos(\theta - 45°)$

7 We have, after expanding:

$\cos\alpha = \dfrac{4}{5}$ and $\sin\alpha = \dfrac{3}{5}$

Since α is acute, it has value 36.9° (to nearest 0.1 of a degree).

Let $f(\theta) = 5\cos(\theta + \alpha) - 4$

$f(\theta)$ has its greatest value when $\theta + \alpha = 0$, since at this point cos has a maximum, i.e. $\theta = -36.9°$. (It only attains this value once every cycle of 360°.) Similarly the minimum value occurs when $\theta + \alpha = 180°$, i.e.

$\theta = 180° - 36.9°$

$\quad = 143.1°$

If $5\cos(\theta + \alpha) = 4$

$\qquad \cos(\theta + \alpha) = \dfrac{4}{5}$

$\qquad \theta + \alpha = -36.9°$ or $+36.9°$

i.e. $\theta = 73.7°$ or $0°$

8 Combining these two functions gives:

$3\cos x + \sin x = \sqrt{10}\cos(x - \alpha)$ where $\tan\alpha = \dfrac{1}{3}$

i.e. $\alpha = 18.43°$

The question becomes equivalent to solving the equation:

$\sqrt{10}\cos(x - \alpha) = 2$

i.e. $\cos(x - \alpha) = \dfrac{2}{\sqrt{10}}$

$x - \alpha = 50.77°$ or $309.23°$

$x = 69.2°$ or $327.7°$

9 (a) $\cos\theta - \sin\theta = \sqrt{2}\cos\left(\theta + \dfrac{\pi}{4}\right)$

(b) The equation becomes:

$\sqrt{2}\cos\left(2x + \dfrac{\pi}{4}\right) = \sqrt{2}$

$\cos\left(2x + \dfrac{\pi}{4}\right) = 1$

$2x + \dfrac{\pi}{4} = 2n\pi \pm 0$

$2x = 2n\pi - \dfrac{\pi}{4}$

$x = n\pi - \dfrac{\pi}{8}$

$\therefore x = \dfrac{7\pi}{8}$ or $\dfrac{15\pi}{8}$

10 The equation becomes $7\cos\theta - 4\sin\theta = 3$

i.e. $\sqrt{65}\cos(\theta + \alpha) = 3$, where $\tan\alpha = \dfrac{4}{7}$

$\theta + \alpha = 68.15°$ or $291.85°$

$\alpha = 29.74° \Rightarrow \theta = 38.4°$ or $262.1°$

11 (a) 4θ

(b) $1 - \dfrac{(2\theta)^2}{2} = 1 - 2\theta^2$

(c) 3θ

(d) $(1 - 2\theta^2)^2$ (Using (b)) $\approx 1 - 4\theta^2$

(e) $\dfrac{2\theta}{\theta} = 2$

(f) $\dfrac{\theta 3\theta}{1 - \left(1 - \dfrac{\theta^2}{2}\right)} = \dfrac{3\theta^2}{\dfrac{\theta^2}{2}} = 6$

12 $\sin\left(\dfrac{1}{6}\pi + x\right) = \sin\dfrac{1}{6}\pi\cos x + \cos\dfrac{1}{6}\pi\sin x$

$\therefore \sin\left(\dfrac{1}{6}\pi + x\right) = \dfrac{1}{2}\cos x + \dfrac{\sqrt{3}}{2}\sin x$

$\therefore 4\sin\left(\dfrac{1}{6}\pi + x\right) = 2\cos x + 2\sqrt{3}\sin x$

$\approx 2\left(1 - \dfrac{x^2}{2}\right) + 2\sqrt{3}x = 2 + 2\sqrt{3}x - x^2$

13 $(1 - \sin^2 2x)\cos 3x \approx (1 - (2x)^2)\left(1 - \dfrac{(3x)^2}{2}\right)$

$= (1 - 4x^2)\left((1 - \dfrac{9x^2}{2}\right) \approx 1 - \dfrac{17}{2}x^2$

14 $\cos x - 6x = x^2$ ∴ $1 - \dfrac{1}{2}x^2 - 6x \approx x^2$

∴ $1.5x^2 + 6x - 1 = 0$. Now use the quadratic formula to get $x = 0.16$.

15 (a) $\dfrac{4}{\sqrt{1 - 16x^2}}$ (b) $\dfrac{-2}{\sqrt{1 - 4x^2}}$ (c) $\dfrac{2}{1 + 4x^2}$

(d) $\dfrac{1}{\sqrt{1 - x^2}}$ (e) $\dfrac{2x}{1 + x^4}$ (f) $\dfrac{e^x}{\sqrt{1 - e^{2x}}}$

(g) $\dfrac{+\dfrac{1}{x^2}}{\sqrt{1 - \left(\dfrac{1}{x}\right)^2}} = \dfrac{1}{x\sqrt{x^2 - 1}}$

(h) $\dfrac{-\dfrac{2}{x^3}}{1 + \dfrac{1}{x^4}} = \dfrac{-2x}{x^4 + 1}$

16 $\cos x + \sin x = R(\cos x \cos A + \sin x \sin A)$

∴ $R \cos A = 1$, $R \sin A = 1$ ∴ $A = \dfrac{\pi}{4}$ and $R = \sqrt{2}$

∴ $\cos x + \sin x = \sqrt{2}\cos\left(x - \dfrac{\pi}{4}\right)$

(a) $\cos\left(x - \dfrac{\pi}{4}\right) = \dfrac{1}{\sqrt{2}}$ ∴ $x - \dfrac{\pi}{4} = 2n\pi \pm \dfrac{\pi}{4}$

∴ $x = 2n\pi$ or $2n\pi + \dfrac{\pi}{2}$

(b) $\sqrt{2}\cos\left(x - \dfrac{\pi}{4}\right)$ reaches its greatest value of $\sqrt{2}$ when $x = \dfrac{\pi}{4}$

17 (a) Differentiate as a product

∴ $\dfrac{x}{\sqrt{1 - x^2}} + \sin^{-1}x$

(b) Another product ∴ $\dfrac{-x^2}{\sqrt{1 - x^2}} + 2x \cos^{-1}x$

(c) $1 + \dfrac{1}{1 + x^2} = \dfrac{2 + x^2}{1 + x^2}$

(d) Another product

∴ $\sqrt{x} \times \dfrac{\dfrac{1}{2}x^{-\frac{1}{2}}}{1 + x} + \dfrac{1}{2}x^{-\frac{1}{2}}\tan^{-1}\sqrt{x}$

$= \dfrac{1}{2(1 + x)} + \dfrac{1}{2\sqrt{x}}\tan^{-1}\sqrt{x}$

Section 4

1 This reduces to $e^x = 1$ ∴ $x = 0$

2 This reduces to $7e^{2x} - 16e^x + 3 = 0$

∴ $e^x = \dfrac{16 \pm \sqrt{172}}{14}$

∴ $e^x = 2.08$ or 0.206

∴ $x = 0.73$ or -1.58 (2 d.p.)

3 This reduces to $3e^{2x} - e^x + 1 = 0$ which has unreal roots

∴ no real solutions

4 $A = 3$ $B = 5$ $C = k$ and so

$x = \ln\dfrac{k \pm \sqrt{(3^2 + k^2 - 5^2)}}{(3 + 5)}$

$= \ln\dfrac{k \pm \sqrt{(k^2 - 16)}}{8}$

In order for this to produce two distinct real roots, the two values of the expression $k \pm \sqrt{(k^2 - 16)}$ must be both real and positive. This is so for any $k > 4$.

5 $A = 3$ $B = k$ $C = 4$

$x = \ln\dfrac{4 \pm \sqrt{(3^2 + 4^2 - k^2)}}{(3 + k)}$

So there are two real roots provided the two values $\dfrac{4 \pm \sqrt{(25 - k^2)}}{(3 + k)}$ are both real and positive.

The expression is real when: $-5 \le k \le 5$

However, $\dfrac{4 - \sqrt{(25 - k^2)}}{(3 + k)}$ is positive when:

either $4 - \sqrt{(25 - k^2)} > 0$ and $3 + k > 0$

i.e. $k > 3$

or $4 - \sqrt{(25 - k^2)} < 0$ and $3 + k < 0$ which cannot happen.

We conclude that: $3 < k \le 5$.

6

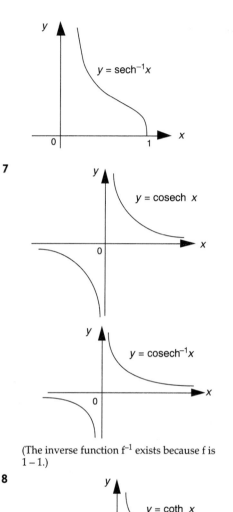

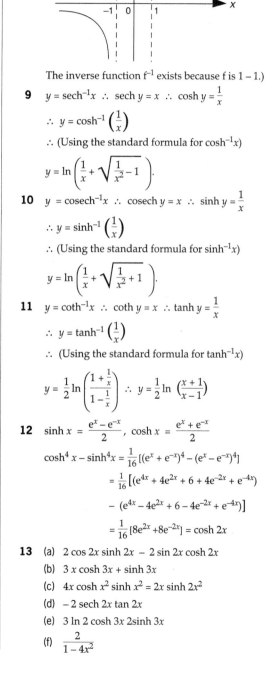

The inverse function f^{-1} exists because f is 1 – 1.)

9 $y = \text{sech}^{-1}x$ $\therefore$ $\text{sech } y = x$ $\therefore$ $\cosh y = \dfrac{1}{x}$

$\therefore$ $y = \cosh^{-1}\left(\dfrac{1}{x}\right)$

$\therefore$ (Using the standard formula for $\cosh^{-1}x$)

$$y = \ln\left(\dfrac{1}{x} + \sqrt{\dfrac{1}{x^2}-1}\,\right).$$

10 $y = \text{cosech}^{-1}x$ $\therefore$ $\text{cosech } y = x$ $\therefore$ $\sinh y = \dfrac{1}{x}$

$\therefore$ $y = \sinh^{-1}\left(\dfrac{1}{x}\right)$

$\therefore$ (Using the standard formula for $\sinh^{-1}x$)

$$y = \ln\left(\dfrac{1}{x} + \sqrt{\dfrac{1}{x^2}+1}\,\right).$$

11 $y = \coth^{-1}x$ $\therefore$ $\coth y = x$ $\therefore$ $\tanh y = \dfrac{1}{x}$

$\therefore$ $y = \tanh^{-1}\left(\dfrac{1}{x}\right)$

$\therefore$ (Using the standard formula for $\tanh^{-1}x$)

$$y = \dfrac{1}{2}\ln\left(\dfrac{1+\frac{1}{x}}{1-\frac{1}{x}}\right) \quad \therefore \quad y = \dfrac{1}{2}\ln\left(\dfrac{x+1}{x-1}\right)$$

12 $\sinh x = \dfrac{e^x - e^{-x}}{2}$, $\cosh x = \dfrac{e^x + e^{-x}}{2}$

$\cosh^4 x - \sinh^4 x = \dfrac{1}{16}[(e^x + e^{-x})^4 - (e^x - e^{-x})^4]$

$= \dfrac{1}{16}[(e^{4x} + 4e^{2x} + 6 + 4e^{-2x} + e^{-4x})$

$\qquad - (e^{4x} - 4e^{2x} + 6 - 4e^{-2x} + e^{-4x})]$

$= \dfrac{1}{16}[8e^{2x} + 8e^{-2x}] = \cosh 2x$

13 (a) $2\cos 2x \sinh 2x - 2\sin 2x \cosh 2x$

(b) $3x \cosh 3x + \sinh 3x$

(c) $4x \cosh x^2 \sinh x^2 = 2x \sinh 2x^2$

(d) $-2\,\text{sech } 2x \tan 2x$

(e) $3\ln 2 \cosh 3x\, 2\sinh 3x$

(f) $\dfrac{2}{1-4x^2}$

7

8

(The inverse function f^{-1} exists because f is 1 – 1.)

14 $2(\cosh^2 x - 1) + 8 = 7 \cosh x$

$\therefore 2\cosh^2 x - 7\cosh x + 6 = 0$

$\therefore (2\cosh x - 3)(\cosh x - 2) = 0$

$\therefore \cosh x = 1.5 \text{ or } 2$

$\therefore x = \pm 0.96 \text{ or } \pm 1.32 \ (2 \text{ d.p.})$

15 (a) $\dfrac{1}{3}\sinh 3x + C$

(b) $\dfrac{x}{3}\sinh 3x - \dfrac{1}{9}\cosh 3x + C$

(c) $x\sinh^{-1} 3x - \dfrac{1}{3}\sqrt{1 + 9x^2} + C$

(d) $\dfrac{1}{2}\ln(\cosh x^2) + C$

(e) $\dfrac{1}{4}\sinh^4 x + C$

(f) $\dfrac{1}{2}\int(\cosh 2x - 1)\,dx = \dfrac{1}{4}\sinh 2x - \dfrac{x}{2} + C$

16 $\dfrac{4\sinh x}{\cosh x} - \dfrac{1}{\cosh x} = 1 \therefore 4\sinh x - 1 = \cosh x$

This reduces to $3e^x - 5e^{-x} - 2 = 0$

$\therefore 3e^{2x} - 2e^x - 5 = 0$

$\therefore (3e^x - 5)(e^x + 1) = 0$

$\therefore e^x = \dfrac{5}{3} \text{ or } -1 \ \therefore x = \ln\left(\dfrac{5}{3}\right)$

Section 5

1 (a) $\dfrac{1}{6}\tan^{-1}\left(\dfrac{3x}{2}\right) + C$ (b) $\dfrac{1}{2}\tan^{-1} 2x + C$

(c) $\dfrac{1}{5}\tan^{-1}\left(\dfrac{x}{5}\right) + C$

2 $\displaystyle\int\left[\dfrac{1}{x-1} - \dfrac{4x+1}{4x^2+1}\right]dx$

$= \displaystyle\int\left(\dfrac{1}{x-1} - \dfrac{4x}{4x^2+1} - \dfrac{1}{4x^2+1}\right)dx$

$= \ln(x-1) - \dfrac{1}{2}\ln(4x^2+1) - \dfrac{1}{2}\tan^{-1} 2x + C$

$= \ln\left[\dfrac{x-1}{\sqrt{4x^2+1}}\right] - \dfrac{1}{2}\tan^{-1} 2x + C$

3 $\displaystyle\int\left[\dfrac{1}{x-1} + \dfrac{2}{x^2+4x+5}\right]dx =$

$\displaystyle\int\left[\dfrac{1}{x-1} + \dfrac{2}{(x+2)^2+1}\right]dx$

$= \ln(x-1) + 2\tan^{-1}(x+2) + C$

4 $dx = 2u\,du$ and so the integral becomes:

$\displaystyle\int\dfrac{2u}{2-u}\,du = \int\left[-2 + \dfrac{4}{2-u}\right]du$

$= -2u - 4\ln(2-u) + c = -2\sqrt{x} - 4\ln(2-\sqrt{x}) + c$

5 $du = \dfrac{1}{x}\,dx$ and the integral is

$\displaystyle\int\dfrac{1}{u}\,du = \ln u + c = \ln(\ln x) + c$

6 $du = e^x dx$ and the limits on u are e^1 and e^2, i.e. e and e^2. The integral is therefore

$\displaystyle\int_e^{e^2}\dfrac{du}{1-u^2} = \dfrac{1}{2}\int_e^{e^2}\left[\dfrac{1}{1-u} + \dfrac{1}{1+u}\right]du$

using partial fractions.

$= \dfrac{1}{2}\left[-\ln(1-u) + \ln(1+u)\right]_e^{e^2}$

$= \dfrac{1}{2}\left[-\ln(1-e^2) + \ln(1+e^2) + \ln(1-e) - \ln(1+e)\right]$

$= \dfrac{1}{2}\ln\left\{\dfrac{(1+e^2)(1-e)}{(1-e^2)(1+e)}\right\}$

$= \dfrac{1}{2}\ln\left\{\dfrac{1+e^2}{(1+e)^2}\right\} = -0.25 \ (2 \text{ d.p.})$

7 $dx = du$ and the limits on u are $5 - 1$ and $2 - 1$, i.e. 4 and 1. The integral is therefore:

$$\int_1^4 \frac{(u + 1)^3 + 2(u + 1)}{u^3} \, du$$

$$= \int_1^4 \frac{u^3 + 3u^2 + 5u + 3}{u^3} \, du$$

$$= \int_1^4 \left[1 + \frac{3}{u} + \frac{5}{u^2} + \frac{3}{u^3} \right] du$$

$$= \left[u + 3 \ln(u) - \frac{5}{u} - \frac{3}{2u^2} \right]_1^4$$

$$= \left[4 + 3 \ln 4 - \frac{5}{4} - \frac{3}{32} \right] - \left[1 + 3 \ln 1 - 5 - \frac{3}{2} \right]$$

$$= 8 + \frac{5}{32} + 3 \ln 4 = 12.3 \text{ (1 d.p.)}$$

8 $du = -\sin x \, dx$ and the limits on u are $\cos(0)$ and $\cos\left(\frac{1}{2}\pi\right)$, i.e. 1 and 0. So:

$$\sin^3 x \, dx = [1 - \cos^2 x] \sin x \, dx = -(1 - u^2) \, du$$

and the integral is:

$$-\int_1^0 \frac{1 - u^2}{(1 + u)^2} \, du = -\int_1^0 \frac{1 - u}{1 + u} \, du$$

$$= \int_1^0 \left[1 - \frac{2}{1 + u} \right] du$$

$$= \left[u - 2 \ln(1 + u) \right]_1^0$$

$$= [0 - 2 \ln(1 + 0)] - [1 - 2\ln(1 + 1)]$$

$$= 2 \ln 2 - 1 = 0.39 \text{ (2 d.p.)}$$

9 $du = e^x \, dx$ and so $e^{3x} \, dx = e^{2x} e^x \, dx = u^2 \, du$
The integral is therefore:

$$\int \frac{u^2}{u^2 - 1} \, du = \int \left[1 + \frac{1}{u^2 - 1} \right] du$$

$$= \int \left[1 + \frac{\frac{1}{2}}{u - 1} - \frac{\frac{1}{2}}{u + 1} \right] du$$

$$= u + \frac{1}{2} \ln(u - 1) - \frac{1}{2} \ln(u + 1)$$

$$= e^x + \frac{1}{2} \ln(e^x - 1) - \frac{1}{2} \ln(e^x + 1) + C$$

$$= e^x + \frac{1}{2} \ln \left(\frac{e^x - 1}{e^x + 1} \right) + C$$

10 (a) Here $a = 1$ and $b = 1$, and so the integral is

$$\left[\sin^{-1} x \right]_0^1 = \frac{1}{2}\pi - 0 = \frac{1}{2}\pi$$

(b) This problem is rather more difficult. We need to do a certain amount of work before we can apply the standard result. First complete the square in the square root bracket:

$$\sqrt{(3 + 2x - x^2)} = \sqrt{\left[4 - (x - 1)^2 \right]}$$

Next use the substitution $u = x - 1$ so that $dx = du$ and the integral becomes:

$$\int_0^2 \frac{du}{\sqrt{(4 - u^2)}}$$

Recognising the standard form, we have $a = 2$ and $b = 1$, so the required solution is:

$$\left[(\sin^{-1} \left(\frac{1}{2} u \right) \right]_0^2 = \sin^{-1}(1) - \sin^{-1}(0)$$

$$= \frac{1}{2}\pi - 0 = \frac{1}{2}\pi$$

11 Set $x^2 - 1 = u^2$ so that $xdx = udu$

$$\therefore \text{ Integral becomes } \int \frac{u}{\sqrt{u^2 + 1}} \times \frac{udu}{\sqrt{u^2 + 1}}$$

$$= \int \frac{u^2}{u^2 + 1} \, du = \int \left(1 - \frac{1}{u^2 + 1} \right) du$$

$$= u - \tan^{-1} u + C$$

$$= \sqrt{x^2 - 1} - \tan^{-1} \sqrt{x^2 - 1} + C$$

12 Set $x = \sin y$ so that $dx = \cos y \, dy$

$$\therefore \text{ Integral becomes } \int \frac{\sin^2 y}{\sqrt{1 - \sin^2 y}} \times \cos y \, dy$$

$$= \int \frac{\sin^2 y}{\cos y} \times \cos y \, dy = \int \sin^2 y \, dy$$

$$= \frac{1}{2} \int (1 - \cos 2y) \, dy$$

$$= \frac{1}{2} \left[y - \frac{1}{2} \sin 2y \right] + C$$

$$= \frac{1}{2} \left[y - \sin y \cos y \right] + C$$

$$= \frac{1}{2} \sin^{-1} x - \frac{x}{2} \sqrt{1 - x^2} + C$$

13 (a) $\frac{1}{2} \tan^{-1} \left(\frac{x}{2} \right) + C$

(b) $\frac{1}{2} \tan^{-1} \left(\frac{x + 1}{2} \right) + C$

(c) $\displaystyle\int \frac{x+2}{(x+1)^2+4}\ dx$ Now substitute $u = x+1$.

∴ Integral becomes $\displaystyle\int \frac{u+1}{u^2+4}\ du$

$= \displaystyle\int \left(\frac{u}{u^2+4} + \frac{1}{u^2+4}\right) du$

$= \dfrac{1}{2}\ln(u^2+4) + \dfrac{1}{2}\tan^{-1}\dfrac{u}{2} + C$

$= \dfrac{1}{2}\ln(x^2+2x+5) + \dfrac{1}{2}\tan^{-1}\left(\dfrac{x+1}{2}\right) + C$

14   (a) $\sinh^{-1}x + C$

    (b) $\cosh^{-1}x + C$

    (c) $\displaystyle\int\left[\frac{x}{\sqrt{4+x^2}} + \frac{3}{\sqrt{4+x^2}}\right]dx$

    $= \sqrt{4+x^2} + 3\sin^{-1}\left(\dfrac{x}{2}\right) + C$

    (d) $\displaystyle\int\left[\frac{x}{\sqrt{4x^2-1}} + \frac{3}{\sqrt{4x^2-1}}\right]dx$

    $= \dfrac{1}{4}\sqrt{4x^2-1} + \dfrac{3}{2}\cosh^{-1}2x + C$

15   (a) $\displaystyle\int \frac{dx}{(x+2)^2+9}$

    $= \dfrac{1}{3}\tan^{-1}\left(\dfrac{x+2}{3}\right) + C$

    (b) $\displaystyle\int \frac{dx}{\sqrt{(x+2)^2-1}} = \cosh^{-1}(x+2) + C$

16 $\tan x = t \Rightarrow$

Also $\sec^2 x\, dx = dt \Rightarrow dx = \dfrac{dt}{1+\tan^2 x} \Rightarrow$

$dx = \dfrac{dt}{1+t^2}$

∴ $\displaystyle\int_0^{\frac{\pi}{4}} \frac{dx}{3\cos^2 x + \sin^2 x} =$

$\displaystyle\int_0^1 \frac{\dfrac{dt}{1+t^2}}{3\left(\dfrac{1}{\sqrt{1+t^2}}\right)^2 + \left(\dfrac{t}{\sqrt{1+t^2}}\right)^2}$

$= \displaystyle\int_0^1 \frac{dt}{3+t^2}$

$= \left[\dfrac{1}{\sqrt{3}}\tan^{-1}\left(\dfrac{t}{\sqrt{3}}\right)\right]_0^1$

$= \dfrac{1}{\sqrt{3}}\tan^{-1}\left(\dfrac{1}{\sqrt{3}}\right) = \dfrac{1}{\sqrt{3}} \times \dfrac{\pi}{6} = \dfrac{\pi}{6\sqrt{3}}$

17   (a) $\displaystyle\int \frac{\dfrac{2dt}{1+t^2}}{1 + \dfrac{1-t^2}{1+t^2}}$

    $= \displaystyle\int \frac{2dt}{(1+t^2)+1-t^2} = \int dt$

    $= t + c = \tan\dfrac{x}{2} + C$

    (b) $\displaystyle\int \frac{\dfrac{2dt}{1+t^2}}{1 + \dfrac{2t}{1+t^2} + \dfrac{1-t^2}{1+t^2}}$

    $= \displaystyle\int \frac{2dt}{(1+t^2)+2t+1-t^2}$

    $= \displaystyle\int \frac{dt}{t+1}$

    $= \ln(t+1) + C$

    $= \ln\left(\tan\dfrac{x}{2}+1\right) + C$

    (c) $\displaystyle\int \left(\frac{1+t^2}{2t}\right) \times \frac{2dt}{1+t^2}$

    $= \displaystyle\int \frac{dt}{t} = \ln t + C$

    $= \ln\left(\tan\dfrac{x}{2}\right) + C$

Section 6

1 (a) scalar (b) vector (c) scalar
   (d) scalar (e) vector (f) scalar

2 Draw a diagram first of all

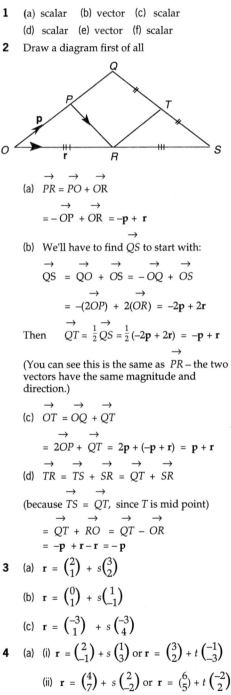

(a) $\overrightarrow{PR} = \overrightarrow{PO} + \overrightarrow{OR}$

$= -\overrightarrow{OP} + \overrightarrow{OR} = -\mathbf{p} + \mathbf{r}$

(b) We'll have to find $\overrightarrow{QS}$ to start with:

$\overrightarrow{QS} = \overrightarrow{QO} + \overrightarrow{OS} = -\overrightarrow{OQ} + \overrightarrow{OS}$

$= -(2\overrightarrow{OP}) + 2(\overrightarrow{OR}) = -2\mathbf{p} + 2\mathbf{r}$

Then $\overrightarrow{QT} = \tfrac{1}{2}\overrightarrow{QS} = \tfrac{1}{2}(-2\mathbf{p} + 2\mathbf{r}) = -\mathbf{p} + \mathbf{r}$

(You can see this is the same as $\overrightarrow{PR}$ – the two vectors have the same magnitude and direction.)

(c) $\overrightarrow{OT} = \overrightarrow{OQ} + \overrightarrow{QT}$

$= 2\overrightarrow{OP} + \overrightarrow{QT} = 2\mathbf{p} + (-\mathbf{p} + \mathbf{r}) = \mathbf{p} + \mathbf{r}$

(d) $\overrightarrow{TR} = \overrightarrow{TS} + \overrightarrow{SR} = \overrightarrow{QT} + \overrightarrow{SR}$

(because $\overrightarrow{TS} = \overrightarrow{QT}$, since T is mid point)

$= \overrightarrow{QT} + \overrightarrow{RO} = \overrightarrow{QT} - \overrightarrow{OR}$

$= -\mathbf{p} + \mathbf{r} - \mathbf{r} = -\mathbf{p}$

3 (a) $\mathbf{r} = \binom{2}{1} + s\binom{3}{2}$

   (b) $\mathbf{r} = \binom{0}{1} + s\binom{1}{-1}$

   (c) $\mathbf{r} = \binom{-3}{1} + s\binom{-3}{4}$

4 (a) (i) $\mathbf{r} = \binom{2}{-1} + s\binom{1}{3}$ or $\mathbf{r} = \binom{3}{2} + t\binom{-1}{-3}$

   (ii) $\mathbf{r} = \binom{4}{7} + s\binom{2}{-2}$ or $\mathbf{r} = \binom{6}{5} + t\binom{-2}{2}$

(b) (i) $\mathbf{r} = \binom{-1}{3} + s\binom{5}{2}$, $0 \le s \le 1$

   (ii) $\mathbf{r} = \binom{0}{-1} + s\binom{-1}{-2}$, $0 \le s \le 1$

5 (a) $\mathbf{r} = \begin{pmatrix}2\\1\\6\end{pmatrix} + \lambda\begin{pmatrix}-1\\2\\-1\end{pmatrix}$ where λ is the parameter (or any other letter)

The corresponding cartesian equation is

$\dfrac{x-2}{-1} = \dfrac{y-1}{2} = \dfrac{z-6}{-1} = \lambda$

(b) $\mathbf{r} = \begin{pmatrix}0\\6\\1\end{pmatrix} + \mu\begin{pmatrix}3\\2\\1\end{pmatrix}$ where μ is the parameter

The corresponding cartesian equation is

$\dfrac{x-0}{3} = \dfrac{y-6}{2} = \dfrac{z-1}{1} = \mu$

6 (a) $\mathbf{r} = \begin{pmatrix}1\\0\\2\end{pmatrix} + s\begin{pmatrix}4\\1\\1\end{pmatrix}$

$\therefore x = 1 + 4s$

$y = s$

$z = 2 + s$

$\therefore \dfrac{x-1}{4} = \dfrac{y-0}{1} = \dfrac{z-2}{1} = s$

(b) $\mathbf{r} = \begin{pmatrix}2\\-1\\0\end{pmatrix} + t\begin{pmatrix}-3\\-3\\3\end{pmatrix}$

$\therefore x = 2 - 3t$

$y = -1 - 3t$

$z = 3t$

$\therefore \dfrac{x-2}{-3} = \dfrac{y+1}{-3} = \dfrac{z-0}{3} = t$

7 (a) $\overrightarrow{AB} = \overrightarrow{OB} - \overrightarrow{OA}$

$= \begin{pmatrix}-2\\3\\6\end{pmatrix}$, length $\sqrt{(-2)^2 + (3)^2 + (6)^2} = 7$

(b) $\overrightarrow{CD} = \begin{pmatrix}3\\-2\\-2\end{pmatrix}$, length $\sqrt{17}$

(c) $\overrightarrow{EF} = -3i + 2j + k$, length $\sqrt{14}$

(d) $|\overrightarrow{OG}| = \sqrt{3^2 + 2^2 + 6^2} = \sqrt{49} = 7$

(e) $|\overrightarrow{OH}| = \sqrt{1^2 + (-1)^2 + 2^2} = \sqrt{6}$

8   (a) $\cos \angle AOB \dfrac{\mathbf{a} \cdot \mathbf{b}}{|\mathbf{a}|\,|\mathbf{b}|}$

$= \dfrac{3 \times 5 + 1 \times -4 + 3 \times 3}{\sqrt{19}\,\sqrt{50}}$

$= \dfrac{20}{\sqrt{19}\,\sqrt{2 \times 25}} = \dfrac{20}{\sqrt{19}\,\sqrt{2} \times 5} = \dfrac{4}{\sqrt{38}}$

9   (a) $\overrightarrow{ML} = \overrightarrow{OL} - \overrightarrow{OM} = a\,(3\mathbf{i} + 4\mathbf{j} + 5\mathbf{k})$

$\overrightarrow{MN} = \overrightarrow{ON} - \overrightarrow{OM} = a(\mathbf{i} + \mathbf{j} + 4\mathbf{k})$

(b) $\cos \angle LMN = \dfrac{a^2(3 + 4 + 20)}{a\,\sqrt{50}\,a\,\sqrt{18}}$

$= \dfrac{27}{5\sqrt{2} \times 3\sqrt{2}} = \dfrac{9}{10}$

10   (a) $\mathrm{Cos}\,\angle AOB = \dfrac{12 + 27 - 36}{\sqrt{121}\,\sqrt{81}} = \dfrac{3}{99} = \dfrac{1}{33}$

$\angle AOB = 88°$

11   A rhombus is a parallelogram with equal sides: i.e. in the figure $AB = AD$.

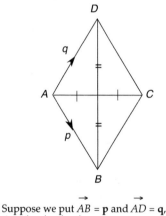

Suppose we put $\overrightarrow{AB} = \mathbf{p}$ and $\overrightarrow{AD} = \mathbf{q}$, then $|\mathbf{p}| = |\mathbf{q}|$

Then since $\overrightarrow{DC} = \overrightarrow{AB}$, $\overrightarrow{DC} = \mathbf{p}$ and similarly $\overrightarrow{BC} = \mathbf{q}$

Now $\overrightarrow{AC} = \overrightarrow{AB} + \overrightarrow{BC} = \mathbf{p} + \mathbf{q}$ and $\overrightarrow{BD} = -\mathbf{p} + \mathbf{q}$

Then $\overrightarrow{AC} \times \overrightarrow{BD} = (\mathbf{q} + \mathbf{p}) \cdot (\mathbf{q} - \mathbf{p})$

$\begin{aligned} &= \mathbf{q} \cdot \mathbf{q} - \mathbf{q} \cdot \mathbf{p} + \mathbf{p} \cdot \mathbf{q} - \mathbf{p} \cdot \mathbf{p} \quad [2] \\ &= \mathbf{q} \cdot \mathbf{q} - \mathbf{p} \cdot \mathbf{q} + \mathbf{p} \cdot \mathbf{q} - \mathbf{p} \cdot \mathbf{p} \quad [1] \\ &= \mathbf{q} \cdot \mathbf{q} - \mathbf{p} \cdot \mathbf{p} = |\mathbf{q}|^2 - |\mathbf{p}|^2 \end{aligned}$

But $|\mathbf{q}| = |\mathbf{p}| \Rightarrow \overrightarrow{AC} \cdot \overrightarrow{BD} = 0 \Rightarrow$ they intersect at right-angles

12

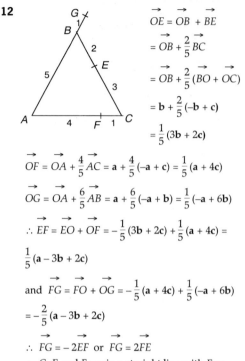

$\overrightarrow{OE} = \overrightarrow{OB} + \overrightarrow{BE}$

$= \overrightarrow{OB} + \dfrac{2}{5}\overrightarrow{BC}$

$= \overrightarrow{OB} + \dfrac{2}{5}(\overrightarrow{BO} + \overrightarrow{OC})$

$= \mathbf{b} + \dfrac{2}{5}(-\mathbf{b} + \mathbf{c})$

$= \dfrac{1}{5}(3\mathbf{b} + 2\mathbf{c})$

$\overrightarrow{OF} = \overrightarrow{OA} + \dfrac{4}{5}\overrightarrow{AC} = \mathbf{a} + \dfrac{4}{5}(-\mathbf{a} + \mathbf{c}) = \dfrac{1}{5}(\mathbf{a} + 4\mathbf{c})$

$\overrightarrow{OG} = \overrightarrow{OA} + \dfrac{6}{5}\overrightarrow{AB} = \mathbf{a} + \dfrac{6}{5}(-\mathbf{a} + \mathbf{b}) = \dfrac{1}{5}(-\mathbf{a} + 6\mathbf{b})$

$\therefore \overrightarrow{EF} = \overrightarrow{EO} + \overrightarrow{OF} = -\dfrac{1}{5}(3\mathbf{b} + 2\mathbf{c}) + \dfrac{1}{5}(\mathbf{a} + 4\mathbf{c}) =$

$\dfrac{1}{5}(\mathbf{a} - 3\mathbf{b} + 2\mathbf{c})$

and $\overrightarrow{FG} = \overrightarrow{FO} + \overrightarrow{OG} = -\dfrac{1}{5}(\mathbf{a} + 4\mathbf{c}) + \dfrac{1}{5}(-\mathbf{a} + 6\mathbf{b})$

$= -\dfrac{2}{5}(\mathbf{a} - 3\mathbf{b} + 2\mathbf{c})$

$\therefore \overrightarrow{FG} = -2\overrightarrow{EF}$ or $\overrightarrow{FG} = 2\overrightarrow{FE}$

$\therefore$ G, E and F are in a straight line with E as mid-point.

13

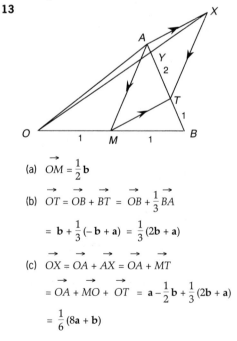

(a) $\overrightarrow{OM} = \dfrac{1}{2}\mathbf{b}$

(b) $\overrightarrow{OT} = \overrightarrow{OB} + \overrightarrow{BT} = \overrightarrow{OB} + \dfrac{1}{3}\overrightarrow{BA}$

$= \mathbf{b} + \dfrac{1}{3}(-\mathbf{b} + \mathbf{a}) = \dfrac{1}{3}(2\mathbf{b} + \mathbf{a})$

(c) $\overrightarrow{OX} = \overrightarrow{OA} + \overrightarrow{AX} = \overrightarrow{OA} + \overrightarrow{MT}$

$= \overrightarrow{OA} + \overrightarrow{MO} + \overrightarrow{OT} = \mathbf{a} - \dfrac{1}{2}\mathbf{b} + \dfrac{1}{3}(2\mathbf{b} + \mathbf{a})$

$= \dfrac{1}{6}(8\mathbf{a} + \mathbf{b})$

(d) We need two routes to Y

$Either\ \ \overrightarrow{OY} = \overrightarrow{OA} + \overrightarrow{AY} = \overrightarrow{OA} + \lambda\,\overrightarrow{AB}$

$= \mathbf{a} + \lambda\,(-\mathbf{a} + \mathbf{b})$

$Or\ \ \overrightarrow{OY} = \mu\overrightarrow{OX} = \dfrac{\mu}{6}\,(8\mathbf{a} + \mathbf{b})$

$\therefore\ \ \mathbf{a} + \lambda\,(-\mathbf{a} + \mathbf{b}) = \dfrac{\mu}{6}\,(8\mathbf{a} + \mathbf{b})$

$\therefore\ \ 1 - \lambda = \dfrac{8\mu}{6}$ and $\lambda = \dfrac{\mu}{6}$ $\ \therefore\ \lambda = \dfrac{1}{9}$ and $\mu = \dfrac{2}{3}$

$\therefore\ \ \overrightarrow{OY} = \dfrac{1}{9}\,(8\mathbf{a} + \mathbf{b})$

14

$\overrightarrow{ED} = \overrightarrow{EO} + \overrightarrow{OD} = -\dfrac{1}{2}\mathbf{a} + \dfrac{1}{2}\mathbf{b} = \dfrac{1}{2}\,(\mathbf{b} - \mathbf{a})$

$\overrightarrow{AB} = \overrightarrow{AO} + \overrightarrow{OB} = -\mathbf{a} + \mathbf{b}$

$\therefore\ \ \overrightarrow{AB} = 2\overrightarrow{ED}$

$\therefore\ \ AB$ and ED are parallel

We need two routes to L.

$Either\ \ \ \overrightarrow{OL} = \overrightarrow{OE} + \overrightarrow{EL} = \overrightarrow{OE} + \lambda\,\overrightarrow{EF} = \dfrac{1}{2}\mathbf{a} + \dfrac{\lambda}{2}\mathbf{b}$

$Or\ \ \ \ \ \ \overrightarrow{OL} = \overrightarrow{OP} + \overrightarrow{PL} = \overrightarrow{OP} + \mu\,\overrightarrow{PA}$

$\qquad = \dfrac{1}{3}\mathbf{b} + \mu\left(-\dfrac{1}{3}\mathbf{b} + \mathbf{a}\right)$

$\therefore\ \dfrac{1}{2}\mathbf{a} + \dfrac{\lambda}{2}\mathbf{b} = \dfrac{1}{3}\mathbf{b} + \mu\left(-\dfrac{1}{3}\mathbf{b} + \mathbf{a}\right)$

$\therefore\ \dfrac{1}{2} = \mu$ and $\dfrac{\lambda}{2} = \dfrac{1}{3} - \dfrac{\mu}{3}$ $\ \therefore\ \mu = \dfrac{1}{2}$ and $\lambda = \dfrac{1}{3}$

$\therefore\ \ \overrightarrow{OL} = \dfrac{1}{2}\mathbf{b} + \dfrac{1}{6}\mathbf{b}$

15 $\mathbf{r} = \begin{pmatrix} -3 \\ 1 \\ -7 \end{pmatrix} + \lambda \begin{pmatrix} 8 \\ 2 \\ 12 \end{pmatrix}$

$\overrightarrow{OP} \cdot \begin{pmatrix} 8 \\ 2 \\ 12 \end{pmatrix} = 0 \Rightarrow \begin{pmatrix} -3 + 8\lambda \\ 1 + 2\lambda \\ -7 + 12\lambda \end{pmatrix} \cdot \begin{pmatrix} 8 \\ 2 \\ 12 \end{pmatrix} = 0$

$\Rightarrow 8\,(-3 + 8\lambda) + 2\,(1 + 2\lambda) + 12\,(12\lambda - 7) = 0$

$\Rightarrow \lambda = \dfrac{1}{2}$

$\therefore\ \ \overrightarrow{OP} = \begin{pmatrix} 1 \\ 2 \\ -1 \end{pmatrix}$ and $|\,\overrightarrow{OP}\,| = \sqrt{1^2 + 2^2 + (-1)^2}$

$\qquad = \sqrt{6}$

16 (a) $\begin{pmatrix} 5 \\ -4 \\ s \end{pmatrix} \cdot \begin{pmatrix} 2 \\ t \\ -3 \end{pmatrix} = 0 \Rightarrow 10 - 4t - 3s = 0$

$\Rightarrow 4t + 3s = 10.$

(b) $\begin{pmatrix} 5 \\ -4 \\ s \end{pmatrix} = \lambda \begin{pmatrix} 2 \\ t \\ -3 \end{pmatrix} \Rightarrow 5 = 2\lambda,\ -4 = \lambda t$ and

$s = -3\lambda$

$\Rightarrow \lambda = \dfrac{5}{2},\ t = \dfrac{-8}{5}$ and $s = \dfrac{-15}{2}$

17 (a) $\begin{pmatrix} \lambda \\ 2\lambda - 1 \\ -1 \end{pmatrix} \cdot \begin{pmatrix} 1 - \lambda \\ 3\lambda \\ 4\lambda - 1 \end{pmatrix} = 0$

$\Rightarrow \lambda\,(1 - \lambda) + 3\lambda\,(2\lambda - 1) - (4\lambda - 1) = 0$

$\Rightarrow 5\lambda^2 - 6\lambda + 1 = 0 \Rightarrow \lambda = \dfrac{1}{5}$ or 1

(b) $\overrightarrow{OA} = \begin{pmatrix} 2 \\ 3 \\ -1 \end{pmatrix},\ \overrightarrow{OB} = \begin{pmatrix} -1 \\ 6 \\ 7 \end{pmatrix} \Rightarrow \overrightarrow{AB} = \begin{pmatrix} -3 \\ 3 \\ 8 \end{pmatrix}$

(c) Use $\overrightarrow{AO} \times \overrightarrow{AB} = |\,\overrightarrow{AO}\,|\,|\,\overrightarrow{AB}\,|\cos\theta$

$\therefore\ \begin{pmatrix} -2 \\ -3 \\ 1 \end{pmatrix} \cdot \begin{pmatrix} -3 \\ 3 \\ 8 \end{pmatrix} =$

$\sqrt{2^2 + 3^2 + (-1)^2}\ \sqrt{(-3)^2 + 3^2 + 8^2}\ \cos\theta$

$\therefore\ 5 = \sqrt{14}\ \sqrt{82}\ \cos\theta$

$\therefore\ \theta = 82°$, the required angle.

18 (a) $\overrightarrow{LM} = \begin{pmatrix} 5 \\ 1 \\ c \end{pmatrix} - \begin{pmatrix} 2 \\ -3 \\ 3 \end{pmatrix} = \begin{pmatrix} 3 \\ 4 \\ c - 3 \end{pmatrix}$

$\therefore\ \overrightarrow{OL} \cdot \overrightarrow{LM} = 0 \Rightarrow \begin{pmatrix} 2 \\ -3 \\ 3 \end{pmatrix} \cdot \begin{pmatrix} 3 \\ 4 \\ c - 3 \end{pmatrix} = 0$

$\Rightarrow 6 - 12 + 3c - 9 = 0 \Rightarrow c = 5$

(b) $\overrightarrow{ON} = \overrightarrow{LM} = \begin{pmatrix} 3 \\ 4 \\ 2 \end{pmatrix}$

(c) $\mathbf{r} = \overrightarrow{OM} + t\overrightarrow{MN} = \begin{pmatrix} 5 \\ 1 \\ 5 \end{pmatrix} + t\begin{pmatrix} -2 \\ 3 \\ -3 \end{pmatrix}$

19 (a) $\overrightarrow{BC} = \begin{pmatrix} 1 \\ -7 \\ -8 \end{pmatrix} + \begin{pmatrix} 1 \\ 2 \\ 1 \end{pmatrix} = \begin{pmatrix} 2 \\ -5 \\ -7 \end{pmatrix}$

∴ the equation of l_2 is $\mathbf{r} = \begin{pmatrix} -1 \\ 7 \\ 8 \end{pmatrix} + \lambda\begin{pmatrix} 2 \\ -5 \\ -7 \end{pmatrix}$

$\overrightarrow{AC} = \begin{pmatrix} -5 \\ -1 \\ -2 \end{pmatrix} + \begin{pmatrix} 1 \\ 2 \\ 1 \end{pmatrix} = \begin{pmatrix} -4 \\ 1 \\ -1 \end{pmatrix}$

∴ the equation of l_1 is $\mathbf{r} = \begin{pmatrix} 5 \\ 1 \\ 2 \end{pmatrix} + \mu\begin{pmatrix} -4 \\ 1 \\ -1 \end{pmatrix}$

(b) We use $\overrightarrow{AO} \cdot \overrightarrow{AB} = |\overrightarrow{AO}| \, |\overrightarrow{AB}| \, \cos\theta$

where $\overrightarrow{OA} = \begin{pmatrix} 5 \\ 1 \\ 2 \end{pmatrix}$ and $\overrightarrow{AB} = \begin{pmatrix} -6 \\ 6 \\ 6 \end{pmatrix}$

∴ $\begin{pmatrix} -5 \\ -1 \\ -2 \end{pmatrix} \times \begin{pmatrix} -6 \\ 6 \\ 6 \end{pmatrix}$

$= \sqrt{(-5)^2 + (-1)^2 + (-2)^2} \, \sqrt{(-6)^2 + 6^2 + 6^2} \, \cos\theta$

∴ $12 = \sqrt{30} \, \sqrt{108} \, \cos\theta$

∴ $\theta = 78°$, the required angle.

20 (a) $\lambda = -1$ gives point A and $\lambda = 0$ gives point B

(b) $\overrightarrow{OP} \cdot \overrightarrow{AB} = 0 \Rightarrow \begin{pmatrix} 5 - 2\lambda \\ 4 + \lambda \\ 6 - 2\lambda \end{pmatrix} \cdot \begin{pmatrix} -2 \\ 1 \\ -2 \end{pmatrix} = 0$

$\Rightarrow -2(5 - 2\lambda) + (4 + \lambda) - 2(6 - 2\lambda) = 0$

$\Rightarrow \lambda = 2 \Rightarrow \overrightarrow{OP} = \begin{pmatrix} 1 \\ 6 \\ 2 \end{pmatrix}$

(c)

Since $\overrightarrow{AP} = \overrightarrow{PC}$, C has coordinates $(-5, 9, -4)$

Section 7

1 (a) $-i$ (b) 1 (c) -1 (d) $-i$
   (e) 1 (f) $-i$ (g) i (h) -1

2 (a) $5 - 2i, -1 - 4i$ (b) $2, -2i$
   (c) $2 + 5i, -8 - 7i$ (d) $2i, -6i$

3 (a) $p = 2, q = -7$ (b) $x = 4, y = 2$
   (c) $u = 2, v = -3$ (d) $r = 4, s = 1$

4 (a) $9 + 7i$ (b) $8 - 6i$
   (c) $z_1 z_1{}^* = (2 + 3i)(2 - 3i) = 4 - 9i^2 = 13$
   (d) $z_2 z_2{}^* = (3 - i)(3 + i) = 10$
   (e) $(z_1{}^*)^2 = (2 - 3i)^2 = -5 - 12i$

5 If $z = a + ib$, $z^* = a - ib$ and
   $zz^* = a^2 + b^2 = 25$ ... ①
   $z + z^* = 2a = 6$ ... ②
   From ②, $a = 3$. This into ① gives $b = \pm 4$, but $b > 0$, so:
   $z = 3 + 4i$

6 $\dfrac{19 + 4i}{5 - 2i} = \dfrac{19 + 4i}{5 - 2i} \times \dfrac{5 + 2i}{5 + 2i}$

$= \dfrac{95 + 20i + 38i + 8i^2}{29}$

$= \dfrac{87}{29} + \dfrac{58i}{29}$

$= 3 + 2i$

7 (a) $z_1 z_2 = (3 + 2i)(4 - 3i) = 12 + 8i - 9i - 6i^2$
   $= 18 - i$

$\dfrac{z_1}{z_2} = \dfrac{3 + 2i}{4 - 3i} \times \dfrac{4 + 3i}{4 + 3i}$

$= \dfrac{12 + 8i + 9i + 6i^2}{25} = \dfrac{6 + 17i}{25}$

$= \dfrac{6}{25} + \dfrac{17}{25}i$

8 $\dfrac{i}{4 + 3i} \times \dfrac{4 - 3i}{4 - 3i} = \dfrac{4i - 3i^2}{25} = \dfrac{3 + 4i}{25} = \dfrac{3}{25} + \dfrac{4}{25}i$

9 Suppose:
   $z = a + ib = \sqrt{3 - 4i}$
   $(a + ib)^2 = 3 - 4i$
   $a^2 - b^2 + 2abi = 3 - 4i$
   $a^2 - b^2 = 3, \, 2ab = -4 \Rightarrow ab = -2$
   This gives $a = \dfrac{-2}{b}$, so:
   $\left(\dfrac{-2}{b}\right)^2 - b^2 = 3 \Rightarrow \dfrac{4}{b^2} - b^2 = 3, \, 4 - b^4 = 3b^2$

$b^4 + 3b^2 - 4 = 0$

$(b^2 + 4)(b^2 - 1) = 0 \Rightarrow b = \pm 1, a \neq 2$

Two square roots are $2 - i$ and $-2 + i$

10   Begin with $z^2 = 5 - 12i$

$\therefore \quad z = \sqrt{5 - 12i}$

$\therefore \quad a^2 - b^2 = 5, \ 2ab = -12$

$a^4 - 5a^2 - 36 = 0$

$a = \pm 3, b = \mp 2$

i.e. $z_1 = 3 - 2i$ and $z_2 = -3 + 2i$

Since $z_2 = -z_1$ then: $z_1 z_2 = z_1(-z_1)$

$= -z_1^2 = -(5 - 12i) = -5 + 12i$

11   (a) $2, 60°$ (b) $2\sqrt{2}, -45°$ (c) $2, -135°$ (d) $2, 90°$

(e) $4, 0°$ (f) $2, 150°$ (g) $3, -90°$ (h) $5, 180°$

12   Work out the modulus and argument for both z_1 and z_2 and the rest is fairly straightforward.

$|z_1| = \sqrt{2}, \arg(z_1) = 45° : |z_2| = 2,$

$\arg(z_2) = 150°$

(a) $2\sqrt{2}, 135°$

(b) $2\sqrt{2}, -165°$ ($195°$ is beyond the limit for arg, which is between $\pm 180°$ so we have to subtract a complete cycle, $360°$)

(c) $\sqrt{2}, 105°$

(d) $\dfrac{1}{2}, -150°$

(e) and (f)

There's no formula for these. The two numbers are first added or subtracted and then the modulus and argument found:

$z_1 + z_2 = 1 - \sqrt{3} + 2i \Rightarrow |z_1 + z_2| = \sqrt{(1 - \sqrt{3})^2 + 2^2}$

$= \sqrt{1 - 2\sqrt{3} + 3 + 4}$

$= \sqrt{8 - 2\sqrt{3}}$

and

$\therefore \tan\theta = \dfrac{2}{\sqrt{3} - 1}$

$\therefore \theta = 69.9°$

$\therefore \arg(z_1 + z_2)$

$= 180 - 69.9°$

$= 110.1°$

$z_2 - z_1 = -\sqrt{3} - 1 \Rightarrow |z_2 - z_1| = \sqrt{3} + 1$

and $\arg(z_2 - z_1) = 180°$

13 $|z_1| = \sqrt{(\sqrt{2})^2 + (-\sqrt{2})^2} = \sqrt{2 + 2} = 2$

$\tan\theta = 1$

$\therefore \theta = 45°$

$\therefore \arg z_1 = -45°$

$|z_2| = \sqrt{1^2 + \sqrt{3}^2} = \sqrt{4} = 2$

$\tan\theta = \sqrt{3}$

$\theta = 60°$

$\therefore \arg z_2 = 60°$

(a) $|z_3| = \left| \dfrac{z_1}{z_2} \right| = \dfrac{|z_1|}{|z_2|} = \dfrac{2}{2} = 1$

(b) $\arg(z_3) = \arg\left(\dfrac{z_1}{z_2}\right) = \arg(z_1) - \arg(z_2)$

$= -45° - 60° = \dfrac{-\pi}{4} - \dfrac{\pi}{3}$ (in radians)

$= \dfrac{-3\pi - 4\pi}{12} = \dfrac{-7\pi}{12}$

14

$|z_1| = \sqrt{1^2 + (-1)^2} = \sqrt{2}, \ |z_2| = \sqrt{1 + (\sqrt{3})^2} = 2$

$|z_1 z_2| = |z_1| \, |z_2| = 2\sqrt{2}$

$\arg z_1 = -\dfrac{\pi}{4}$

$\arg z_2 = \pi - \dfrac{\pi}{3} = \dfrac{2\pi}{3}$

(see original diagram)

Then: $\arg(z_1 z_2) = \arg(z_1) + \arg(z_2)$

$= \dfrac{-\pi}{4} + \dfrac{2\pi}{3}$

$= \dfrac{-3\pi + 8\pi}{12} = \dfrac{5\pi}{12}$

$z_1 z_2 = (1 - i)(-1 + i\sqrt{3}) = -1 + i\sqrt{3} + i + \sqrt{3}$

$= (\sqrt{3} - 1) + i(\sqrt{3} + 1)$ ... ①

At this point we need to draw a diagram:

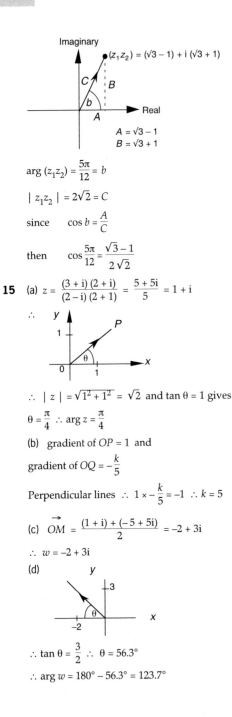

arg $(z_1 z_2) = \dfrac{5\pi}{12} = b$

$|\, z_1 z_2 \,| = 2\sqrt{2} = C$

since $\cos b = \dfrac{A}{C}$

then $\cos\dfrac{5\pi}{12} = \dfrac{\sqrt{3}-1}{2\sqrt{2}}$

15   (a) $z = \dfrac{(3+i)(2+i)}{(2-i)(2+1)} = \dfrac{5+5i}{5} = 1+i$

∴

$\therefore\ |\,z\,| = \sqrt{1^2 + 1^2} = \sqrt{2}$ and $\tan\theta = 1$ gives

$\theta = \dfrac{\pi}{4}\ \therefore\ \arg z = \dfrac{\pi}{4}$

(b)   gradient of $OP = 1$ and

gradient of $OQ = -\dfrac{k}{5}$

Perpendicular lines $\therefore\ 1 \times -\dfrac{k}{5} = -1\ \therefore\ k = 5$

(c) $\overrightarrow{OM} = \dfrac{(1+i) + (-5+5i)}{2} = -2+3i$

$\therefore\ w = -2+3i$

(d)

$\therefore\ \tan\theta = \dfrac{3}{2}\ \therefore\ \theta = 56.3°$

$\therefore\ \arg w = 180° - 56.3° = 123.7°$

16

$\therefore\ |\,1+i\sqrt{3}\,| = \sqrt{1^2 + (\sqrt{3})^2} = 2$

and $\tan\theta = \sqrt{3}\ \Rightarrow\ \theta = 60°$

$\therefore\ 1+i\sqrt{3} = 2\,(\cos 60° + i \sin 60°)$

The modulus of $(1+i\sqrt{3})^6$ will be $2^6 = 64$ and

the argument of $(1+i\sqrt{3})^6$ will be $6 \times 60° = 360°$

i.e. $0°$

$\therefore\ (1+i\sqrt{3})^6 = 64\,(\cos 0° + i \sin 0°)$

$\therefore\ (1+i\sqrt{3})^6 = 64$

17   Let $\sqrt{10i-24} = a+ib$

$\therefore\ 10i-24 = (a+ib)^2$

$\therefore\ 10 = 2ab$ and $-24 = a^2 - b^2$

Solve simultaneously and get

$a = \pm 1,\ b = \pm 5$

$\therefore\ \sqrt{10i-24} = 1+5i$

18   Let $\sqrt{i} = a+ib$

$\therefore\ i = (a+ib)^2$

$\therefore\ 0 = a^2 - b^2$ and $1 = 2ab$

Solve simultaneously and get

$a = \pm\dfrac{1}{\sqrt{2}},\ b = \pm\dfrac{1}{\sqrt{2}}$

$\therefore\ \sqrt{i} = \pm\dfrac{1}{\sqrt{2}}\,(1+i)$

Section 8

1 (a) $\dfrac{dy}{dx} = 4 - y$ $\therefore$ $\displaystyle\int \dfrac{dy}{4-y} = \int dx$

$\therefore -\ln(4-y) = x + C \therefore 4 - y = Ae^{-x}$

$\therefore y = 4 - Ae^{-x}$

(b) $\dfrac{dy}{dx} = x(4-y)$ $\therefore$ $\displaystyle\int \dfrac{dy}{4-y} = \int x\, dx$

$\therefore -\ln(4-y) = \dfrac{x^2}{2} + C$

$\therefore 4 - y = Ae^{-x^2/2}$ $\quad y = 4 - Ae^{-x^2/2}$

(c) $\displaystyle\int \dfrac{dy}{y^2+4}$ $\displaystyle\int xe^{-x}\, dx$

$\therefore \dfrac{1}{2}\tan^{-1}\dfrac{y}{2} = -xe^{-x} - e^{-x} + C$

(integrating by parts)

$\therefore \tan^{-1}\dfrac{y}{2} = -2xe^{-x} - e^{-x} + D$

$\therefore y = 2\tan[D - 2xe^{-x} - e^{-x}]$

2 (a) $e^x\dfrac{dy}{dx} + e^x y = xe^x$ $\therefore$ $\dfrac{d}{dx}(e^x y) = xe^x$

$\therefore e^x y = xe^x - e^x + C$ (integrating by parts)

$\therefore y = x - 1 + Ce^{-x}$

(b) $\dfrac{dy}{dx} - \dfrac{1}{x}y = x$ $\therefore$ integrating factor $= e^{\int -\frac{1}{x}dx}$

$= e^{-\ln x} = e^{\ln\left(\frac{1}{x}\right)} = \dfrac{1}{x}$

$\therefore \dfrac{d}{dx}\left(\dfrac{1}{x}\times y\right) = x \times \dfrac{1}{x} = 1$

$\therefore \dfrac{y}{x} = x + C$ $\therefore$ $y = x^2 + Cx$

(c) integrating factor $= e^{\int \cot x\, dx}$

$= e^{\ln\sin x} = \sin x$

$\therefore \dfrac{d}{dx}(y\sin x) = \sin x\cos x$

$\therefore \dfrac{d}{dx}(y\sin x) = \dfrac{1}{2}\sin 2x$

$\therefore y\sin x = -\dfrac{1}{4}\cos 2x + C$

(d) $\dfrac{dy}{dx} + \dfrac{2x}{x^2-1}y = \dfrac{x}{x^2-1}$

$\therefore$ integrating factor $= e^{\int \frac{2x}{x^2-1}dx} \quad e^{\ln(x^2-1)}$

$= x^2 - 1$

$\therefore \dfrac{d}{dx}\big((x^2-1)y\big) = \dfrac{x}{x^2-1}\times(x^2-1)$

$\therefore \dfrac{d}{dx}\big((x^2-1)y\big) = x$

$\therefore (x^2-1)y = \dfrac{x^2}{2} + C$

(e) integrating factor $= e^{\int 3dx} = e^{3x}$

$\therefore e^{3x}\dfrac{dy}{dx} + 3e^{3x}y = e^{5x}$

$\therefore \dfrac{d}{dx}(e^{3x}y) = e^{5x}$

$\therefore ye^{3x} = \dfrac{1}{5}e^{5x} + C$

$\therefore y = 0.2e^{2x} + Ce^{-3x}$

3 (a) $m^2 - 4 = 0$ $\therefore m = \pm 2$ $\therefore y = Ae^{2x} + Be^{-2x}$

(b) $m^2 - m - 2 = 0$ $\therefore$ $m = 2$ or -1

$\therefore y = Ae^{2x} + Be^{-x}$

(c) $m^2 - 2m + 1 = 0$ $\therefore$ $m = 1$ repeated

$\therefore y = e^x(Ax + B)$

(d) $m^2 + 1 = 0$ $\therefore$ $m = \pm i$ $\therefore y = A\cos x + B\sin x$

(e) $4m^2 + 4m + 1 = 0$ $\therefore m = -\dfrac{1}{2}$ repeated

$\therefore y = e^{-\frac{x}{2}}(Ax + B)$

(f) $m^2 + m + 1 = 0$ $\therefore m = \dfrac{-1}{2} \pm \dfrac{i\sqrt{3}}{2}$

$\therefore y = e^{-\frac{x}{2}}\left(A\cos\dfrac{\sqrt{3}}{2}x + B\sin\dfrac{\sqrt{3}}{2}x\right)$

4 (a) $m^2 - 3m + 2 = 0 \Rightarrow m = 1$ or $2 \Rightarrow$

C.F. is $Ae^x + Be^{2x}$

Then try $y = ke^{4x}$ $\therefore 16k - 12k + 2k = 1$ $\therefore k = \dfrac{1}{6}$

$\therefore y = Ae^x + Be^{2x} + \dfrac{1}{6}e^{4x}$

(b) C.F. as (a) Try $y = Axe^x$

so $\dfrac{dy}{dx} = Axe^x + Ae^x$ and $\dfrac{d^2y}{dx^2} = Axe^x + 2Ae^x$.

Substitution then gives

$(Ax + 2A) - 3(Ax + A) + 2Ax = 1$

$\therefore A = -1$

$\therefore y = Ae^x + Be^{2x} - xe^x$

(c) $m^2 - 2m + 1 = 0 \Rightarrow m = 1$ repeated

$\Rightarrow$ C.F. is $(A + Bx)e^x$

Then try $y = A\cos x$ so $\dfrac{dy}{dx} = -A\sin x$

and $\dfrac{d^2y}{dx^2} = -A\cos x$.

Substitution then gives

$-A \cos x + 2A \sin x + A \cos x = 2 \sin x \quad \therefore \ A = 1$

$\therefore \ y = (A + Bx) e^x + \cos x$

(d) $m^2 - 1 = 0 \Rightarrow m = \pm 1 \Rightarrow$ C.F. is $Ae^x + Be^{-x}$

Then try $y = Ax^2 + Bx + C$ so $\dfrac{dy}{dx} = 2Ax + B$

and $\dfrac{d^2y}{dx^2} = 2A$

Substitution then gives $2A - (Ax^2 + Bx + C) = x^2$
$\therefore \ A = -1, B = 0, C = -2$

$\therefore \ y = Ae^x + Be^{-x} - x^2 - 2$

(e) $m^2 - 9 = 0 \Rightarrow m = \pm 3$

$\Rightarrow$ C.F. is $y = Ae^{3x} + Be^{-3x}$

Then try $y = ke^{2x} \quad \therefore \ 4k - 9k = 2 \quad \therefore \ k = -\dfrac{2}{5}$

$\therefore \ y = Ae^{3x} + Be^{-3x} - \dfrac{2}{5} e^{2x}$

(f) $4m^2 - 3m - 1 = 0 \Rightarrow m = 1 \ \text{or} -\dfrac{1}{4}$

$\Rightarrow$ C.F. is $y = Ae^x + Be^{-\frac{x}{4}}$

The particular solution is $y = -2$

$\therefore \ y = Ae^x + Be^{-\frac{x}{4}} - 2$

(g) $m^2 + 1 = 0 \Rightarrow m = \pm i$

$\Rightarrow$ C.F. is $y = A \cos x + B \sin x$

Then try $y = k \cos 2x$ so $\dfrac{d^2y}{dx^2} = -4k \cos 2x$

Substitution gives $-4k \cos 2x + k \cos 2x$

$= 3 \cos 2x \quad \therefore \ k = -1$

$\therefore \ y = A \cos x + B \sin x - \cos 2x$

(h) $m^2 - 2m + 5 = 0 \Rightarrow m = 1 \pm 2i$

$\Rightarrow$ C.F. is $y = e^x (A \cos 2x + B \sin 2x)$

Then try $y = ke^{3x}$ which gives $9k - 6k + 5k = 80$
$\therefore \ k = 10$

$\therefore \ y = e^x (A \cos 2x + B \sin 2x) + 10e^{3x}$

(i) $m^2 + 9 = 0 \Rightarrow m = \pm 3i$

$\Rightarrow$ C.F. is $y = A \cos 3x + B \sin 3x$

Then try $y = A \cos 2x + B \sin 2x$ so that

$(-4A \cos 2x - 4B \sin 2x) + 9 (A \cos 2x + B \sin 2x)$
$= 3 \cos 2x - \sin 2x$

$\therefore \ A = \dfrac{3}{5} \ \text{and} \ B = -\dfrac{1}{5}$

$\therefore \ y = A \cos 3x + B \sin 3x + \dfrac{3}{5} \cos 2x - \dfrac{1}{5} \sin 2x$

5 (a) $y = vx \quad \Rightarrow \quad \dfrac{dy}{dx} = v + x \dfrac{dv}{dx}$

$\therefore \quad x^2 v \left(v + x \dfrac{dv}{dx} \right) = v^2 x^2 + x^2 e^v$

$\Rightarrow \quad xv \dfrac{dv}{dx} = e^v \Rightarrow ve^{-v} dv = \dfrac{dx}{x}$

Now integrate by parts to get

$-ve^{-v} - e^{-v} = \ln x + c.$

But $v = \dfrac{y}{x}$

$\therefore \quad -\dfrac{y}{x} e^{-y/x} - e^{-y/x} = \ln x + c$

$\therefore \quad (x + y)e^{-y/x} = Dx - x \ \ln x \ .$

(b) You are meant to realise that t is a function of x.

$\therefore \quad y = t - x^2$

$\Rightarrow \dfrac{dy}{dx} = \dfrac{dt}{dx} - 2x \Rightarrow \dfrac{d^2y}{dx^2} = \dfrac{d^2t}{dx^2} - 2.$

Substitution in the given equation now gives

$\dfrac{d^2t}{dx^2} - 2 + x^2 + t - x^2 + 2 = 0$

$\therefore \quad \dfrac{d^2t}{dx^2} + t = 0 \ .$

$\therefore \quad t = A \cos x + B \sin x$
(the auxiliary equation $m^2 + 1 = 0 \Rightarrow m = \pm i$)

$\therefore \quad y + x^2 = A \cos x + B \sin x.$

(c) $y = v^2 \quad \Rightarrow \dfrac{dy}{dx} = 2v \dfrac{dv}{dx} \ .$

Substitute and get $\dfrac{1}{2} \dfrac{dy}{dx} + \dfrac{y}{2a} = -\mu x$

$\Rightarrow \dfrac{dy}{dx} + \dfrac{1}{a} y = -2\mu x.$

Using the integrating factor method we get

$ye^{(1/a)x} = -\displaystyle\int 2\mu x e^{(1/a)x} \, dx.$

Integration by parts gives

$ye^{(1/a)x} = -2\mu a x e^{(1/a)x} + 2\mu a^2 e^{(1/a)x} + c^*$

$\therefore \quad y = -2\mu a x + 2\mu a^2 + ce^{-(1/a)x}$

$\therefore \quad v^2 = -2\mu a x + 2\mu a^2 + ce^{-(1/a)x}$

But $v = 0$ when $x = a \quad \Rightarrow \quad c = 0$

$\therefore \quad v^2 = -2\mu a x + 2\mu a^2$

$\therefore \quad x = 0 \Rightarrow v^2 = 2\mu a^2$, as required.

(*I hope you didn't forget the $+ c$ at this stage, even though it turns out to be zero!)

(d) $z = \tan y \Rightarrow \dfrac{dz}{dx} = \sec^2 y \dfrac{dy}{dx} \Rightarrow$

$\dfrac{dy}{dx} = \cos^2 y \dfrac{dz}{dx}$

$\therefore \dfrac{dy}{dx} + x \sin 2y = x^3 \cos^2 y$

$\Rightarrow \cos^2 y \dfrac{dz}{dx} + 2x \sin y \cos y = x^3 \cos^2 y$

$\Rightarrow \dfrac{dz}{dx} + 2x \tan y = x^3$

$\Rightarrow \dfrac{dz}{dx} + 2xz = x^3$

The integrating factor is e^{x^2}

$\therefore \dfrac{d}{dx} \left(z e^{x^2} \right) = x^3 e^{x^2} \quad \therefore z e^{x^2} = \int x^3 e^{x^2} dx \ \dots (*)$

$\left[\text{To integrate } \int x^3 e^{x^2} dx, \text{ substitute } x^2 = u \text{ so } 2x\,dx = du \right.$

$\therefore$ The integral becomes

$\int x^2 e^{x^2} \times x\,dx = \int u e^u \dfrac{du}{2}$

$= \dfrac{1}{2} (u e^u - e^u) + C \quad \text{(integrated by parts)}$

$= \dfrac{1}{2} (x^2 - 1) e^{x^2} + C$

$\therefore$ Equation (*) gives us $z e^{x^2} = \dfrac{1}{2}(x^2 - 1) e^{x^2} + C$

$\therefore 2z = x^2 - 1 + A e^{-x^2} \quad \therefore 2 \tan y = x^2 - 1 + A e^{-x^2}$

(e) $y = \dfrac{1}{u} \Rightarrow \dfrac{dy}{dx} = -\dfrac{1}{u^2} \dfrac{du}{dx}$

$\therefore \dfrac{dy}{dx} + \dfrac{y}{x} = y^2$ becomes $\dfrac{-1}{u^2} \dfrac{du}{dx} + \dfrac{1}{ux} = \dfrac{1}{u^2}$

$\Rightarrow \dfrac{du}{dx} - \dfrac{u}{x} = -1$

The integrating factor is $e^{\int - \frac{1}{x} dx}$

$= e^{-\ln x} = e^{\ln\left(\frac{1}{x}\right)} = \dfrac{1}{x}$

$\therefore \dfrac{d}{dx} \left(\dfrac{u}{x} \right) = -\dfrac{1}{x} \quad \therefore \dfrac{u}{x} = -\ln x + C$

$\therefore u = -x \ln x + Cx$

$\therefore \dfrac{1}{y} = -x \ln x + Cx$

$\therefore 1 + xy \ln x = Cxy$

6 $\dfrac{dy}{dx} = -e^x \Rightarrow dy = -e^x dx \Rightarrow y = -e^x + C$

The family of solution curves consists of $y = -e^x$ being translated up and down the y-axis.

If a curve passes through $(0, 0)$ then $0 = -1 + C$
$\therefore C = 1$

$\therefore$ The particular equation required is $y = 1 - e^x$

7 $x = e^t \Rightarrow \dfrac{dx}{dt} = e^t \Rightarrow \dfrac{dt}{dx} = e^{-t}$ $\qquad \dots ①$

$\therefore \dfrac{dy}{dx} = \dfrac{dy}{dt} \times \dfrac{dt}{dx} = \dfrac{dy}{dt} \times e^{-t}$

(using equation ①) $\qquad \dots ②$

$\therefore \dfrac{d^2 y}{dx^2} = \dfrac{d}{dx} \left[\dfrac{dy}{dt} \times e^{-t} \right]$ (using equation ②)

$= \dfrac{d}{dt} \left[\dfrac{dy}{dt} \times e^{-t} \right] \times \dfrac{dt}{dx}$

$= \left(-\dfrac{dy}{dt} e^{-t} + \dfrac{d^2 y}{dt^2} e^{-t} \right) \times e^{-t}$

(differentiating a product)

$= \left(\dfrac{d^2 y}{dt^2} - \dfrac{dy}{dt} \right) e^{-2t}$, as required.

$\therefore$ Using the above expressions for x, $\dfrac{dy}{dx}$ and

$\dfrac{d^2 y}{dx^2}$ we have $x^2 \dfrac{d^2 y}{dx^2} - 4x \dfrac{dy}{dx} + 6y = 3$

$\Rightarrow e^{2t} \left(\dfrac{d^2 y}{dt^2} - \dfrac{dy}{dt} \right) e^{-2t} - 4e^t \times \dfrac{dy}{dt} e^{-t} + 6y = 3$

$\left(\dfrac{d^2 y}{dt^2} - \dfrac{dy}{dt} \right) - \dfrac{4dy}{dt} + 6y = 3$

$\Rightarrow \dfrac{d^2 y}{dt^2} - 5 \dfrac{dy}{dt} + 6y = 3$, as required

$\therefore m^2 - 5m + 6 = 0 \Rightarrow m = 2$ or 3

$\Rightarrow$ C.F. is $y = A e^{2t} + B e^{3t}$

A particular solution is simply $y = \dfrac{1}{2}$

$\therefore$ The general solution is $y = A e^{2t} + B e^{3t} + \dfrac{1}{2}$

$\Rightarrow y = Ax^2 + Bx^3 + \dfrac{1}{2}$

Section 9

1 $f(x) = e^{-x} - \tan x$ ∴ $f(0.5) = 0.06 > 0$ And

$f(0.6) = -0.14 < 0$. Change of sign ∴ a root.

2

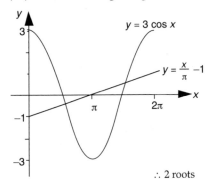

∴ 2 roots

Note: $\dfrac{x}{\pi} - 1 = 3\cos x \Rightarrow x - \pi = 3\pi \cos x$

3 Suppose $f(x) = e^x - 4\sin x$

Using radians, $f(0) = 1$ $f(0.5) = -0.27$

$f(1) = -0.65$ $f(1.5) = 0.49$

There are two changes of sign, so there are two roots, one between 0 and 0.5, the other between 1 and 1.5.

4

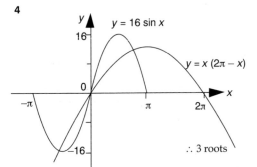

∴ 3 roots

5 (a) $1.7 + 6.7 = 8.4$

∴ approximation to root is $2 + \dfrac{1.7}{8.4} = 2.2$

(b) $4.2 + 0.6 = 4.8$

∴ approximation to root is $1.1 + \dfrac{4.2}{4.8} \times \dfrac{1}{10} = 1.19$

6 (a) 1.15 is three-quarters of way between 1.0 and 1.2, so we would expect y-value to be three-quarters of way between 3.70 and 3.82: i.e. at 3.79.

(b) The difference between the y values on either side of the given value is $4.51 - 4.15$ $= 0.36$. We want to be 0.25 above the lower value, and we would expect the corresponding x value to be:

$1.4 + \dfrac{0.25}{0.36} \times 0.2 = 1.54$

7 Take everything to one side first of all and let this side be $f(x)$, i.e.

$f(x) = x^5 - x^3 - 25$

then $f'(x) = 5x^4 - 3x^2$

$a_0 = 2;\ a_1 = a_0 - \dfrac{f(a_0)}{f'(a_0)} = 2 - \dfrac{(-1)}{68}$

$= 2.015$ to 3 d.p.

8 x must be less than zero, otherwise both terms would be positive.

If $f(x) = x + 2e^x$

$f(0) = 2$

$f(-1) = -0.26$

The two consecutive integers are -1 and 0 and we take -1 as first approximation, since $0.26 < 2$

$f'(x) = 1 + 2e^x$

$a_0 = -1;\ a_1 = a_0 - \dfrac{f(a_0)}{f'(a_0)} = -1 - \dfrac{(-0.264)}{1.736}$

$= -0.85$

9 Let $f(x) = x^3 + x^2 + x + (x-1)^2$;

$f'(x) = 3x^2 + 2x + 1 + 2x - 2 = 3x^2 + 4x - 1$

$f(-2) = 3\ f(-3) = -5$

Change of sign, so root between -3 and -2.

$a_0 = -3;\ a_1 = a_0 - \dfrac{f(a_0)}{f'(a_0)} = -3 - \dfrac{(-5)}{14}$

$= -2.6$ to 1 d.p.

10

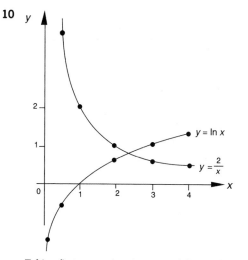

Taking first approximation as $x = 2.3$, putting

$$f(x) = \ln x - \frac{2}{x}, \quad f'(x) = \frac{1}{x} + \frac{2}{x^2}$$

$$a_0 = 2.3; \ a_1 = a_0 - \frac{f(a_0)}{f'(a_0)} = 2.3 - \frac{(-0.0367)}{0.8129} = 2.35$$

$$a_2 = a_1 - \frac{f(a_1)}{f'(a_1)} = 2.35 - \frac{0.003351}{0.7877} = 2.346$$

$\therefore$ Since $a_1 = a_2 = 2.35$, correct to 2 d.p., this must be the required root.

11 $\dfrac{dy}{dx} = 3x^2 + 1 > 0$ $\therefore$ increasing $\therefore$ 1 root

The root is between –1 and 0.

Linear interpolation gives –0.5 as an approximate root.

The Newton-Raphson process eventually gives –0.7.

12 $f(x) = x + \ln x - 3$ $\therefore$ $f(2) = -0.307 < 0$ and $f(3) = 1.099 > 0$. Change of sign $\therefore$ a root

Interpolation gives 2.3. Final answer 2.2

13

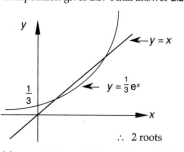

$\therefore$ 2 roots

(a) $1 \to 0.906 \to 0.825 \to 0.761 \to 0.713 \to$
$0.680 \to 0.66 \to 0.64 \to 0.63 \to 0.63 \to 0.63 \to$

$0.62 \to 0.62$ $\therefore$ 0.6 (using memories throughout and rounding off answers as above)

(b) $e^x = 3x \Rightarrow x = \ln(3x)$

$2 \to 1.79 \to 1.68 \to 1.62 \to 1.58 \to 1.56 \to 1.54$
$\to 1.53 \to 1.52 \to 1.52$ $\therefore$ 1.5

14

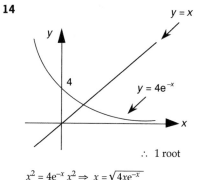

$\therefore$ 1 root

$x^2 = 4e^{-x} x^2 \Rightarrow x = \sqrt{4xe^{-x}}$

$\therefore x = 2\sqrt{xe^{-x}}$. The final answer is 1.2

15 (a) $f(2.7) = 0.719$ and $f(2.8) = -0.12$.
Sign change $\Rightarrow$ root.

(b) $f'(x) = 8 \cos x - 1$ $\therefore$ $x_1 = 2.8 - \left[\dfrac{-0.120}{-8.5378} \right]$

$= 2.786$

(c) $f\left(\dfrac{5\pi}{2}\right) = 0.146$

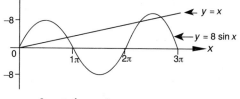

$\therefore$ 3 roots for $x > 0$

16 (a) $x^3 + 3x^2 - 3 = 0 \Rightarrow x^2(x + 3) = 3$

$\Rightarrow x^2 = \dfrac{3}{x + 3} \Rightarrow x = \sqrt{\dfrac{3}{x + 3}}$

(b) $1 \to 0.866 \to 0.88$ $\therefore$ $x_2 = 0.88$

Solutions

Section 10

1 (a) (1,3),4 (b) (−4,0),5 (c) (0,−2),2 (d) (−3,−4),5

2 $x^2 + y^2 - 2x - 4y - 4 = 0$

3 Circle centre (0,0), radius 3.

4 Circle centre (0,0), radius 5. (3,4) and (−4,−3)

5 (a) Circle centre (1,5), radius 1

    (b) Circle centre (2,1), radius 3

    (c) Circle centre (0,0), radius a

6 $x = 2 + 5 \cos \theta, y = -3 + 5 \sin \theta$

7 $3y - 4x + 34 = 0$

8 1

9 $m = -3, (2,-6). \ m = \frac{13}{9}, \left(-3\frac{3}{5}, -5\frac{1}{5}\right)$

10 $m = 2, (1,5). \ m = -\frac{1}{2}, (-2, 4)$

11 (6,3)

12 $x^2 + (mx + c)^2 = a^2$

$\Rightarrow (1 + m^2) x^2 + 2m cx + c^2 - a^2 = 0$

This has repeated roots

$\therefore (2 mc)^2 = 4 (1 + m^2) (c^2 - a^2)$

$\therefore 4m^2c^2 = 4 (1 + m^2) (c^2 - a^2)$

$\therefore c^2 = a^2 (1 + m^2)$

13 $x^2 + y^2 - 2x + 4y - 8 = 0.$

Both gradients $= -\frac{2}{3}$

14 $\dfrac{y - 2at}{2as - 2at} = \dfrac{x - at^2}{as^2 - at^2}$

$\Rightarrow \dfrac{y - 2at}{2a(s - t)} = \dfrac{x - at^2}{a(s - t)(s + t)}$

$\Rightarrow \dfrac{y - 2at}{2} = \dfrac{x - at^2}{s + t}$

$\Rightarrow y (s + t) = 2x + 2ats$

Letting $s = t$, this becomes $2yt = 2x + 2at^2$

i.e. $yt = x + at^2$

15 PQ has equation

$\dfrac{y - b\sin \theta}{b\sin \theta - b\sin \psi} = \dfrac{x - a\cos \theta}{a\cos \theta - a\cos \psi}$

This passes through $(ae,0)$

$\therefore \dfrac{-\sin \theta}{\sin \theta - \sin \psi} = \dfrac{e - \cos \theta}{\cos \theta - \cos \psi}$

$\therefore \dfrac{-\sin \theta}{2 \cos \dfrac{\theta + \psi}{2} \sin \dfrac{\theta - \psi}{2}}$

$= \dfrac{e - \cos \theta}{-2 \sin \dfrac{\theta + \psi}{2} \sin \dfrac{\theta - \psi}{2}}$

$\therefore \sin \theta \sin \dfrac{\theta + \psi}{2} = (e - \cos \theta) \cos \dfrac{\theta + \psi}{2}$

$\therefore e \cos \dfrac{\theta + \psi}{2}$

$= \cos \theta \cos \dfrac{\theta + \psi}{2} + \sin \theta \sin \dfrac{\theta + \psi}{2}$

$\therefore e \cos \dfrac{\theta + \psi}{2} = \cos \dfrac{\theta - \psi}{2}$

or $e \cos \dfrac{\psi + \theta}{2} = \cos \dfrac{\psi - \theta}{2}$

16 $\dfrac{x^2}{a^2} + \dfrac{(mx + c)^2}{b^2} = 1$

$\Rightarrow x^2 (b^2 + m^2a^2) + 2mca^2x + c^2a^2 - a^2b^2 = 0$

Repeated roots

$\Rightarrow (2mca^2)^2 = 4(b^2 + m^2a^2) (c^2 - b^2)a^2$

$\Rightarrow m^2c^2a^2 = (b^2 + m^2a^2) (c^2 - b^2)$

This simplifies to give $c^2 = a^2m^2 + b^2$

17 Solve $y = \dfrac{x}{t} + at$ and $y = \dfrac{x}{s} + as$ simultaneously

to give $x = ast$ and $y = a(s + t)$

Then $t = 2s \Rightarrow x = 2as^2$ and $y = 3as$

Now eliminate s to get $x = 2a \left(\dfrac{y}{3a}\right)^2$

i.e. $2y^2 = 9xa$

18 From $y + tx = at (2 + t^2)$ we get $X \left(a(2 + t^2), 0\right)$

and $Y \left(0, at (2 + t^2)\right)$

Pythagoras now gives $XY = a(2 + t^2) \sqrt{1 + t^2}$

19 From $yt = x + at^2$ we get $X(-at^2, 0)$ and $Y(0, at)$

Pythagoras now gives $XY = at \sqrt{1 + t^2}$

20 Solve $y = -tx + 2at + at^3$ and $y = -sx + 2as + as^3$ simultaneously to give

$-tx + 2at + at^3 = -sx + 2as + as^3$

$\Rightarrow x(s - t) = 2a(s - t) + a(s - t)(s^2 + st + t^2)$

$\Rightarrow x = 2a + a(s^2 + st + t^2)$

$\Rightarrow y = -ast(s + t)$

21 Let tangent be $\dfrac{x \cos \theta}{a} + \dfrac{y \sin \theta}{b} = 1$

$\therefore \quad M\left(a, \dfrac{(1 - \cos \theta) b}{\sin \theta}\right)$ and

$M'\left(-a, \dfrac{(1 + \cos \theta) b}{\sin \theta}\right)$

If F is $(ae, 0)$ then

gradient of $FM = \dfrac{(1 - \cos \theta) b}{\sin \theta} + a(1 - e)$

and gradient of $FM' = \dfrac{(1 + \cos \theta) b}{\sin \theta} \div -a(1 + e)$

$\therefore$ Product of these gradients

$= \dfrac{(1 - \cos \theta) b}{a \sin \theta (1 - e)} \times \dfrac{(1 + \cos \theta) b}{-a \sin \theta (1 + e)}$

$= \dfrac{(1 - \cos^2 \theta) b^2}{-a^2 \sin \theta (1 - e^2)}$

But $b^2 = a^2(1 - e^2)$ and $\sin^2 \theta = 1 - \cos^2 \theta$

$\therefore$ this product of gradients $= -1$, as required. Similarly for the other focus $(-ae, 0)$.

22 $\dfrac{x \cos \theta}{a} + \dfrac{y \sin \theta}{b} = 1 \Rightarrow T(a \sec \theta, 0)$

$\dfrac{ax}{\cos \theta} - \dfrac{by}{\sin \theta} = a^2 - b^2$

$\Rightarrow G\left(\dfrac{(a^2 - b^2)}{a}\right) \cos \theta, 0 \bigg)$

Also $C(0, 0)$ and $N(a \cos \theta, 0)$

$\therefore NG = \dfrac{b^2}{a} \cos \theta$

$\therefore CT \times NG = a \sec \theta \times \dfrac{b^2}{a} \cos \theta = b^2$,

as required.

23 $\sin \theta = \dfrac{b^2}{a^2 - b^2}$

24 $\dfrac{x^2}{a^2} - \dfrac{y^2}{b^2} = 1 \Rightarrow \dfrac{2x}{a^2} - \dfrac{2y}{b^2}\dfrac{dy}{dx} = 0 \Rightarrow \dfrac{dy}{dx} = \dfrac{b^2 x}{a^2 y}$

$\therefore$ Tangent is $y - y_1 = \dfrac{b^2 x_1}{a^2 y_1}(x - x_1)$

$\Rightarrow \dfrac{yy_1}{b^2} - \dfrac{y_1^2}{b^2} = \dfrac{xx_1}{a^2} - \dfrac{x_1^2}{a^2}$

$\Rightarrow \dfrac{xx_1}{a^2} - \dfrac{yy_1}{b^2} = \dfrac{x_1^2}{a^2} - \dfrac{y_1^2}{b^2}$

$\Rightarrow \dfrac{xx_1}{a^2} - \dfrac{yy_1}{b^2} = 1$, as required

25 Let the asymptote $y = \dfrac{x}{\sqrt{2}}$ meet the tangent at

$A\left(\alpha, \dfrac{\alpha}{\sqrt{2}}\right)$

Let the asymptote $y = \dfrac{-x}{\sqrt{2}}$ meet the tangent at

$B\left(\beta, \dfrac{-\beta}{\sqrt{2}}\right)$

$\therefore$ Area of $\triangle AOB = \dfrac{1}{2} \times OA \times OB \times \sin 2\theta$

where $\tan \theta = \dfrac{1}{\sqrt{2}}$

$= \dfrac{1}{2}\sqrt{\alpha^2 + \left(\dfrac{\alpha}{\sqrt{2}}\right)^2} \times \sqrt{\beta^2 + \left(\dfrac{\beta}{\sqrt{2}}\right)^2}$

$\times 2 \sin \theta \cos \theta$, where

$= \dfrac{1}{2} \times \dfrac{\sqrt{3}\alpha}{\sqrt{2}} \times \dfrac{\sqrt{3}\beta}{\sqrt{2}} \times 2 \times \dfrac{1}{\sqrt{3}} \times \dfrac{\sqrt{2}}{\sqrt{3}} = \dfrac{\alpha\beta}{\sqrt{2}}$

If the tangent is $\dfrac{xx_1}{4} - \dfrac{yy_1}{2} = 1$ then, solving

simultaneously with $y = \dfrac{x}{\sqrt{2}}$, we get

$\alpha = \dfrac{4}{x_1 - y_1\sqrt{2}}, \quad \beta = \dfrac{4}{x_1 + y_1\sqrt{2}}$

$\therefore \alpha\beta = \dfrac{16}{x_1^2 - 2y_1^2}$ i.e. $\alpha\beta = \dfrac{16}{4} = 4$

$\therefore$ Area of $\triangle ADB = \dfrac{\alpha\beta}{\sqrt{2}} = \dfrac{4}{\sqrt{2}} = 2\sqrt{2}$,

a constant.

26 Tangent is $\dfrac{xx_1}{a^2} - \dfrac{yy_1}{b^2} = 1$

$\Rightarrow \dfrac{x}{a^2} \times \dfrac{a}{2}\left(t + \dfrac{1}{t}\right) - \dfrac{y}{b^2} \times \dfrac{b}{2}\left(t - \dfrac{1}{t}\right) = 1$

$\Rightarrow bx(t^2 + 1) - ay(t^2 - 1) = 2abt$

27 $\dfrac{y-\frac{c}{t}}{\frac{c}{s}-\frac{c}{t}} = \dfrac{x-ct}{cs-ct} \Rightarrow \dfrac{y-\frac{c}{t}}{\frac{c}{st}(t-s)} = \dfrac{x-ct}{c(s-t)}$

$\Rightarrow \dfrac{y-\frac{c}{t}}{\frac{-1}{st}} = \dfrac{x-ct}{1} \Rightarrow -yst + cs = x - ct$

$\Rightarrow x + sty = c\,(s+t)$, as required

28 $x = ct \Rightarrow \dfrac{dx}{dt} = c$ and $y = \dfrac{c}{t} \Rightarrow \dfrac{dy}{dt} = \dfrac{-c}{t^2}$

$\Rightarrow \dfrac{dy}{dx} = \dfrac{-c}{t^2} \div c = \dfrac{-1}{t^2}$

$\therefore$ gradient of normal $= t^2$

$\therefore$ Normal is $y - \dfrac{c}{t} = t^2 (x-ct)$

$\Rightarrow y - t^2 x = \dfrac{c}{t} - ct^3$, as required.

Let normal meet curve again at $\left(cs, \dfrac{c}{s}\right)$.

$\therefore \dfrac{c}{s} - \dfrac{c}{t} = t^2 (cs - ct) \Rightarrow \dfrac{c(t-s)}{st} = t^2 c\,(s-t)$

$\Rightarrow s = \dfrac{-1}{t^3}$

$\therefore$ Intersection point is $\left(-\dfrac{c}{t^3}, -ct^3\right)$

29 Tangents are $y - \dfrac{c}{t} = \dfrac{-1}{t^2}(x-ct)$

and $y - \dfrac{c}{s} = \dfrac{-1}{s^2}(x-cs)$

$\Rightarrow$ subtracting gives

$\dfrac{c}{s} - \dfrac{c}{t} = \dfrac{1}{s^2}(x-cs) - \dfrac{1}{t^2}(x-ct)$

$= x\left(\dfrac{1}{s^2} - \dfrac{1}{t^2}\right) - \dfrac{c}{s} + \dfrac{c}{t}$

$\Rightarrow x = \dfrac{2c\left(\frac{1}{s}-\frac{1}{t}\right)}{\frac{1}{s^2}-\frac{1}{t^2}} = \dfrac{2cst}{s+t} \Rightarrow y = \dfrac{2c}{s+t}$

$s = \dfrac{1}{t} \Rightarrow Q\left(\dfrac{2c}{\frac{1}{t}+t}, \dfrac{2c}{\frac{1}{t}+t}\right) \Rightarrow Q$ on line $y = x$

30 (a) $r = 3$ (b) $r = 4 \sec\theta$ (c) $r = \sec\left(\tfrac{1}{4}\pi - \theta\right)$

(d) $r = 2\cos\theta$

31 (a)

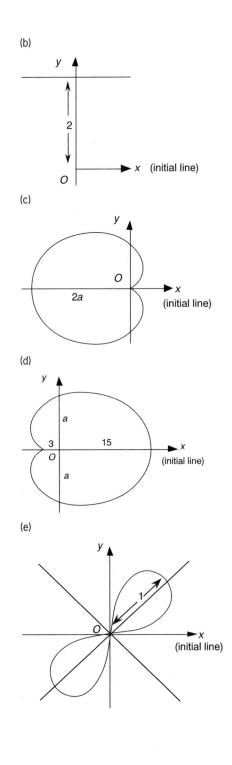

(b)

(c)

(d)

(e)

32 $2 \times \dfrac{1}{2} \displaystyle\int_0^{\frac{\pi}{4}} a^2 \sin^2 2\theta \, d\theta$

$= \dfrac{a^2}{2} \displaystyle\int_0^{\frac{\pi}{4}} (1 - \cos 4\theta) \, d\theta$

$= \dfrac{a^2}{2} \left[\theta - \dfrac{1}{4} \sin 4\theta \right]_0^{\frac{\pi}{4}} = \dfrac{\pi a^2}{8}$

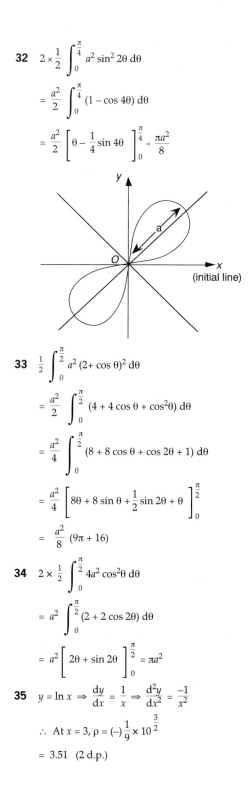

33 $\dfrac{1}{2} \displaystyle\int_0^{\frac{\pi}{2}} a^2 (2 + \cos\theta)^2 \, d\theta$

$= \dfrac{a^2}{2} \displaystyle\int_0^{\frac{\pi}{2}} (4 + 4\cos\theta + \cos^2\theta) \, d\theta$

$= \dfrac{a^2}{4} \displaystyle\int_0^{\frac{\pi}{2}} (8 + 8\cos\theta + \cos 2\theta + 1) \, d\theta$

$= \dfrac{a^2}{4} \left[8\theta + 8\sin\theta + \dfrac{1}{2}\sin 2\theta + \theta \right]_0^{\frac{\pi}{2}}$

$= \dfrac{a^2}{8} (9\pi + 16)$

34 $2 \times \dfrac{1}{2} \displaystyle\int_0^{\frac{\pi}{2}} 4a^2 \cos^2\theta \, d\theta$

$= a^2 \displaystyle\int_0^{\frac{\pi}{2}} (2 + 2\cos 2\theta) \, d\theta$

$= a^2 \left[2\theta + \sin 2\theta \right]_0^{\frac{\pi}{2}} = \pi a^2$

35 $y = \ln x \Rightarrow \dfrac{dy}{dx} = \dfrac{1}{x} \Rightarrow \dfrac{d^2y}{dx^2} = \dfrac{-1}{x^2}$

$\therefore$ At $x = 3$, $\rho = (-)\dfrac{1}{9} \times 10^{\frac{3}{2}}$

$= 3.51 \quad (2 \text{ d.p.})$

36 $y = c \cosh\left(\dfrac{x}{c}\right) \Rightarrow \dfrac{dy}{dx} = \sinh\left(\dfrac{x}{c}\right)$

$\Rightarrow \dfrac{d^2y}{dx^2} = \dfrac{1}{c} \cosh\left(\dfrac{x}{c}\right)$

$\rho = \dfrac{\left[1 + \sinh^2\left(\frac{\pi}{c}\right)\right]^{\frac{3}{2}}}{\dfrac{1}{c}\cosh\left(\frac{x}{c}\right)} = \dfrac{\cosh^3\left(\frac{x}{c}\right)}{\dfrac{1}{c}\cosh\left(\frac{x}{c}\right)}$

$= c \cosh^2\left(\dfrac{x}{c}\right) = \dfrac{y^2}{c}$ as required

37 $y = c \cosh\left(\dfrac{x}{c}\right) \Rightarrow \dfrac{dy}{dx} = \sinh\left(\dfrac{x}{c}\right)$

$\Rightarrow \dfrac{ds}{dx} = \sqrt{1 + \sinh^2\left(\dfrac{x}{c}\right)} = \cosh\left(\dfrac{x}{c}\right)$

$\therefore$ Integration gives $s = c \sinh\left(\dfrac{x}{c}\right)$

$\Rightarrow s = c \times \dfrac{dy}{dx} \Rightarrow s = c \tan\psi$, as required.

38 Curvature = zero $\Rightarrow$ radius of curvature is infinite

$\Rightarrow \dfrac{d^2y}{dx^2} = 0 \Rightarrow 6 - 6x = 0 \Rightarrow x = 1 \Rightarrow y = 2$

$\therefore$ required point is $(1, 2)$.

39 $\rho = \dfrac{\left[4\sinh^2\theta + \cosh^2\theta\right]^{\frac{3}{2}}}{2\sinh^2\theta - 2\cosh^2\theta}$ and $\theta = 0$

$\Rightarrow \rho = (-)\dfrac{1}{2}$ i.e. $\dfrac{1}{2}$

40 $\rho = \dfrac{\left[a^2(1 + \cos\theta)^2 + a^2 \sin^2\theta\right]^{\frac{3}{2}}}{-a^2(1 + \cos\theta)\cos\theta - a^2 \sin^2\theta}$

$= \dfrac{a^3 (2 + 2\cos\theta)^{\frac{3}{2}}}{-a^2(1 + \cos\theta)}$

$= (-)\, a \times 2^{\frac{3}{2}} \sqrt{1 + \cos\theta}$

$= (-)\, a \times 2^{\frac{3}{2}} \sqrt{2\cos^2\dfrac{\theta}{2}}$

$= (-)\, 4a \cos\dfrac{\theta}{2}$ as required

41 $\rho = \dfrac{\left[c^2 + \dfrac{c^2}{t^4}\right]^{\frac{3}{2}}}{\dfrac{2c^2}{t^3}} = \dfrac{\dfrac{c^3}{t^3}\left(t^2 + \dfrac{1}{t^2}\right)^{\frac{3}{2}}}{\dfrac{2c^2}{t^3}}$

$= \dfrac{c}{2}\left(t^2 + \dfrac{1}{t^2}\right)^{\frac{3}{2}}$ as required

Section 11

1 (a) $\ln (e^{ix}) = ix$ $\ln e = ix$

∴ $ix - ix = 0$, as required

(b) $\cosh (x + iy) = \cosh x \ \cosh iy \ + \sinh x \sinh iy$

etc.

2 (a) $\dfrac{e^{i\theta}}{e^{-i\theta}} = e^{2i\theta} = \cos 2\theta + i \sin 2\theta$

(b) $(e^{2i\theta})^{10} = e^{20\iota\theta} = \cos 20\theta + i \sin 20\theta$

3 (a) $z = r (\cos \theta + i \sin \theta)$

$\Rightarrow r^3 (\cos 3\theta + i \sin 3\theta) = -8$

$\Rightarrow r^3 \cos 3\theta = -8$ and $r^3 \sin 3\theta = 0$

∴ $r = 2$, $\sin 3\theta = 0$ and $\cos 3\theta = -1$

∴ $r = 2$ and $3\theta = \pi, 3\pi$ or 5π

∴ $z = 2\left(\cos \dfrac{\pi}{3} + i \sin \dfrac{\pi}{3} \right)$ or $2(\cos \pi + i \sin \pi)$

or $2 \left(\cos \dfrac{5\pi}{3} + i \sin \dfrac{5\pi}{3} \right)$

∴ the three solutions are $1 + i\sqrt{3}$, -2 and

$1 - i\sqrt{3}$

(b) $r^4 (\cos 4\theta + i \sin 4\theta) = 16i \Rightarrow r^4 \cos 4\theta = 0$
and $r^4 \sin 4\theta = 16$

∴ $r = 2$, $\cos 4\theta = 0$ and $\sin 4\theta = 1$ ∴ $r = 2$ and
$4\theta = \dfrac{\pi}{2}, \dfrac{5\pi}{2}$ or $\dfrac{9\pi}{2}$

∴ $z = 2 \left(\cos \dfrac{\pi}{8} + i \sin \dfrac{\pi}{8} \right)$

or $2 \left(\cos \dfrac{5\pi}{8} + i \sin \dfrac{5\pi}{8} \right)$

or $2 \left(\cos \dfrac{9\pi}{8} + i \sin \dfrac{9\pi}{8} \right)$

(c) $z^5 = -1 \Rightarrow r^5 (\cos 5\theta + i \sin 5\theta) = -1$

$\Rightarrow r = 1$, $\cos 5\theta = -1$ and $\sin 5\theta = 0$

∴ $r = 1$ and $5\theta = \pi, 3\pi, 5\pi, 7\pi$ or 9π

∴ $z = \cos \dfrac{\pi}{5} + i \sin \dfrac{\pi}{5}$ or $\cos \dfrac{3\pi}{5} + i \sin \dfrac{3\pi}{5}$ or -1

or $\cos \dfrac{7\pi}{5} + i \sin \dfrac{7\pi}{5}$ or $\cos \dfrac{9\pi}{5} + i \sin \dfrac{9\pi}{5}$

4 $\cos 4\theta + i \sin 4\theta = (c + i s)^4$

$= c^4 + 4c^3 (is) + 6c^2 (is)^2 + 4c (is)^3 + (is)^4$, etc.

(d) $c^4 - 6c^2 s^2 + s^4 = c^4 - 6c^2 (1 - c^2) + (1 - c^2)^2$

$= 8c^4 - 8c^2 + 1 \Rightarrow a = 8, b = -8$ and $c = 1$

5 $2^6 c^3 s^4 = \dfrac{(e^{i\theta} + e^{-i\theta})^3 (e^{i\theta} - e^{-i\theta})^4}{2}$

$= \dfrac{(e^{2i\theta} - e^{-2i\theta})^3 (e^{i\theta} - e^{-i\theta})}{2}$

$= \dfrac{1}{2} \left(e^{6i\theta} - 3e^{2i\theta} + 3e^{-2i\theta} - e^{-6i\theta} \right) \left(e^{i\theta} - e^{-i\theta} \right)$

$= \dfrac{1}{2} \left(e^{7\theta} + e^{-7i\theta} - e^{5i\theta} - e^{-5i\theta} - 3e^{3i\theta} - 3e^{-3i\theta} \right.$

$\left. + 3e^{i\theta} + 3e^{-i\theta} \right)$

$= \cos 7\theta - \cos 5\theta - 3 \cos 3\theta + 3 \cos \theta$, as
required

6 $2^5 \left(\dfrac{e^{i\theta} + e^{-i\theta}}{2} \right)^6$

$= \dfrac{1}{2} \left(e^{6\theta} + 6e^{4i\theta} + 15e^{2i\theta} + 20 + 15e^{-2i\theta} \right.$

$\left. + 6e^{-4i\theta} + e^{-6i\theta} \right)$

$= \cos 6\theta + 6 \cos 4\theta + 15 \cos 2\theta + 10$

∴ $a = 1$, $b = 6$, $c = 15$ and $d = 10$

7 $(z^{-1})^* = \left(\dfrac{1}{r} e^{-i\theta} \right)^* = \dfrac{1}{r} e^{i\theta} = \dfrac{1}{re^{-i\theta}} = (z^*)^{-1}$

∴ $(z_1 z_2^{-1})^* = z_1^* (z_2^{-1})^* = z_1^* (z_2^*)^{-1}$

8 (a) Circle centre $(0,1)$, radius 2

(b) Line $y = x$ for $x > 0$

(c) The line $x + y = 5$

(d) Circle centre $\left(0, +\dfrac{9}{8} \right)$, radius $\dfrac{3}{8}$

9 $1 + i$ and $1 - i$ are roots

∴ $(x - (1 + i)) (x - (1 - i)) = x^2 - 2x + 2$ is a factor

The other factor is $(x + 1)$

∴ roots are $1 + i$, $1 - i$ and -1

10 $4 - 5i$ and $4 + 5i$ are roots

∴ $x^2 - 8x + 41$ is a factor

The other factor is $x - 2$ ∴ real root is 2.

11 $\pm i$ are roots ∴ $x^2 + 1$ is a factor

∴ other factor is $x^2 - 4x + 5$

∴ roots are $\pm i$, $2 + i$, $2 - i$

12 $\dfrac{3}{2} + \dfrac{i}{2}, \dfrac{1}{2} + \dfrac{i}{2}$; imaginary coefficients;

$\dfrac{3}{2} - \dfrac{i}{2}, \dfrac{1}{2} - \dfrac{i}{2}$.

13 $|z| = 1 \Rightarrow z = \cos\theta + i\sin\theta$

$\Rightarrow u + iv = \dfrac{c + i(s+2)}{-(2s+1) + 2ic}$

$= \dfrac{[c + i(s+2)]}{[-(2s+1) + 2ic]}\left[\dfrac{(2s+1)\,2ic}{(2s+1) + 2ic}\right]$

$= \dfrac{i(4+5s) - 3c}{-5 - 4s}$

$\therefore\ u = \dfrac{3c}{5+4s}$ and $v = \dfrac{-4-5s}{5+4s}$ $\therefore\ u^2 + v^2 = 1$

$\therefore\ |w| = 1$

14 $u + iv = \dfrac{(1-y) + ix}{x + i(y+1)}$

$= \dfrac{[(1-y) + ix]\,[x - i(y+1)]}{[x + i(y+1)]\,[x - i(y+1)]}$

$= \dfrac{2x + i(x^2 + y^2 - 1)}{x^2 + (y+1)^2}$

$\therefore\ u = \dfrac{2x}{x^2 + (y+1)^2}$ and $v = \dfrac{x^2 + y^2 - 1}{x^2 + (y+1)^2}$

Then $u = 0$ and $-1 \le v \le 1$ $\therefore\ x = 0$ and $y \ge 0$

$\therefore\ Q$ describes the positive half of the imaginary axis.

15 $z = x + \dfrac{1}{2}i$

$\Rightarrow u + iv = \dfrac{x - \frac{1}{2}i}{x + \frac{1}{2}i}$

$\Rightarrow u + iv = \dfrac{x^2 - \frac{1}{4} - ix}{x^2 + \frac{1}{4}}$

$\Rightarrow u = \dfrac{x^2 - \frac{1}{4}}{x^2 + \frac{1}{4}},\ v = \dfrac{-x}{x^2 + \frac{1}{4}}$

$\Rightarrow u^2 + v^2 = 1$, as required

The image is $|w - 3 + i| = 2$

i.e. $\left|\dfrac{w - 3 + i}{2}\right| = 1$

$\therefore$ Replacing w with $\dfrac{w - 3 + i}{2}$ in the original transformation, we get

$\dfrac{w - 3 + i}{2} = \dfrac{z - i}{z}$ i.e. $w = \dfrac{(5 - i)z - 2i}{z}$

Section 12

1 $p - 12 = 0$ $\therefore\ p = 12$

2 (a) $-2i - j + 5k$ (b) $\begin{pmatrix} 5 \\ 5 \\ -5 \end{pmatrix}$

3 $\mathbf{a} \times \mathbf{b} = \begin{pmatrix} -14 \\ 10 \\ -2 \end{pmatrix}$ Unit vector $= \dfrac{1}{\sqrt{300}}\begin{pmatrix} -14 \\ 10 \\ -2 \end{pmatrix}$

4 $\mathbf{b}_1 \times \mathbf{b}_2 = \begin{pmatrix} -4 \\ 3 \\ 2 \end{pmatrix} \times \begin{pmatrix} -4 \\ 1 \\ 1 \end{pmatrix} = \begin{pmatrix} 1 \\ -4 \\ 8 \end{pmatrix}$

Also $\mathbf{a}_1 - \mathbf{a}_2 = \begin{pmatrix} -3 \\ 6 \\ 0 \end{pmatrix} - \begin{pmatrix} -2 \\ 0 \\ 7 \end{pmatrix} = \begin{pmatrix} -1 \\ 6 \\ -7 \end{pmatrix}$

$\therefore$ Shortest distance $= \dfrac{\begin{pmatrix} -1 \\ 6 \\ -7 \end{pmatrix} \cdot \begin{pmatrix} 1 \\ -4 \\ 8 \end{pmatrix}}{\sqrt{1^2 + (-4)^2 + 8^2}}$

$= \dfrac{-81}{\sqrt{81}} = -9$

$\therefore$ Shortest distance $= 9$ (ignore negative sign).

5 (a) $(10, 8, 14)$ (b) $\begin{pmatrix} 7 \\ 4 \\ 7 \end{pmatrix} \times \begin{pmatrix} 2 \\ 2 \\ 4 \end{pmatrix} = \begin{pmatrix} 2 \\ -14 \\ 6 \end{pmatrix}$

$\therefore$ Area $= \sqrt{2^2 + (-14)^2 + 6^2} = \sqrt{236}$

(c) $\mathbf{r} = \begin{pmatrix} 1 \\ 2 \\ 3 \end{pmatrix} + \lambda\begin{pmatrix} 2 \\ 2 \\ 4 \end{pmatrix}$

(d) $\dfrac{x - 1}{2} = \dfrac{y - 2}{2} = \dfrac{z - 3}{4}$

(e) $\begin{pmatrix} 2 \\ 2 \\ 4 \end{pmatrix} \times \begin{pmatrix} 9 \\ -2 \\ 0 \end{pmatrix} = \begin{pmatrix} 8 \\ 36 \\ -22 \end{pmatrix}$

$\therefore$ distance $= \dfrac{\sqrt{8^2 + 36^2 + (-22)^2}}{\sqrt{2^2 + 2^2 + 4^2}}$

$= \sqrt{76\dfrac{5}{6}}$

6 A straight line through A and B could be:

$\mathbf{r} = \begin{pmatrix} 3 \\ -2 \\ 1 \end{pmatrix} + \lambda\begin{pmatrix} -4 \\ 3 \\ 1 \end{pmatrix}$,

If this is perpendicular to $\begin{pmatrix} 1 \\ 2 \\ p \end{pmatrix}$ then:

$\begin{pmatrix} -4 \\ 3 \\ 1 \end{pmatrix} \cdot \begin{pmatrix} 1 \\ 2 \\ p \end{pmatrix} = -4 + 6 + p = 0$, i.e. $p = -2$

7 $\overrightarrow{AB}$ is $\begin{pmatrix} 3 \\ -5 \\ 3 \end{pmatrix}$

So the angle between $\overrightarrow{AB}$ and the given line is given by

$$\cos\theta = \frac{\begin{pmatrix} 3 \\ -5 \\ 3 \end{pmatrix} \cdot \begin{pmatrix} 1 \\ -2 \\ -2 \end{pmatrix}}{\sqrt{43}\,\sqrt{9}} = \frac{7}{3\sqrt{43}}$$

then $\theta = 69°$ (correct to the nearest degree)

8 Given by $\cos\theta = \dfrac{24 + 0 + 4}{7 \times \sqrt{20}} = \dfrac{2}{\sqrt5}$

then $\theta = 26.6°$ (correct to one decimal place)

9 $\begin{pmatrix} 3+\lambda \\ 1 \\ 4+4\lambda \end{pmatrix} = \begin{pmatrix} 2+3\mu \\ \mu \\ 7+5\mu \end{pmatrix}$ Simultaneous equations

give $\lambda = 2$ and $\mu = 1$

∴ Meet at (5, 1, 12)

10 $\left[\mathbf{r} - \begin{pmatrix} 1 \\ 2 \\ 5 \end{pmatrix} \right] \times \begin{pmatrix} 1 \\ 1 \\ -3 \end{pmatrix} = 0$

11 $\begin{pmatrix} x \\ y \\ z \end{pmatrix} \cdot \begin{pmatrix} 4 \\ -2 \\ 1 \end{pmatrix} = \begin{pmatrix} 3 \\ 1 \\ 2 \end{pmatrix} \cdot \begin{pmatrix} 4 \\ -2 \\ 1 \end{pmatrix}$

∴ $\mathbf{r} \cdot \begin{pmatrix} 4 \\ -2 \\ 1 \end{pmatrix} = 12$ is the vector equation of Π

and

$4x - 2y + z = 12$ is the cartesian equation of Π.

12 $\begin{pmatrix} 2 \\ 0 \\ 2 \end{pmatrix} \times \begin{pmatrix} 2 \\ -1 \\ 3 \end{pmatrix} = \begin{pmatrix} 2 \\ -2 \\ -2 \end{pmatrix}$

∴ $\mathbf{r} \cdot \begin{pmatrix} 2 \\ -2 \\ -2 \end{pmatrix} = \begin{pmatrix} 1 \\ 2 \\ 4 \end{pmatrix} \cdot \begin{pmatrix} 2 \\ -2 \\ -2 \end{pmatrix}$ ∴ $\mathbf{r} \cdot \begin{pmatrix} 2 \\ -2 \\ -2 \end{pmatrix} = -10$

∴ the equation of the plane ABC is

$\mathbf{r} \cdot \begin{pmatrix} 1 \\ -1 \\ -1 \end{pmatrix} = -5$

13 (a) $\overrightarrow{AB} = \begin{pmatrix} 2 \\ 4 \\ -2 \end{pmatrix}$, $\overrightarrow{AC} = \begin{pmatrix} -1 \\ -5 \\ 1 \end{pmatrix}$, $\overrightarrow{AB} \times \overrightarrow{AC} = \begin{pmatrix} -6 \\ 0 \\ -6 \end{pmatrix}$

(b) $\begin{pmatrix} -6 \\ 0 \\ -6 \end{pmatrix}$ is normal to the plane

∴ equation of plane is $-6x - 6z = k$.

Now substitute in the coordinates of A (say)

∴ $k = -6$

∴ equation of plane is $-6x - 6z = -6$

$\Rightarrow x + z = 1$.

(c) Volume $= \overrightarrow{OA} \times \overrightarrow{OB} \cdot \overrightarrow{OC}$

$= \begin{pmatrix} 1 \\ 1 \\ 0 \end{pmatrix} \times \begin{pmatrix} 3 \\ 5 \\ -2 \end{pmatrix} \cdot \begin{pmatrix} 0 \\ -4 \\ 1 \end{pmatrix}$

$= \begin{pmatrix} -2 \\ 2 \\ 2 \end{pmatrix} \cdot \begin{pmatrix} 0 \\ -4 \\ 1 \end{pmatrix} = -6$

∴ Volume $= +6$ (ignore negative sign).

14 $\overrightarrow{AB} = \begin{pmatrix} 2 \\ 4 \\ -3 \end{pmatrix}$ and $\overrightarrow{AC} = \begin{pmatrix} 1 \\ 6 \\ 2 \end{pmatrix}$

∴ $\overrightarrow{AB} \times \overrightarrow{AC} = \begin{pmatrix} 26 \\ -7 \\ 8 \end{pmatrix}$

∴ $\mathbf{r} \times \begin{pmatrix} 26 \\ -7 \\ 8 \end{pmatrix} = \begin{pmatrix} 1 \\ 1 \\ 1 \end{pmatrix} \times \begin{pmatrix} 26 \\ -7 \\ 8 \end{pmatrix}$

∴ $\mathbf{r} \times \begin{pmatrix} 26 \\ -7 \\ 8 \end{pmatrix} = 27$ i.e. $26x - 7y + 8z = 27$

15 $\overrightarrow{AB} \times \overrightarrow{AC} = \begin{pmatrix} 2 \\ 3 \\ 4 \end{pmatrix} \times \begin{pmatrix} -1 \\ 6 \\ -1 \end{pmatrix} = \begin{pmatrix} -27 \\ -2 \\ 15 \end{pmatrix}$

∴ $\mathbf{r} \cdot \begin{pmatrix} -27 \\ -2 \\ 15 \end{pmatrix} = \begin{pmatrix} 1 \\ 2 \\ 3 \end{pmatrix} \cdot \begin{pmatrix} -27 \\ -2 \\ 15 \end{pmatrix} = 14$

∴ Equation of plan is $\mathbf{r} \cdot \begin{pmatrix} -27 \\ -2 \\ 15 \end{pmatrix} = 14$

16 $\mathbf{r} = \begin{pmatrix} 1 \\ 0 \\ 3 \end{pmatrix} + \lambda \begin{pmatrix} -1 \\ 2 \\ 1 \end{pmatrix} + \mu \begin{pmatrix} 2 \\ 1 \\ 1 \end{pmatrix}$

17 $\cos\theta = \dfrac{\begin{pmatrix} 3 \\ 1 \\ 4 \end{pmatrix} \cdot \begin{pmatrix} 2 \\ 4 \\ 5 \end{pmatrix}}{\sqrt{26}\,\sqrt{45}} = \dfrac{30}{\sqrt{26}\,\sqrt{45}}$

∴ $\theta = 28.7°$ (1 d.p.)

18 $\cos\theta = \dfrac{\begin{pmatrix} 2 \\ 3 \\ 4 \end{pmatrix} \cdot \begin{pmatrix} 5 \\ 1 \\ 2 \end{pmatrix}}{\sqrt{29}\,\sqrt{30}} = \dfrac{21}{\sqrt{29}\,\sqrt{30}}$ ∴ $\theta = 44.6°$

∴ Answer $= 45.4°$ (1 d.p.)

19 $\cos\theta = \dfrac{\begin{pmatrix}3\\4\\7\end{pmatrix}\cdot\begin{pmatrix}2\\1\\1\end{pmatrix}}{\sqrt{74}\ \sqrt{6}} = \dfrac{17}{\sqrt{74}\ \sqrt{6}}$ ∴ $\theta = 36.2°$

∴ Answer = 53.8° (1 d.p.)

20 Substitute $\mathbf{r} = \begin{pmatrix}1+4\lambda\\2+\lambda\\3+3\lambda\end{pmatrix}$ into $\mathbf{r}\cdot\begin{pmatrix}2\\3\\1\end{pmatrix} = 39$

∴ $\begin{pmatrix}1+4\lambda\\2+\lambda\\3+3\lambda\end{pmatrix}\cdot\begin{pmatrix}2\\3\\1\end{pmatrix} = 39$

∴ $2(1+4\lambda) + 3(2+\lambda) + (3+3\lambda) = 39$ ∴ $\lambda = 2$

∴ meet at (9, 4, 9)

21 (a) $\begin{pmatrix}3\\1\\-1\end{pmatrix}\times\begin{pmatrix}2\\4\\1\end{pmatrix} = \begin{pmatrix}5\\-5\\10\end{pmatrix}$ ∴ $\begin{pmatrix}1\\-1\\2\end{pmatrix}$ gives

direction of the line.

(b) $\begin{pmatrix}1\\2\\3\end{pmatrix}\cdot\begin{pmatrix}3\\1\\-1\end{pmatrix} = 2$ and $\begin{pmatrix}1\\2\\3\end{pmatrix}\cdot\begin{pmatrix}2\\4\\1\end{pmatrix} = 13$

(c) $\mathbf{r} = \begin{pmatrix}1\\2\\3\end{pmatrix} + \lambda\begin{pmatrix}1\\-1\\2\end{pmatrix}$

22 (a) $\begin{pmatrix}-1\\0\\1\end{pmatrix}\times\begin{pmatrix}0\\2\\-1\end{pmatrix} = \begin{pmatrix}-2\\-1\\-2\end{pmatrix}$

(b) $\mathbf{r}\cdot\begin{pmatrix}-2\\-1\\-2\end{pmatrix} = \begin{pmatrix}2\\0\\1\end{pmatrix}\cdot\begin{pmatrix}-2\\-1\\-2\end{pmatrix} = -6$ ∴ $2x + y + 2z = 6$

(c) You need here the result that if the equation of a plane is written $\mathbf{r}\cdot\hat{\mathbf{n}} = d$, where $\hat{\mathbf{n}}$ is a *unit* normal vector, then d is the perpendicular distance of the plane from the origin.

∴ $2x + y + 2z = 6$

⇒ $\dfrac{2x + y + 2z}{\sqrt{2^2 + 1^2 + 2^2}} = \dfrac{6}{\sqrt{2^2 + 1^2 + 2^2}}$

⇒ $\dfrac{2x + y + 2z}{3} = 2$

∴ perpendicular distance required = 2

(d) Line $\mathbf{r} = \lambda\begin{pmatrix}2\\1\\2\end{pmatrix}$ meets plane $\mathbf{r}\cdot\begin{pmatrix}2\\1\\1\end{pmatrix} = 6$

when $\lambda\begin{pmatrix}2\\1\\2\end{pmatrix}\cdot\begin{pmatrix}2\\1\\2\end{pmatrix} = 6$ ∴ $\lambda = \dfrac{2}{3}$

∴ Line meets plane at $\dfrac{4}{3}, \dfrac{2}{3}, \dfrac{4}{3}$

∴ R has coordinates $\dfrac{8}{3}, \dfrac{4}{3}, \dfrac{8}{3}$

23 (a) $\begin{pmatrix}1\\-2\\3\end{pmatrix}\times\begin{pmatrix}-2\\3\\-5\end{pmatrix} = \begin{pmatrix}1\\-1\\-1\end{pmatrix}$

(b) $\begin{pmatrix}2\\-1\\5\end{pmatrix}\cdot\begin{pmatrix}1\\-1\\-1\end{pmatrix} = -2$

(c) $\dfrac{-2}{\left|\begin{pmatrix}1\\-1\\-1\end{pmatrix}\right|} = \dfrac{-2}{\sqrt{3}}$ ∴ distance $= \dfrac{2}{\sqrt{3}}$

24 (a) $s = 2$ and $t = -1$ gives $\begin{pmatrix}3\\-1\\2\end{pmatrix}$

(b) $\begin{pmatrix}0\\1\\2\end{pmatrix}\times\begin{pmatrix}5\\4\\-2\end{pmatrix} = \begin{pmatrix}-10\\10\\-5\end{pmatrix}$

(c) $\mathbf{r}\cdot\begin{pmatrix}-10\\10\\-5\end{pmatrix} = \begin{pmatrix}3\\-1\\2\end{pmatrix}\cdot\begin{pmatrix}-10\\10\\-5\end{pmatrix} = -50$

∴ $2x - 2y + z = 10$

(d) $\overrightarrow{A_1P} = \begin{pmatrix}0\\2\\4\end{pmatrix} = 2\mathbf{b}_1$ and $\overrightarrow{A_2P} = \begin{pmatrix}-5\\-4\\2\end{pmatrix} = -\mathbf{b}_2$

∴ Area triangle $= \dfrac{1}{2}\left|\overrightarrow{A_1P}\times\overrightarrow{A_2P}\right|$

$= \left|\mathbf{b}_1\times\mathbf{b}_2\right| = \sqrt{(-10)^2 + 10^2 + (-5)^2} = 15$

25 (a) $\begin{pmatrix}2\\0\\-1\end{pmatrix}\times\begin{pmatrix}4\\3\\1\end{pmatrix} = \begin{pmatrix}3\\-6\\6\end{pmatrix}$

(b) ∴ $\mathbf{r}\cdot\begin{pmatrix}3\\-6\\4\end{pmatrix} = \begin{pmatrix}0\\0\\0\end{pmatrix}\cdot\begin{pmatrix}3\\-6\\6\end{pmatrix} = 0$

∴ $3x - 6y + 6z = 0$ ∴ $x - 2y + 2z = 0$

(c) $\begin{pmatrix}4\\3\\1\end{pmatrix}\cdot\begin{pmatrix}3\\1\\-1\end{pmatrix} = 14$ ∴ $d = 14$

(d) Direction of L is $\begin{pmatrix}3\\1\\-1\end{pmatrix}\times\begin{pmatrix}1\\-2\\2\end{pmatrix} = \begin{pmatrix}0\\-7\\-7\end{pmatrix}$

i.e. $\begin{pmatrix}0\\1\\1\end{pmatrix}$

Point B lies on L

∴ $\mathbf{r} = \begin{pmatrix}4\\3\\1\end{pmatrix} + t\begin{pmatrix}0\\1\\1\end{pmatrix}$

(e) $\begin{pmatrix}4\\3+t\\1+t\end{pmatrix}\cdot\begin{pmatrix}0\\1\\1\end{pmatrix} = 0 \Rightarrow t = -2 \Rightarrow \mathbf{r} = \begin{pmatrix}4\\1\\-1\end{pmatrix}$

Section 13

1 $I_n = \int_0^{\frac{\pi}{2}} \sin x^{n-1}x \; \sin x \; dx$

$= \left[\sin^{n-1}x \cos x \right]_0^{\frac{\pi}{2}}$

$+ (n-1) \int_0^{\frac{\pi}{2}} \sin x^{n-2}x \; \sin x \cos^2 x \; dx$

$= 0 + (n-1) \int_0^{\frac{\pi}{2}} \sin x^{n-2}(1 - \sin^2 x) \; dx$

$\therefore I_n = (n-1)\left\{ I_{n-2} - I_n \right\}$

$\therefore I_n = \left(\frac{n-1}{n} \right) I_{n-2}$

(a) $I_7 = \frac{6}{7} I_5 = \frac{6}{7} \times \frac{4}{5} \times I_3$

$= \frac{6}{7} \times \frac{4}{5} \times \frac{2}{3} I_1 = \frac{6}{7} \times \frac{4}{5} \times \frac{2}{3} \times \left[-\cos x \right]_0^{\frac{\pi}{2}}$

$= \frac{16}{35}$

(b) $I_{10} = \frac{9}{10} \times \frac{7}{8} \times \frac{5}{6} \times \frac{3}{4} \times \frac{1}{2} \times I_0$

Since $I_0 = \frac{\pi}{2}$, $I_{10} = \frac{63\pi}{512}$

2 $I_n - I_{n-2} = \int \frac{\sin nx - \sin (n-2)x}{\sin x} \; dx$

$= \int \frac{2 \cos (n-1) x \; \sin x}{\sin x} \; dx$

$= \int 2 \cos (n-1)x \; dx$

$\therefore I_n - I_{n-2} = \frac{2}{(n-1)} \sin (n-1) x$

$I_4 = \frac{2}{3} \sin 3x + I_2$ and

$I_2 = \int \frac{\sin 2x}{\sin x} \; dx = \int 2 \cos x \; dx = 2 \sin x$

$\therefore I_4 = \left[\frac{2}{3} \sin 3x + 2 \sin x \right]_{\frac{\pi}{4}}^{\frac{\pi}{2}}$

$= \frac{-4}{3} (\sqrt{2} - 1) = -0.55 \text{ (2 d.p.)}$

3 $I_n = \left[-x^n \cos x \right]_0^{\frac{\pi}{2}}$

$+ n \int x^{n-1} \cos x \; dx = 0 + n \left[x^{n-1} \sin x \right]_0^{\frac{\pi}{2}}$

$- n (n-1) \int_0^{\frac{\pi}{2}} x^{n-2} \sin x \; dx$

$\therefore I_n = n \left(\frac{\pi}{2} \right)^{n-1} - n (n-1) I_{n-2}$

4 $I_{m,n} = \left[-\cos^m x \; \frac{\cos nx}{n} \right]_0^{\frac{\pi}{2}}$

$- \frac{m}{n} \int_0^{\frac{\pi}{2}} \cos^{m-1} x \sin x \cos nx \; dx$

$= \frac{1}{n} - \frac{m}{n} \int_0^{\frac{\pi}{2}} \cos^{m-1}x \; (\sin nx \cos x - \sin (n-1) x) \; dx$

$\therefore I_{m,n} = \frac{1}{n} - \frac{m}{n} I_{m,n} + \frac{m}{n} I_{m-1, n-1}$

$\therefore \left(1 + \frac{m}{n} \right) I_{m,n} = \frac{1}{n} + \frac{m}{n} I_{m-1, n-1}$

$\therefore (n + m) I_{m,n} = 1 + m \; I_{m-1, n-1}$

Then $I_{5,2} = \frac{1}{7} + \frac{5}{7} I_{4,1}$ and

$I_{4,1} = \int_0^{\frac{\pi}{2}} \cos^4 x \sin x \; dx = \left[-\frac{\cos^5 x}{5} \right]_0^{\frac{\pi}{2}} = \frac{1}{5}$

$\therefore I_{5,2} = \frac{2}{7}$

5 $\frac{dy}{dx} = \frac{3}{2} \sqrt{x}$

$\therefore s = \int_0^2 \sqrt{1 + \frac{9}{4}x} \; dx = \left[\frac{8}{27} \left(1 + \frac{9x}{4} \right)^{\frac{3}{2}} \right]_0^2$

$= \frac{8}{27} \left\{ \left(\frac{11}{2} \right)^{\frac{3}{2}} - 1 \right\} = 3.53 \text{ (2 d.p.)}$

6 $\int_0^\pi \sqrt{a^2 (1 + \cos \theta)^2 + a^2 \sin^2 \theta} \; d\theta$

$= \int_0^\pi a \sqrt{2 + 2 \cos \theta} \; d\theta = \int_0^\pi a \sqrt{4 \cos^2 \frac{\theta}{2}} \; d\theta$

$$= \int_0^\pi 2a \cos\frac{\theta}{2}\, d\theta = \left[4a \sin\frac{\theta}{2}\right]_0^\pi = 4a$$

7

$$\int \sqrt{\left(e^\theta \cos\theta + e^\theta \sin\theta\right)^2 + \left(-e^\theta \sin\theta + e^\theta \cos\theta\right)^2}\, d\theta$$

$$= \int \sqrt{e^{2\theta} \times 2}\ \, d\theta = \int \sqrt{2} \times e^\theta\, d\theta = \sqrt{2}e^\theta + c$$

8 Line meets parabola at $y = \dfrac{3a}{2}$. Also $\dfrac{dy}{dx} = \dfrac{2a}{y}$

$$\therefore \text{\i\in(, ,\r(1 + \f(4a^2,y^2)\s(, ,))} \times\ dx$$

$$= \int_{\frac{1}{2a}} \sqrt{1 + \frac{4a^2}{y^2}} \times \frac{ydy}{2a}$$
$$= \int_{\frac{1}{2a}} \frac{\sqrt{y^2 + 4a^2}}{\ } \frac{ydy}{dy}$$

The hyperbolic substitution $y = 2a \sinh\theta$ leads to the required answer.

9 $\ 2\pi \displaystyle\int_0^h x \tan\alpha \sqrt{1 + \tan^2\alpha}\ dx$

$$= 2\pi \int_0^h x \tan\alpha \sec\alpha\, dx = \pi h^2 \tan\alpha \sec\alpha$$

10 $\ 2\pi \displaystyle\int y \sqrt{1 + \left(\frac{dx}{dy}\right)^2}\, dy = 2\pi \int y \sqrt{1 + \frac{y^2}{4a^2}}\, dy$

$$= \frac{\pi}{a} \int y \sqrt{y^2 + 4a^2}\, dy$$

$$= \left[\frac{\pi}{3a}(y^2 + 4a^2)^{\frac{3}{2}}\right]_0^{\sqrt{4ah}}$$

And this gives $\dfrac{8\pi\sqrt{a}}{3}\left\{(h + a)^{\frac{3}{2}} - a^{\frac{3}{2}}\right\}$

as required.

11 $\ 2\pi \displaystyle\int_0^{\frac{\pi}{2}} a \sin^3 t \sqrt{1 + (-\tan t)^2}\ (-3a \cos^2 t \sin t)$
dt

$$= -6\pi a^2 \int_0^{\frac{\pi}{2}} \sin^4 t \cos t\, dt$$

$$= \frac{-6\pi a^2}{5}\left[\sin^5 t\right]_0^{\frac{\pi}{2}} = (-)\frac{6\pi a^2}{5}\ \therefore \text{Area} = \frac{6\pi a^2}{5}$$

$$\therefore \text{ The total surface area} = 2 \times \frac{6\pi a^2}{5} = \frac{12\pi a^2}{5}$$

12 $\ \dfrac{dx}{d\theta} = a \sec\theta - a \cos\theta = \dfrac{a \sin^2\theta}{\cos\theta}\ \therefore \dfrac{dy}{dx} = -\cot\theta$

$$\therefore\ 2\pi \int_0^{\frac{\pi}{2}} y \sqrt{1 + \left(\frac{dy}{dx}\right)^2}\ dx$$

$$= 2\pi \int_0^{\frac{\pi}{2}} a \cos\theta\ \sqrt{1 + \cot^2\theta}\ \left(\frac{a \sin^2\theta}{\cos\theta}\right) d\theta$$

$$= -2\pi a^2 \left[\cos\theta\right]_0^{\frac{\pi}{2}} = 2\pi a^2$$

13 $\ \displaystyle\int_0^1 \sqrt{1 + \sinh^2\theta}\, d\theta$

$$= \int_0^1 \cosh\theta\, d\theta = \left[\sinh\theta\right]_0^1 = \sinh(1) = 1.175$$

14 $\ \dfrac{dy}{dx} = x^{\frac{1}{2}}\ \therefore \left(\dfrac{dy}{dx}\right)^2 = x$

$$\therefore\ S = 2\pi \int y \sqrt{1 + \left(\frac{dy}{dx}\right)^2}\ \cdot dx$$

$$= 2\pi \int \frac{2}{3} x^{\frac{3}{2}} \sqrt{1 + x}\ \cdot dx$$

$$= \frac{4\pi}{3} \int x^{\frac{3}{2}}\sqrt{1 + x}\ \cdot dx, \text{ as required}$$

15 $\ I_n = \displaystyle\int_0^{\frac{\pi}{2}} \sin^n x \cdot e^{\sin x} \cos x\, dx$

$$= \left[\sin^n x \cdot e^{\sin x}\right]_0^{\frac{\pi}{2}} - \int_0^{\frac{\pi}{2}} e^{\sin x} \cdot n \sin^{n-1} x \cos x\, dx$$

$$= e - n \int e^{\sin x} \sin^{n-1} x \cos x\, dx$$

$$\therefore\quad I_n = e - n\ I_{n-1}$$
$$\therefore\quad I_3 = e - 3I_2 = e - 3(e - 2I_1)$$
$$= -2e + 6I_1$$
$$= -2e + 6(e - I_0)$$
$$= 4e - 6I_0$$

$$= 4e - 6 \int_0^{\frac{\pi}{2}} e^{\sin x} \cos x\, dx$$

$$= 4e - 6\left[e^{\sin x}\right]_0^{\frac{\pi}{2}}$$

$$= 4e - 6(e - 1) = 6 - 2e$$

361

Section 14

1   (a) $\begin{pmatrix} 47 \\ 32 \end{pmatrix}$ (b) $\begin{pmatrix} 17 \\ 24 \end{pmatrix}$ (c) $\begin{pmatrix} 110 \\ 218 \\ 326 \end{pmatrix}$ (d) $\begin{pmatrix} 14 \\ 11 \\ 11 \end{pmatrix}$

2   (a) $\begin{pmatrix} 0 & -1 \\ 1 & 0 \end{pmatrix}$ (b) $\begin{pmatrix} -1 & 0 \\ 0 & -1 \end{pmatrix}$ (c) $\begin{pmatrix} 0 & 1 \\ 1 & 0 \end{pmatrix}$ (d) $\begin{pmatrix} 0 & -1 \\ -1 & 0 \end{pmatrix}$

(e) $\begin{pmatrix} 1 & 0 \\ 0 & -1 \end{pmatrix}$ (f) $\begin{pmatrix} -1 & 0 \\ 0 & 1 \end{pmatrix}$

3   (a) $\begin{pmatrix} \cos\theta & -\sin\theta & 0 \\ \sin\theta & \cos\theta & 0 \\ 0 & 0 & 1 \end{pmatrix}$ (b) $\begin{pmatrix} 1 & 0 & 0 \\ 0 & 1 & 0 \\ 0 & 0 & -1 \end{pmatrix}$

4   (a) $\begin{pmatrix} 19 & 22 \\ 43 & 50 \end{pmatrix}$ (b) $\begin{pmatrix} 23 & 34 \\ 31 & 46 \end{pmatrix}$ (c) $\begin{pmatrix} 11 & 11 & 14 \\ 29 & 29 & 32 \\ 47 & 47 & 50 \end{pmatrix}$

(d) $\begin{pmatrix} 12 & 14 & 16 \\ 6 & 7 & 8 \\ 18 & 21 & 24 \end{pmatrix}$

5 $\begin{pmatrix} -1 & 0 \\ 0 & 1 \end{pmatrix} \begin{pmatrix} 0 & 1 \\ 1 & 0 \end{pmatrix} \begin{pmatrix} 0 & -1 \\ 1 & 0 \end{pmatrix} = \begin{pmatrix} -1 & 0 \\ 0 & -1 \end{pmatrix}.$

A 180° spin about the origin.

6   (a) $\dfrac{1}{14}\begin{pmatrix} 5 & -2 \\ -3 & 4 \end{pmatrix}$ (b) $\dfrac{1}{26}\begin{pmatrix} 2 & 4 \\ 5 & -3 \end{pmatrix}$

(c) $\dfrac{1}{8}\begin{pmatrix} 9 & -12 & 29 \\ -1 & 4 & -13 \\ -3 & 4 & -7 \end{pmatrix}$ (d) $\begin{pmatrix} 11 & -12 & -7 \\ -8 & 9 & 5 \\ 7 & -8 & -4 \end{pmatrix}$

7 $\begin{pmatrix} x \\ y \end{pmatrix} = \dfrac{1}{7}\begin{pmatrix} 5 & -4 \\ -2 & 3 \end{pmatrix} \begin{pmatrix} 9 \\ 11 \end{pmatrix}$ $\therefore x = \dfrac{1}{7}, y = \dfrac{15}{7}$

8 $AB = BA = I$, $A^{-1} = B$, $\alpha = 1, \beta = 1, \gamma = 1$

9 $WV = VW = 2I$, $W^{-1} = \dfrac{1}{2}V$, $F = \left(W^{-1}\right)^2$

$= \dfrac{1}{4}V^2 = \dfrac{1}{4}\begin{pmatrix} 10 & 12 & -4 \\ 0 & 4 & 0 \\ -4 & 3 & 2 \end{pmatrix}$

10 $\begin{vmatrix} 2-\lambda & 4 \\ 3 & 6-\lambda \end{vmatrix} = 0$

$\Rightarrow (2-\lambda)(6-\lambda) - 12 = 0 \Rightarrow \lambda = 0$ or 8.

(a) $\lambda = 0 \Rightarrow \begin{pmatrix} 2 & 4 \\ 3 & 6 \end{pmatrix}\begin{pmatrix} x \\ y \end{pmatrix} = 0$

$\Rightarrow \begin{array}{l} 2x + 4y = 0 \\ 3x + 6y = 0 \end{array} \Rightarrow x = -2y$

∴ the corresponding eigenvector is

$\begin{pmatrix} -2y \\ y \end{pmatrix} = y\begin{pmatrix} -2 \\ 1 \end{pmatrix}.$

(b) $\lambda = 8 \Rightarrow \begin{pmatrix} 2 & 4 \\ 3 & 6 \end{pmatrix}\begin{pmatrix} x \\ y \end{pmatrix} = 8\begin{pmatrix} x \\ y \end{pmatrix}$

$\Rightarrow \begin{array}{l} 2x + 4y = 8x \\ 3x + 6y = 8y \end{array}$

$\Rightarrow 2y = 3x \Rightarrow \dfrac{2}{3}y = x$

∴ the corresponding eigenvector is

$\begin{pmatrix} \frac{2}{3}y \\ y \end{pmatrix} = \dfrac{y}{3}\begin{pmatrix} 2 \\ 3 \end{pmatrix} = y\begin{pmatrix} 2 \\ 3 \end{pmatrix}$

∴   The matrix **A** has eigenvalues 0 and 8 with corresponding

eigen vectors scalar multiples of $\begin{pmatrix} -2 \\ 1 \end{pmatrix}$ and $\begin{pmatrix} 2 \\ 3 \end{pmatrix}$ respectively.

11 $\begin{vmatrix} 2-\lambda & -2 & 3 \\ 1 & 1-\lambda & 1 \\ 1 & 3 & -1-\lambda \end{vmatrix} = 0$

$\Rightarrow (2-\lambda)[(1-\lambda)(-1-\lambda)-3] + 2[1(-1-\lambda)-1]$
$+ 3[3 - 1(1-\lambda)] = 0$

$\Rightarrow (2-\lambda)(\lambda^2 - 4) + 2(-\lambda - 2) + 3(\lambda + 2) = 0$

$\Rightarrow -\lambda^3 + 2\lambda^2 + 5\lambda - 6 = 0$

$\Rightarrow \lambda^3 - 2\lambda^2 - 5\lambda + 6 = 0$

$\Rightarrow (\lambda - 1)(\lambda + 2)(\lambda - 3) = 0 \Rightarrow \lambda = 1, -2$ or 3

(a) $\lambda = 1 \Rightarrow \begin{pmatrix} 2 & -2 & 3 \\ 1 & 1 & 1 \\ 1 & 3 & -1 \end{pmatrix}\begin{pmatrix} x \\ y \\ z \end{pmatrix} = 1\begin{pmatrix} x \\ y \\ z \end{pmatrix}$

$\begin{array}{l} x - 2y + 3z = 0 \\ x + z = 0 \\ x + 3y - 2z = 0 \end{array} \Rightarrow x + z = 0 \Rightarrow \begin{array}{l} x = -z \\ \text{and} \\ y = z \end{array}$

∴ the corresponding eigenvector is

$\begin{pmatrix} -z \\ z \\ z \end{pmatrix} = z\begin{pmatrix} -1 \\ 1 \\ 1 \end{pmatrix}.$

(b) $\lambda = -2 \Rightarrow \begin{pmatrix} 2 & -2 & 3 \\ 1 & 1 & 1 \\ 1 & 3 & -1 \end{pmatrix}\begin{pmatrix} x \\ y \\ z \end{pmatrix} = -2\begin{pmatrix} x \\ y \\ z \end{pmatrix}$

$\begin{array}{l} 4x - 2y + 3z = 0 \\ x + 3y + z = 0 \\ x + 3y + z = 0 \end{array} \Rightarrow \begin{array}{l} x = 11y \\ \text{and} \\ z = -14y \end{array}$

∴ the corresponding eigenvector is

$\begin{pmatrix} 11y \\ y \\ -14y \end{pmatrix} = y\begin{pmatrix} 11 \\ 1 \\ -14 \end{pmatrix}$

(c) $\lambda = 3 \Rightarrow$

$\begin{pmatrix} 2 & -2 & 3 \\ 1 & 1 & 1 \\ 1 & 3 & -1 \end{pmatrix}\begin{pmatrix} x \\ y \\ z \end{pmatrix} = 3\begin{pmatrix} x \\ y \\ z \end{pmatrix} \Rightarrow \begin{array}{l} -x - 2y + 3z = 0 \\ x - 2y + z = 0 \\ x + 3y - 4z = 0 \end{array}$

$\Rightarrow x = y = z$

∴ the corresponding eigenvector is

$\begin{pmatrix} x \\ x \\ x \end{pmatrix} = x\begin{pmatrix} 1 \\ 1 \\ 1 \end{pmatrix}$

∴ The matrix **A** has eigenvalues 1, –2 and 3 with corresponding eigenvectors scalar multiples of

$$\begin{pmatrix} -1 \\ 1 \\ 1 \end{pmatrix}, \begin{pmatrix} 11 \\ 1 \\ -14 \end{pmatrix} \text{ and } \begin{pmatrix} 1 \\ 1 \\ 1 \end{pmatrix} \text{ respectively.}$$

12 $\mathbf{P} = \begin{pmatrix} -2 & 2 \\ 1 & 3 \end{pmatrix}$, $\mathbf{P}^{-1} = -\dfrac{1}{8} \begin{pmatrix} 3 & -2 \\ -1 & -2 \end{pmatrix}$ and

$\mathbf{P}^{-1}\mathbf{AP} = \begin{pmatrix} 0 & 0 \\ 0 & 8 \end{pmatrix}$

The verification:

$\mathbf{P}^{-1}\mathbf{AP} = -\dfrac{1}{8} \begin{pmatrix} 3 & -2 \\ -1 & -2 \end{pmatrix} \begin{pmatrix} 2 & 4 \\ 3 & 6 \end{pmatrix} \begin{pmatrix} -2 & 2 \\ 1 & 3 \end{pmatrix}$

$= -\dfrac{1}{8} \begin{pmatrix} 0 & 0 \\ -8 & -16 \end{pmatrix} \begin{pmatrix} -2 & 2 \\ 1 & 3 \end{pmatrix}$

$= -\dfrac{1}{8} \begin{pmatrix} 0 & 0 \\ 0 & -64 \end{pmatrix} = \begin{pmatrix} 0 & 0 \\ 0 & 8 \end{pmatrix}$, as required.

13 $\mathbf{P} = \begin{pmatrix} -1 & 11 & 1 \\ 1 & 1 & 1 \\ 1 & -14 & 1 \end{pmatrix}$, $\mathbf{P}^{-1} = \dfrac{-1}{30} \begin{pmatrix} 15 & -25 & 10 \\ 0 & -2 & 2 \\ -15 & -3 & -12 \end{pmatrix}$

and $\mathbf{P}^{-1}\mathbf{AP} = \begin{pmatrix} 1 & 0 & 0 \\ 0 & -2 & 0 \\ 0 & 0 & 3 \end{pmatrix}$

The verification:

$\mathbf{P}^{-1}\mathbf{AP} = -\dfrac{1}{30} \begin{pmatrix} 15 & -25 & 10 \\ 0 & -2 & 2 \\ -15 & -3 & -12 \end{pmatrix}$

$\begin{pmatrix} 2 & -2 & 3 \\ 1 & 1 & 1 \\ 1 & 3 & -1 \end{pmatrix} \begin{pmatrix} -1 & 11 & 1 \\ 1 & 1 & 1 \\ 1 & -14 & 1 \end{pmatrix}$

$= -\dfrac{1}{30} \begin{pmatrix} 15 & -25 & 10 \\ 0 & 4 & -4 \\ -45 & -9 & -36 \end{pmatrix} \begin{pmatrix} -1 & 11 & 1 \\ 1 & 1 & 1 \\ 1 & -14 & 1 \end{pmatrix}$

$= -\dfrac{1}{30} \begin{pmatrix} -30 & 0 & 0 \\ 0 & 60 & 0 \\ 0 & 0 & -90 \end{pmatrix} = \begin{pmatrix} 1 & 0 & 0 \\ 0 & -2 & 0 \\ 0 & 0 & 3 \end{pmatrix}$,

as required.

14 $\mathbf{P} = \begin{pmatrix} -1 & 1 & 1 \\ 0 & 1 & 1 \\ 1 & 1 & 0 \end{pmatrix}$, $\mathbf{P}^{-1} = \begin{pmatrix} -1 & 1 & 0 \\ 1 & -1 & 1 \\ -1 & 2 & -1 \end{pmatrix}$ and

$\mathbf{P}^{-1}\mathbf{AP} = \begin{pmatrix} 2 & 0 & 0 \\ 0 & 4 & 0 \\ 0 & 0 & 5 \end{pmatrix}$

The verification:

$\mathbf{P}^{-1}\mathbf{AP} =$

$\begin{pmatrix} -1 & 1 & 0 \\ 1 & -1 & 1 \\ -1 & 2 & -1 \end{pmatrix} \begin{pmatrix} 1 & 4 & -1 \\ -1 & 6 & -1 \\ 2 & -2 & 4 \end{pmatrix} \begin{pmatrix} -1 & 1 & 1 \\ 0 & 1 & 1 \\ 1 & 1 & 0 \end{pmatrix}$

$= \begin{pmatrix} -2 & 2 & 0 \\ 4 & -4 & 4 \\ -5 & 10 & -5 \end{pmatrix} \begin{pmatrix} -1 & 1 & 1 \\ 0 & 1 & 1 \\ 1 & 1 & 0 \end{pmatrix}$

$= \begin{pmatrix} 2 & 0 & 0 \\ 0 & 4 & 0 \\ 0 & 0 & 5 \end{pmatrix}$, as required.

15 The trick here is to notice that

$(\mathbf{P}^{-1}\mathbf{AP})(\mathbf{P}^{-1}\mathbf{AP}) = \mathbf{P}^{-1}\mathbf{A}(\mathbf{PP}^{-1})\mathbf{AP} = \mathbf{P}^{-1}\mathbf{A}^2\mathbf{P}$

∴ $(\mathbf{P}^{-1}\mathbf{AP})^2 = \mathbf{P}^{-1}\mathbf{A}^2\mathbf{P}$

Similarly $(\mathbf{P}^{-1}\mathbf{AP})^3 = (\mathbf{P}^{-1}\mathbf{A}^2\mathbf{P})(\mathbf{P}^{-1}\mathbf{AP})$

$= \mathbf{P}^{-1}\mathbf{A}^2(\mathbf{PP}^{-1})\mathbf{AP} = \mathbf{P}^{-1}\mathbf{A}^3\mathbf{P}$

∴ $(\mathbf{P}^{-1}\mathbf{AP})^3 = \mathbf{P}^{-1}\mathbf{A}^3\mathbf{P}$

∴ $\mathbf{P}^{-1}\mathbf{A}^n\mathbf{P} = (\mathbf{P}^{-1}\mathbf{AP})^n \Rightarrow \begin{pmatrix} \lambda_1 & 0 \\ 0 & \lambda_2 \end{pmatrix}^n$

$= \begin{pmatrix} \lambda_1^n & 0 \\ 0 & \lambda_2^n \end{pmatrix}$

You probably found that a bit tricky. The *important point* is to remember how you square diagonal matrices. For example:

$\mathbf{A} = \begin{pmatrix} 5 & 0 \\ 0 & 4 \end{pmatrix} \Rightarrow \mathbf{A}^2 = \begin{pmatrix} 5^2 & 0 \\ 0 & 4^2 \end{pmatrix} = \begin{pmatrix} 25 & 0 \\ 0 & 16 \end{pmatrix}$

$\mathbf{B} = \begin{pmatrix} 3 & 0 & 0 \\ 0 & 2 & 0 \\ 0 & 0 & 4 \end{pmatrix}$

$\Rightarrow \mathbf{B}^2 = \begin{pmatrix} 3^2 & 0 & 0 \\ 0 & 2^2 & 0 \\ 0 & 0 & 4^2 \end{pmatrix} = \begin{pmatrix} 9 & 0 & 0 \\ 0 & 4 & 0 \\ 0 & 0 & 16 \end{pmatrix}$

And, in reverse:

$\mathbf{G}^2 = \begin{pmatrix} 16 & 0 & 0 \\ 0 & 9 & 0 \\ 0 & 0 & 25 \end{pmatrix} \Rightarrow \mathbf{G} = \begin{pmatrix} \pm 4 & 0 & 0 \\ 0 & \pm 3 & 0 \\ 0 & 0 & \pm 5 \end{pmatrix}$

Ditto for higher powers. For example:

$\mathbf{H} = \begin{pmatrix} 2 & 0 & 0 \\ 0 & 5 & 0 \\ 0 & 0 & 3 \end{pmatrix} \Rightarrow \mathbf{H}^3 = \begin{pmatrix} 8 & 0 & 0 \\ 0 & 125 & 0 \\ 0 & 0 & 27 \end{pmatrix}$

This is a most important property of diagonal matrices.

16 (a) $\lambda = 1 \Rightarrow \begin{pmatrix} 1 & -3 & -3 \\ -8 & 6 & -3 \\ 8 & -2 & 7 \end{pmatrix} \begin{pmatrix} x \\ y \\ z \end{pmatrix} = 1 \begin{pmatrix} x \\ y \\ z \end{pmatrix}$

$\Rightarrow x = y = -z$

∴ $\lambda = 1 \Rightarrow x \begin{pmatrix} 1 \\ 1 \\ -1 \end{pmatrix}$.

(b) $\lambda = 4 \Rightarrow \begin{pmatrix} 1 & -3 & -3 \\ -8 & 6 & -3 \\ 8 & -2 & 7 \end{pmatrix} \begin{pmatrix} x \\ y \\ z \end{pmatrix} = 4 \begin{pmatrix} x \\ y \\ z \end{pmatrix}$

$\Rightarrow x = y$ and $z = -2x$

$\therefore \lambda = 4 \Rightarrow y \begin{pmatrix} 1 \\ 1 \\ -2 \end{pmatrix}$

(c) $\lambda = 9 \Rightarrow \begin{pmatrix} 1 & -3 & -3 \\ -8 & 6 & -3 \\ 8 & -2 & 7 \end{pmatrix} \begin{pmatrix} x \\ y \\ z \end{pmatrix} = 9 \begin{pmatrix} x \\ y \\ z \end{pmatrix}$

$\Rightarrow x = 0$ and $z = -y$

$\therefore \lambda = 9 \Rightarrow y \begin{pmatrix} 0 \\ 1 \\ -1 \end{pmatrix}$

$\therefore$ The eigenvectors are scalar multiples of

$\begin{pmatrix} 1 \\ 1 \\ -1 \end{pmatrix} \begin{pmatrix} 1 \\ 1 \\ -2 \end{pmatrix}$ and $\begin{pmatrix} 0 \\ 1 \\ -1 \end{pmatrix}$.

$\therefore \mathbf{P} = \begin{pmatrix} 1 & 1 & 0 \\ 1 & 1 & 1 \\ -1 & -2 & -1 \end{pmatrix}$ and $\mathbf{P}^{-1} = \begin{pmatrix} 1 & 1 & 1 \\ 0 & -1 & -1 \\ -1 & 1 & 0 \end{pmatrix}$

$\therefore \mathbf{P}^{-1}\mathbf{AP} = \mathbf{D}$.

$\mathbf{C} = \begin{pmatrix} 1 & 0 & 0 \\ 0 & 2 & 0 \\ 0 & 0 & 3 \end{pmatrix}$ (by inspection)

Now comes the tricky bit!

$\mathbf{P}^{-1}\mathbf{AP} = \mathbf{C}^2 \Rightarrow \mathbf{P}^1\mathbf{B}^2\mathbf{P} = \mathbf{C}^2 \Rightarrow \mathbf{P}^{-1}\mathbf{BP} = \mathbf{C}$ *

$\Rightarrow \mathbf{B} = \mathbf{PCP}^{-1}$

$\therefore \mathbf{B} = \begin{pmatrix} 1 & 1 & 0 \\ 1 & 1 & 1 \\ -1 & -2 & -1 \end{pmatrix} \begin{pmatrix} 1 & 0 & 0 \\ 0 & 2 & 0 \\ 0 & 0 & 3 \end{pmatrix} \begin{pmatrix} 1 & 1 & 1 \\ 0 & -1 & -1 \\ -1 & 1 & 0 \end{pmatrix}$

$\Rightarrow \mathbf{B} = \begin{pmatrix} 1 & -1 & -1 \\ -2 & 2 & -1 \\ 2 & 0 & 3 \end{pmatrix}$

*This is the clever step. Refer back to question 15 if necessary.

17 $\begin{vmatrix} 1-\lambda & 0 & 2 \\ 0 & 2-\lambda & 0 \\ 2 & 0 & 1-\lambda \end{vmatrix} = 0$

$\Rightarrow (1-\lambda)(2-\lambda)(1-\lambda) - 4(2-\lambda) = 0$

$\Rightarrow -\lambda^3 + 4\lambda^2 - \lambda - 6 = 0$

By inspection $\lambda = -1, 2$ and 3.

(a) $\lambda = -1 \Rightarrow \begin{pmatrix} 1 & 0 & 2 \\ 0 & 2 & 0 \\ 2 & 0 & 1 \end{pmatrix} \begin{pmatrix} x \\ y \\ z \end{pmatrix}$

$\Rightarrow y = 0$ and $x = -z$

$\therefore$ corresponding eigenvector has

the form $x \begin{pmatrix} 1 \\ 0 \\ -1 \end{pmatrix}$

$\therefore$ corresponding eigenvector of unit length

is $\dfrac{1}{\sqrt{2}} \begin{pmatrix} 1 \\ 0 \\ -1 \end{pmatrix}$

(b) $\lambda = 2 \Rightarrow$ corresponding eigenvector

has the form $y \begin{pmatrix} 0 \\ 1 \\ 0 \end{pmatrix}$

$\therefore$ corresponding eigenvector of unit length

is $\begin{pmatrix} 0 \\ 1 \\ 0 \end{pmatrix}$

(c) $\lambda = 3 \Rightarrow$ corresponding eigenvector

has the form $x \begin{pmatrix} 1 \\ 0 \\ 1 \end{pmatrix}$

$\therefore$ corresponding eigenvector of unit length

is $\dfrac{1}{\sqrt{2}} \begin{pmatrix} 1 \\ 0 \\ 1 \end{pmatrix}$

$\therefore$ Unit eigenvectors for **A** are

$\dfrac{1}{\sqrt{2}} \begin{pmatrix} 1 \\ 0 \\ -1 \end{pmatrix}, \begin{pmatrix} 0 \\ 1 \\ 0 \end{pmatrix}$ and $\dfrac{1}{\sqrt{2}} \begin{pmatrix} 1 \\ 0 \\ 1 \end{pmatrix}$

and they are mutually perpendicular.

Let $\mathbf{P} = \begin{pmatrix} \frac{1}{\sqrt{2}} & 0 & \frac{1}{\sqrt{2}} \\ 0 & 1 & 0 \\ \frac{-1}{\sqrt{2}} & 0 & \frac{1}{\sqrt{2}} \end{pmatrix}$

Since A is symmetric $\Rightarrow \mathbf{P}^{-1} = \mathbf{P}^{\mathrm{T}} =$

$\begin{pmatrix} \frac{1}{\sqrt{2}} & 0 & \frac{-1}{\sqrt{2}} \\ 0 & 1 & 0 \\ \frac{1}{\sqrt{2}} & 0 & \frac{1}{\sqrt{2}} \end{pmatrix}$

Finally $\mathbf{P}^{-1}\mathbf{AP} = \mathbf{P}^{\mathrm{T}}\mathbf{AP} = \begin{pmatrix} -1 & 0 & 0 \\ 0 & 2 & 0 \\ 0 & 0 & 3 \end{pmatrix}$.

18 $\begin{vmatrix} 3-\lambda & -6 & -4 \\ -6 & 4-\lambda & 2 \\ -4 & 2 & -1-\lambda \end{vmatrix} = 0$

$\Rightarrow (3-\lambda)\big[(4-\lambda)(-1-\lambda) - 4\big]$
$+ 6\big[6(1+\lambda) + 8\big] - 4\big[-12 + 4(4-\lambda)\big] = 0$

$\Rightarrow -\lambda^3 + 6\lambda^2 + 51\lambda + 44 = 0$

$\Rightarrow (\lambda + 1)(\lambda + 4)(\lambda - 11) = 0$

$\therefore \lambda = -1, -4,$ or 11

'Normalised' eigenvectors *means* eigenvectors of *unit length*.

$$\therefore \lambda = -1 \Rightarrow \begin{pmatrix} \frac{1}{3} \\ \frac{2}{3} \\ \frac{-2}{3} \end{pmatrix} : \lambda = -4 \Rightarrow \begin{pmatrix} \frac{2}{3} \\ \frac{1}{2} \\ \frac{2}{3} \end{pmatrix}$$

$$\lambda = 11 \Rightarrow \begin{pmatrix} \frac{-2}{3} \\ \frac{2}{3} \\ \frac{1}{3} \end{pmatrix}$$

Mutually perpendicular because each pair of scalar products is zero.

$$\text{Let } \mathbf{B} = \begin{pmatrix} \frac{1}{3} & \frac{2}{3} & \frac{-2}{3} \\ \frac{2}{3} & \frac{1}{2} & \frac{2}{3} \\ \frac{-2}{3} & \frac{2}{3} & \frac{1}{3} \end{pmatrix}$$

Since $\mathbf{A}$ *is symmetric*, $\mathbf{B}^{-1} = \mathbf{B}^T = \begin{pmatrix} \frac{1}{3} & \frac{2}{3} & \frac{-2}{3} \\ \frac{2}{3} & \frac{1}{3} & \frac{2}{3} \\ \frac{-2}{3} & \frac{2}{3} & \frac{1}{3} \end{pmatrix}$

$$\therefore \mathbf{B}^{-1}\mathbf{AB} = \mathbf{B}^T\mathbf{B} = \begin{pmatrix} -1 & 0 & 0 \\ 0 & -4 & 0 \\ 0 & 0 & 11 \end{pmatrix} = \mathbf{L}.$$

Don't be put off by the phrasing of the question! $\mathbf{AB} = \mathbf{BL}$ is the same thing as $\mathbf{B}^{-1}\mathbf{AB} = \mathbf{L}$. Therefore all *you* have to do is to verify that $\mathbf{B}^T\mathbf{AB} = \mathbf{L}$, where $\mathbf{A}$, $\mathbf{B}$, $\mathbf{B}^T$ and $\mathbf{L}$ are as given above. I'll leave that to you.

19 $\begin{vmatrix} -\lambda & 1 \\ -1 & -\lambda \end{vmatrix} = 0 \Rightarrow \lambda^2 + 1 = 0 \Rightarrow \lambda = \pm i$

(a) $\begin{pmatrix} 0 & 1 \\ -1 & 0 \end{pmatrix} \begin{pmatrix} x \\ y \end{pmatrix} = i \begin{pmatrix} x \\ y \end{pmatrix}$

$\Rightarrow \begin{matrix} y = ix \\ -x = iy \end{matrix} \Rightarrow y = ix$

$\therefore$ corresponding eigenvector has the form

$$x \begin{pmatrix} 1 \\ i \end{pmatrix}$$

(b) $\lambda = -i \Rightarrow$ corresponding eigenvector has the form $x \begin{pmatrix} 1 \\ -i \end{pmatrix}$

$\therefore$ Let $\mathbf{P} = \begin{pmatrix} 1 & 1 \\ i & -i \end{pmatrix}$

It's important to note in this example that the original matrix $\mathbf{A}$ *is not symmetric*. Therefore there is no need to worry about unit vectors.

20 $\begin{pmatrix} -1 & -2 & 0 \\ -2 & 0 & 2 \\ 0 & 2 & 1 \end{pmatrix} \begin{pmatrix} 1 \\ -2 \\ -2 \end{pmatrix} = \lambda_1 \begin{pmatrix} 1 \\ -2 \\ -2 \end{pmatrix} \Rightarrow \lambda_1 = 3$

$\begin{pmatrix} -1 & -2 & 0 \\ -2 & 0 & 2 \\ 0 & 2 & 1 \end{pmatrix} \begin{pmatrix} -2 \\ -2 \\ 1 \end{pmatrix} = \lambda_2 \begin{pmatrix} -2 \\ -2 \\ 1 \end{pmatrix} \Rightarrow \lambda_2 = -3$

$\therefore$ We've got the eigenvalues of 3 and -3 already.

$\begin{vmatrix} -1-\lambda & -2 & 0 \\ -2 & -\lambda & 2 \\ 0 & 2 & 1-\lambda \end{vmatrix} = 0 \Rightarrow \lambda^3 - 9\lambda = 0$

$\Rightarrow \lambda = 0, 3$ or -3

Corresponding to $\lambda = 0$ we have

$\begin{pmatrix} -1 & -2 & 0 \\ -2 & 0 & 2 \\ 0 & 2 & 1 \end{pmatrix} \begin{pmatrix} x \\ y \\ z \end{pmatrix} = 0 \begin{pmatrix} x \\ y \\ z \end{pmatrix} \Rightarrow \begin{matrix} -x - 2y = 0 \\ -2x + 2z = 0 \\ 2y + z = 0 \end{matrix}$

$\Rightarrow \begin{matrix} x = -2y \\ \text{and} \\ z = -2y \end{matrix}$

$\therefore$ The third eigenvector has the form $y \begin{pmatrix} -2 \\ 1 \\ -2 \end{pmatrix}$.

21 $\det \mathbf{A} = 0$. $\mathbf{A}^{-1}$ does not exist.

22 $(1 - a)^2 (1 + a + a^2)^2 = (1 - a^3)^2$

23 $-1, 11$ or -4

24 $\frac{1}{2} \begin{pmatrix} 2 & 0 & 0 \\ -x & 1 & 0 \\ x-6 & -1 & 2 \end{pmatrix}$

Section 15

1 Five strips, so the x coordinates are 0, 0.2, 0.4, 0.6, 0.8 and 1.0. The corresponding values of the function are

$x = 0$	$f(0)$	$= 1$	
0.2			$f(0.2) = 1.58489$
0.4			$f(0.4) = 2.51189$
0.6			$f(0.6) = 3.98107$
0.8			$f(0.8) = 6.30957$
1.0	$f(1) = 10$		

Sum is 11   Sum is 14.38742

Then approximate area is given by

$$\frac{h}{2}\left\{ \text{first} + \text{last} + 2\,(\text{rest}) \right\}$$

i.e. $\dfrac{0.2}{2}\left\{ 11 + 2\,(14.38742) \right\}$

$$= 0.1 \{ 39.77484 \} = 3.977484$$

To three significant figures, approximate area is 3.98

(This can in fact be integrated directly.)

$$\int_0^1 10^x \, dx = \left[\frac{10^x}{\ln 10} \right]_0^1$$

$$= \frac{1}{\ln 10}\,(10 - 1) = \frac{9}{\ln 10} = 3.91$$

The gradient changes very rapidly, so the approximation is not quite so good as in other cases.

2 | $x = 1$ | $f(1)$ | $= \sqrt{39}$ |
|---|---|---|
| $x = 2$ | | $f(2) = \sqrt{32}$ |
| $x = 3$ | $f(3) = \sqrt{13}$ | |

Sum is 9.851   Sum is 5.657

Area is approximately

$$\frac{1}{2} \times 1 \times \left\{ 9.851 + 2\,(5.657) \right\}$$

$$= \frac{1}{2} \{ 21.165 \}$$

$$= 10.58 \text{ to 2 decimal places}$$

3 | $x = 1$ | $f(1)$ | $= e^{-1}$ |
|---|---|---|
| $x = 1.5$ | | $f(1.5) = e^{-2.25}$ |
| $x = 2$ | $f(2) = e^{-4}$ | |

Sum is 0.3862   Sum is 0.1054

Approximate area is

$$\frac{1}{2} \times \frac{1}{2}\left\{ 0.3862 + 2(0.1054) \right\}$$

$$= 0.149 \text{ to 2 decimal places}$$

4 $x = 0.01$ $f(0.01) = \dfrac{1}{1.2}$

0.25 $f(0.25) = \dfrac{1}{2}$

0.49 $f(0.49) = \dfrac{1}{2.4}$

Approximate area is $\dfrac{1}{2} \times 0.24 \left\{ 1.25 + 2(0.5) \right\}$

$$= 0.12\left\{ 2.25 \right\} = 0.27$$

$$\int_{0.01}^{0.49} \frac{1}{1 + 2\sqrt{x}} \, dx \quad \text{Put } x = u^2 \quad \text{so } dx = 2u \, du$$

When $x = 0.49$, $u = 0.7$
When $x = 0.01$, $u = 0.1$

$$\therefore \quad = \int_{0.1}^{0.7} \frac{1}{1 + 2u} \, 2u \, du$$

We have to divide through here:

$$
\begin{array}{r}
1 \\
2u + 1 \overline{\smash{\big)}\, 2u} \\
\underline{2u + 1} \\
-1
\end{array}
$$

$$= \int_{0.1}^{0.7} \left(1 - \frac{1}{2u + 1} \right) du$$

$$= \left[u - \frac{1}{2}\ln\,(2u + 1) \right]_{0.1}^{0.7}$$

$$= \left[0.7 - \frac{1}{2}\ln\,(2.4) \right] - \left[0.1 - \frac{1}{2}\ln\,(1.2) \right]$$

$$= 0.6 - \frac{1}{2}\ln 2 = 0.253 \dots$$

5 $\dfrac{0.5}{3}\left[\dfrac{1}{2} + \dfrac{1}{1 + \sqrt{2}} + \dfrac{4}{1 + \sqrt{1.5}} \right] = 0.452$

6 $\dfrac{0.5}{3}\left[\sqrt{2} + \sqrt{1 + \dfrac{1}{3}} + 4\left(\sqrt{1 + \dfrac{1}{1.5}} + \sqrt{1 + \dfrac{1}{2.5}} \right) \right.$

$$\left. + 2\sqrt{1 + \frac{1}{2}} \right] = 2.486$$

7 3 ordinates $\Rightarrow$ 2 equally spaced intervals.

x:	0	$\dfrac{\pi}{4}$	$\dfrac{\pi}{2}$
$y = \sqrt{\cos x}$:	1	$\sqrt{\cos \dfrac{\pi}{4}} \approx 0.8409$	0

$\therefore$ integral $\approx \dfrac{\frac{\pi}{4}}{3}\left[1 + 0 + 4 \times 0.8409\right] = 1.142$

8 9 ordinates $\Rightarrow$ 8 equally spaced intervals

$\therefore$ integral $\Rightarrow$

$\dfrac{0.5}{3}\left\{\left[\dfrac{1}{1} + \dfrac{1}{17}\right] + 4\left[\dfrac{1}{1 + 0.5^2} + \dfrac{1}{1 + 1.5^2} + \right.\right.$

$\left.\left. \dfrac{1}{1 + 2.5^2} + \dfrac{11}{1 + 3.5^2}\right] + 2\left[\dfrac{1}{2} + \dfrac{1}{5} + \dfrac{1}{10}\right]\right\}$

$= 1.324$

Exact answer $= \left[\tan^{-1} x\right]_0^4 = 1.326$ (3 d.p.)

$\therefore$ Simpson's rule only accurate to 1 d.p. this time.

9 $y' = 4x + 5y^2 \Rightarrow y'' = 4 + 10yy'$

(The aim of this question was to check your implicit differentiation! Ditto the next one.)

10 $y' = x^2 + y^2 \Rightarrow y'' = 2x + 2yy'$

$\Rightarrow y''' = 2 + 2yy'' + 2(y')^2$

11 Given that $y' = 2x^2 + 3y$

and $y(0) = 1 \Rightarrow y'(0) = 3$

$\therefore y'' = 4x + 3y' \Rightarrow y''(0) = 9$

$\therefore y''' = 4 + 3y'' \Rightarrow y'''(0) = 31$

$\therefore y'''' = 3y''' \Rightarrow y''''(0) \Rightarrow 93$

$\therefore y = 1 + \dfrac{3}{1!}x + \dfrac{9}{2!}x^2 + \dfrac{31}{3!}x^3 + \dfrac{93}{4!}x^4 + \dots$

$\therefore y = 1 + 3x + 4.5x^2 + 5\tfrac{1}{6}x^3 + 3\tfrac{7}{8}x^4 + \dots$

12 Given that $y' = x^2 + 3y^2$ and $y(0) = 2$

$\Rightarrow y'(0) = 12$

$\therefore y'' = 2x + 6yy' \Rightarrow y''(0) = 144$

$\therefore y''' = 2 + 6yy'' + 6(y')^2 \Rightarrow y'''(0) = 2594$

$\therefore y'''' = 6yy''' + 18y'y'' \Rightarrow y''''(0) = 62232$

$\therefore y = 2 + \dfrac{12}{1!}x + \dfrac{144}{2!}x^2 + \dfrac{2594}{3!}x^3 + \dfrac{62232}{4!}x^4 + \dots$

$\therefore y = 2 + 12x + 72x^2 + 432\tfrac{1}{3}x^3 + 2593x^4 + \dots$

13 Given that $y'' = -xy' - y$ and $y(0) = 1$, $y'(0) = 0$.

$\therefore y''(0) = -0 - 1 = -1 \Rightarrow y''(0) = -1$

$\therefore y''' = -xy'' - y' - y' = -xy'' - 2y' \Rightarrow y'''(0) = 0$

$\therefore y'''' = -xy''' - 3y'' \Rightarrow y''''(0) = 3$

$\therefore y = 1 + \dfrac{0}{1!}x - \dfrac{1}{2!}x^2 + \dfrac{0}{3!}x^3 + \dfrac{3}{4!}x^4 + \dots$

$\therefore y = 1 - \dfrac{1}{2}x^2 + \dfrac{1}{8}x^4 \dots$

14 $y' = x^2 - y^2$ and $y(2) = 1$ $\therefore y'(2) = 3$

$\therefore y(2.2) \approx y(2) + 0.2 \times y'(2) = 1 + 0.2 \times 3 = 1.6$.

15 $y' = 2x + y$ and $y(0) = 2$ $\therefore y'(0) = 2$

$\therefore y(0.2) \approx y(0) + 0.2 \times y'(0) = 2 + 0.2 \times 2 = 2.4$

But $y'(0.2) \approx 2 \times 0.2 + 2.4 = 2.8$

$\therefore y(0.4) \approx y(0.2) + 0.2 \times y'(0.2) = 2.4 + 0.2 \times 2.8$
$= 2.96$

But $y'(0.4) \approx 2 \times 0.4 + 2.96 = 3.76$

$\therefore y(0.6) \approx y(0.4) + 0.2 \times y'(0.4)$
$= 2.96 + 0.2 \times 3.76 = 3.712$

This is summarised as:

x:	0	0.2	0.4	0.6
y:	2	2.4	2.96	3.712

16 $y' = \dfrac{4}{x^2}$ and $y(2) = 0$ $\therefore y'(2) = 1$

$\therefore y(2.2) \approx y(2) + 0.2 \times y'(2) = 0 + 0.2 \times 1 = 0.2$

Separation of variables gives

$\int dy = \int \dfrac{4dx}{x^2} \Rightarrow y = \dfrac{-4}{x} + c \Rightarrow y = \dfrac{-4}{x} + 2$

(Using the initial conditions $y = 0$ when $x = 2$).

$\therefore$ the *exact* value of y when $x = 2.2$ is given by

$y(2.2) = \dfrac{-4}{2.2} + 2 = \dfrac{2}{11}$

$\therefore$ overestimate percentage $= \dfrac{0.2 - \dfrac{2}{11}}{\dfrac{2}{11}} \times 100$

$= 10\%$ exactly

17 $y' = xe^{-x^2}$ and $y(0.1) = -0.495$

$\therefore y'(0.1) = 0.0990$

$\therefore y(0.2) \approx -0.495 + 0.1 \times 0.0990 = -0.4851$

$\therefore y'(0.2) \approx 0.2e^{-0.2^2} = 0.19216$

$\therefore y(0.3) \approx -0.4851 + 0.1 \times 0.19216 = -0.4659$

$\therefore y'(0.3) \approx 0.3e^{-0.3^2} = 0.27418$

$\therefore y(0.4) \approx -0.4659 + 0.1 \times 0.27418 = -0.4384$

Rounding off to three decimal places gives

x:	0.1	0.2	0.3	0.4
y:	−0.495	−0.485	−0.466	−0.438

367

18 $y' = x^2 + y$ with $y(0) = 1$ and $y(0.1) = 1.106$

$\therefore \ y'(0.1) = 0.1^2 + 1.106 \Rightarrow y'(0.1) = 1.116$

$\therefore \ y(0.2) \approx y(0) + 2 \times 0.1 \times y'(0.1)$

$= 1 + 2 \times 0.1 \times 1.116 = 1.2232$

$\therefore \ y'(0.2) = 0.2^2 + 1.2232 \Rightarrow y'(0.2) = 1.2632$

$\therefore \ y(0.3) \approx y(0.1) + 2 \times 0.1 \times y'(0.2)$

$= 1.106 + 2 \times 0.1 \times 1.2632 = 1.35864$

$\therefore \ y'(0.3) = 0.3^2 + 1.35864 \Rightarrow y'(0.3) = 1.44864$

$\therefore \ y(0.4) \approx y(0.2) + 2 \times 0.1 \times y'(0.3)$

$= 1.2232 + 2 \times 0.1 \times 1.44864 = 1.512928$

This is summarised as (correct to 4 d.p.):

$x:$	0	0.1	0.2	0.3	0.4
$y:$	1	1.106	1.2232	1.3586	1.5129

19 $y' = x^2 - y^2$ with $y(0) = 1$ and $y(0.1) = 0.9094$

$\therefore \ y'(0.1) = 0.1^2 - 0.9094^2 \Rightarrow y'(0.1) = -0.8170$

$\therefore \ y(0.2) \approx y(0) + 2 \times 0.1 \times y'(0.1)$

$= 1 + 2 \times 0.1 \times -0.8170 = 0.8366$

$\therefore \ y'(0.2) = 0.2^2 - 0.8366^2 \Rightarrow y'(0.2) = -0.6599$

$\therefore \ y(0.3) \approx y(0.1) + 2 \times 0.1 \times y'(0.2)$

$= 0.9094 + 2 \times 0.1 \times -0.6599 = 0.7774$

$\therefore \ y'(0.3) = 0.3^2 - 0.7774^2 \Rightarrow y'(0.3) = -0.5144$

$\therefore \ y(0.4) \approx y(0.2) + 2 \times 0.1 \times y'(0.3)$

$= 0.8366 + 2 \times 0.1 \times -0.5144 = 0.7377$

This summarises to give (correct to 4 d.p.)

f(0.2) = 0.8366, f(0.3) = 0.7774, f(0.4) = 0.7337

20 $y'' = x + y$ with $y(0) = 2$ and $y(0.1) = 1.91$

$\therefore \ y''(0.1) = 0.1 + 1.91 = 2.01$

$\therefore \ y(0.2) \approx 2y(0.1) - y(0) + 0.1^2 \times y''(0.1)$

$= 2 \times 1.91 - 2 + 0.1^2 \times 2.01 = 1.8401$

$\therefore \ y''(0.2) = 0.2 + 1.8401 = 2.0401$

$\therefore \ y(0.3) \approx 2y(0.2) - y(0.1) + 0.1^2 \times y''(0.2)$

$= 2 \times 1.8401 - 1.91 + 0.1^2 \times 2.0401 = 1.790601$

$\therefore \ y''(0.3) = 0.3 + 1.790601 = 2.090601$

$\therefore \ y(0.4) \approx 2y(0.3) - y(0.2) + 0.1^2 \times y''(0.3)$

$= 2 \times 1.790601 - 1.8401 + 0.1^2 \times 2.090601$

$= 1.7620$

This summarises as (correct to 4 d.p.):

$x:$	0	0.1	0.2	0.3	0.4
$y:$	2	1.91	1.8401	1.7906	1.7620

21 $y'' = 1 - y$ with $y(0) = 2$ and $y(0.1) = 2.095$

$\therefore \ y''(0.1) = 1 - 2.095 = -1.095$

$\therefore \ y(0.2) \approx 2y(0.1) - y(0) + 0.1^2 \times y''(0.1)$

$= 2 \times 2.095 - 2 + 0.1^2 \times -1.095 = 2.17905$

$\therefore \ y''(0.2) = 1 - 2.17905 = 1.17905$

$\therefore \ y(0.3) \approx 2y(0.2) - y(0.1) + 0.1^2 \times y''(0.2)$

$= 2 \times 2.17905 - 2.095 + 0.1^2 \times -1.17905$

$= 2.2513095$

$\therefore \ y''(0.3) = 1 - 2.2513095 = -1.2513095$

$\therefore \ y(0.4) \approx 2y(0.3) - y(0.2) + 0.1^2 \times y''(0.3)$

$= 2 \times 2.2513095 - 2.17905 + 0.1^2 \times -1.2513095$

$= 2.31096$

This summarises to give (correct to 4 d.p.):

$x:$	0	0.1	0.2	0.3	0.4
$y:$	2	2.095	2.1791	2.2513	2.3110

22   (a) $y'' = y + y^2$ and $y(0) = 1$, $y'(0) = 0.2$

$\therefore \ y''(0) = 1 + 1^2 = 2$

$y''' = y' + 2yy' \Rightarrow y'''(0) = 0.2 + 2 \times 1 \times 0.2 = 0.6$

$\therefore \ y = 1 + \dfrac{0.2}{1!}\, x + \dfrac{2}{2!}\, x^2 + \dfrac{0.6}{3!}\, x^3 + \ \ldots$

$\therefore \ y \approx 1 + 0.2x + x^2 + 0.1x^3$

$\therefore \ y(0.1) \approx 1 + 0.2 \times 0.1 + 0.1^2 + 0.1 \times 0.1^3$

$= 1.0301$

(b) $y''(0.1) \approx y(0.1) + y^2(0.1)$

$\approx 1.0301 + 1.0301^2 = 2.0912$

$\therefore \ y(0.2) \approx 2y(0.1) - y(0) + 0.1^2\, y''(0.1)$

$\approx 2 \times 1.0301 - 1 + 0.1^2 \times 2.0912 = 1.0811.$

Section 16

1 (a) Assume true for $n = k$.

$\therefore 1^2 + 2^2 + \dots k^2 + (k+1)^2$

$= \dfrac{k(k+1)(2k+1)}{6} + (k+1)^2$

$= \dfrac{(k+1)}{6} \left[k(2k+1) + 6(k+1) \right]$

$= \dfrac{(k+1)}{6} (k+2)(2k+3)$

$\therefore$ Result true for $n = k + 1$

Also true when $n = 1$ because $1^2 = 1 = \dfrac{1 \times 2 \times 3}{6}$

$\therefore$ By induction true for all n.

(b) Assume true for $n = k$

$\therefore 1.2 + 2.3 + \dots + k(k+1) + (k+1)(k+2)$

$= \dfrac{k(k+1)(k+2)}{3} + (k+1)(k+2)$

$= \dfrac{(k+1)(k+2)(k+3)}{3}$

$\therefore$ Result true for $n = k + 1$

Also true when $n = 1$ because $1.2 = \dfrac{1 \times 2 \times 3}{3}$

$\therefore$ By induction true for all n.

(c) Assume true for $n = k$

$\therefore 2 + 3.2 + 4.2^2 + \dots + (k+1).2^{k-1} + (k+2).2^k$
$= k.2^k + (k+2).2^k$

$= 2^k(2k+2) = 2^{k+1}.(k+1)$

$\therefore$ Result true for $n = k + 1$

Also true when $n = 1$ because $2 = 1.2^1$

$\therefore$ By induction true for all n.

(d) Assume true for $n = k$

$\therefore \dfrac{1}{1.3} + \dfrac{1}{2.4} + \dots + \dfrac{1}{k(k+2)} + \dfrac{1}{(k+1)(k+3)}$

$= \dfrac{k(3k+5)}{4(k+1)(k+2)} + \dfrac{1}{(k+1)(k+3)}$

$= \dfrac{k(3k+5)(k+3) + 4(k+2)}{4(k+1)(k+2)(k+3)}$

$= \dfrac{3k^3 + 14k^2 + 19k + 8}{4(k+1)(k+2)(k+3)}$

$= \dfrac{(k+1)(3k^2 + 11k + 8)}{4(k+1)(k+2)(k+3)}$

$= \dfrac{(k+1)(k+1)(3k+8)}{4(k+1)(k+2)(k+3)}$

$= \dfrac{(k+1)(3k+8)}{4(k+2)(k+3)}$

$\therefore$ Result true for $n = k + 1$

Also true when $n = 1$ because $\dfrac{1}{1.3} = \dfrac{1}{3} = \dfrac{1.8}{4.2.3}$

$\therefore$ By induction true for all n.

(e) Assume $3^{2k} - 1 = 8\lambda$

$\therefore 3^{2(k+1)} - 1 = 3^{2k}.9 - 1 = (8\lambda + 1)9 - 1$
(from the assumption)

$= 72\lambda + 8$

$= 8(9\lambda + 1)$, which is also divisible by 8

$\therefore$ true for $n = k + 1$

True when $n = 1$ because $3^2 - 1 = 8$

$\therefore$ By induction true for all n.

(f) Assume $2^{k+2} + 3^{2k+1} = 7\lambda$

$\therefore 2^{k+3} + 3^{2(k+1)+1} = 2.2^{k+2} + 3^{2k+3}$

$= 2(7\lambda - 3^{2k+1}) + 3^{2k+3}$ (from the assumption)

$= 14\lambda - 2.3^{2k+1} + 9.3^{2k+1}$

$= 14\lambda + 7.3^{2k+1}$

$= 7(2\lambda + 3^{2k+1})$, which is also divisible by 7.

$\therefore$ Result true for $n = k + 1$

Result also true when $n = 1$ because $2^3 + 3^3 = 35$

$\therefore$ By induction true for all n

(g) Assume true for $n = k$

$\therefore A^{k+1} = A^k . A$

$= \begin{pmatrix} 2k+1 & -k \\ 4k & 1-2k \end{pmatrix} \begin{pmatrix} 3 & -1 \\ 4 & -1 \end{pmatrix}$

$= \begin{pmatrix} 2k+3 & -(k+1) \\ 4k+4 & 1-2(k+1) \end{pmatrix}$

$\therefore$ Result true for $n = k + 1$

Result clearly true when $n = 1$

$\therefore$ By induction true for all n.

2 $\left(1 - \dfrac{4}{1}\right) = \dfrac{-3}{1}$, $\left(1 - \dfrac{4}{1}\right)\left(1 - \dfrac{4}{9}\right) = \dfrac{-5}{3}$,

$\left(1 - \dfrac{4}{1}\right)\left(1 - \dfrac{4}{9}\right)\left(1 - \dfrac{4}{25}\right) = \dfrac{-7}{5}$ etc.

$\therefore$ Conjectured formula is $\dfrac{1+2n}{1-2n}$

Assume true for $n = k$

$\therefore \left(1 - \dfrac{4}{1}\right)\left(1 - \dfrac{4}{9}\right) \dots$

$\qquad \left(1 - \dfrac{4}{(2k-1)^2}\right)\left(1 - \dfrac{4}{(2k+1)^2}\right)$

$= \dfrac{(1+2k)}{(1-2k)} \left(1 - \dfrac{4}{(2k+1)^2}\right)$

$= \dfrac{(1+2k)(4k^2 + 4k - 3)}{(1-2k)(2k+1)^2}$

$$= \frac{(1 + 2k)\,(2k + 3)\,(2k - 1)}{(1 - 2k)\,(2k + 1)^2}$$

$$= \frac{2k + 3}{1 - 2(k + 1)}$$

$\therefore$ Result true for $n = k + 1$

We already know that result is true for $n = 1$.

$\therefore$ By induction true for all n.

3   Assume $(1 + x)^k > 1 + kx$

$\therefore$ $(1 + x)^{k+1} = (1 + x)^k (1 + x) > (1 + kx)(1 + x)$, since $1 + x$ is positive (from the assumption)

$= 1 + (k + 1)\,x + kx^2$

$> 1 + (k + 1)\,x$

$\therefore$ Result true for $n = k + 1$

Result is also true for $n = 2$ because

$(1 + x)^2 = 1 + 2x + x^2 > 1 + 2x$

$\therefore$ By induction true for all n.

4   Assume true for $n = k$

$\therefore$ $\dfrac{1}{2} + \dfrac{2}{3} + \ldots + \dfrac{k}{k + 1} + \dfrac{k + 1}{k + 2} < k + \dfrac{k + 1}{k + 2}$

$= k + 1 - \dfrac{1}{k + 2}$ (after long division)

$< k + 1$, since $k \geq 1$

$\therefore$ Result true for $n = k + 1$

Result clearly true when $n = 1$ because $\dfrac{1}{2} < 1$

$\therefore$ By induction true for all n.

5   (a) $n = 3$ gives $1 + \dfrac{1}{4} + \dfrac{1}{9} = \dfrac{7}{5}$ which is false.

$\therefore$ Conjecture is false.

(b)   True. Proof by induction as follows:

Assume $8^k + 6 = 14\lambda$

$\therefore$ $8^{k+1} + 6 = 8 \cdot 8^k + 6 = 8(14\lambda - 6) + 6$ (from the assumption)

$= 112\lambda - 42$

$= 14\,(8\lambda - 3)$, which is also divisible by 14.

$\therefore$ True for $n = k + 1$.

Clearly true when $n = 1$.

$\therefore$ By induction true for all n.

6   Assume that $\sqrt{2} = \dfrac{p}{q}$ where p and q are positive integers in their lowest terms.

$\therefore$ $2 = \dfrac{p^2}{q^2}$ $\therefore$ $p^2 = 2q^2$

$\therefore$ p^2 is even.

$\therefore$ p is even.

$\therefore$ p^2 is divisible by 4.

$\therefore$ (from $p^2 = 2q^2$) it follows that q^2 is also even.

$\therefore$ q is even.

$\therefore$ p and q are both even.

$\therefore$ they have a factor of 2 in common.

This contradicts the initial assumption.

$\therefore$ The initial assumption is wrong.

$\therefore$ $\sqrt{2}$ must be irrational.

7   Suppose there is only a finite number of primes so that they will be 2, 3, 5, 7, 11, ... , p_n, where p_n is the biggest prime number possible. Now consider the number

$2 \times 3 \times 5 \times 7 \times 11 \times \ldots \times p_n + 1$

This number leaves a remainder of 1 when divided by any of the primes 2, 3, 5, 7, 11, ... p_n. Therefore either it is a prime number (bigger than p_n) or it is divisible by another prime number larger than p_n). In either case, we have found a prime bigger than p_n. But this contradicts our initial assumption. Therefore our initial assumption is false. Therefore there must be infinitely many prime numbers.